KU-787-390

AUTOMOTIVE

SUSPENSIONS, STEERING, ALIGNMENT, AND BRAKES

Third Edition

BY

ERNEST VENK, M.A., Voc Ed., Assistant Dean, Technical Division, Henry Ford Community College, Dearborn, Michigan. Formerly Instructor in Auto and Aviation Mechanics, Fordson High School.

WALTER E. BILLIET, M.ED., Coordinator of Automotive Training, Henry Ford Community College, Dearborn, Michigan. Formerly Automotive Instructor, Fordson High School.

WALTER V. ALLEY, Jr., M.S. (Industrial Ed.), Coordinator of Alignment, Brake Service, and Unitized Body and Frame Straightening, Ferris Institute, Big Rapids, Michigan. Formerly Instructor, Product Service, General Motors Institute.

AMERICAN TECHNICAL SOCIETY · CHICAGO, ILLINOIS

LONDON
THE TECHNICAL PRESS LTD.

LIBRARY OF CONGRESS CARD CATALOG NO.: 62-15244

FIRST EDITION
1st Printing 1951

SECOND EDITION (REVISED)
2nd Printing 1955
3rd Printing 1960
4th Printing 1961

THIRD EDITION (REVISED)
5th Printing 1962
6th Printing 1964
7th Printing 1967

Former editions and printings appeared under the title: AUTOMOTIVE SUSPENSIONS, STEERING, AND WHEEL ALIGNMENT.

PRINTED IN THE UNITED STATES OF AMERICA

FOREWORD

When the automobile was first developed, steering, suspensions and brakes were relatively simple mechanisms. For the light weight, low speed automobiles of that era they were adequate for the purpose. However, as the automobile developed in complexity these simple mechanisms were no longer adequate to provide the steering and braking control necessary to handle the higher speeds and heavier weights of the modern vehicle.

The ever increasing demands made upon the entire suspension system (the axle, springs, steering gear and linkages) made necessary a series of almost constant refinements which have resulted in the entire suspension system evolving into a complex arrangement of parts requiring precision measurement and adjustment. For this reason, the mechanic who desires to become an expert needs to thoroughly understand the construction, maintenance and repair of automotive suspensions and steering systems; and the knowledge of how to measure, interpret, and correct these systems.

The development of the brake system has paralleled the other improvements in the automobile. As refinements and increased performance have taken place the demands on the brake system also increased. The complexity of the modern brake system and the need for more exacting service requires a thorough understanding of the operating principles and construction of brakes.

Involved with wheel alignment is the need for checking and correcting any frame damage or misalignment which may be present, since the frame is the foundation on which the suspension, and steering linkages are mounted. The newer type of unitized body construction calls for different procedures and techniques that require a thorough knowledge on the part of the mechanic who services them. This book supplies the information necessary to the understanding and development of those procedures.

A chapter of special interest is devoted to the thorough treatment of Customized Vehicle Alignment utilizing the latest equipment. The complex suspensions and steering linkages of todays automobiles demand precision measurement and adjustment for safe, efficient operation. To provide this precision requires familiarity with the equipment used for alignment. This chapter supplies the information necessary to the efficient use of this equipment and the procedures of precision alignment.

The subjects of frame and wheel alignment, and brakes, are unique in that other portions of the vehicle are rarely involved. This means that the reader can become a frame and wheel alignment or brake specialist, or both, without the knowledge or experience in other aspects of service.

This book thoroughly covers frame designs and methods of correcting frame damage. Likewise, the entire subject of suspension systems, steering control, tire wear, vehicle alignment, and brakes and brake service is presented completely and logically in a simple straight forward manner. This book is intended not only to teach the beginner but also to be invaluable as a reference book for the accomplished mechanic.

THE PUBLISHERS

ACKNOWLEDGMENTS

The publishers, editors, and authors wish to acknowledge and express their appreciation to the following companies who supplied artwork and information used in this volume:

Chevrolet Division, General Motors Corporation
Ford Division, Ford Motor Company
Plymouth Division, Chrysler Corporation
Lincoln Mercury Division, Ford Motor Company
John Bean Corporation
Cadillac Division, General Motors Corporation
Oldsmobile Division, General Motors Corporation
Pontiac Division, General Motors Corporation
Buick Division, General Motors Corporation
Studebaker Corporation
K. R. Wilson Company
Dodge Division, Chrysler Corporation
Stewart Warner Corporation
Barrett Equipment Company

CONTENTS

PAGE

Chapter 1. The Frame ... 1
- I. General Description of Frame ... 1
- II. Types of Frames ... 2
- III. General Principles of Frame Repair ... 5
- IV. Analysis of Kinds of Frame Damage ... 6
- V. Correction Sequence of Frame Repair ... 14
- VI. Estimating ... 29

Chapter 2. Front Suspension Systems ... 32
- I. Independent Front Wheel Suspension Systems ... 32
- II. Axle Suspension with Leaf Springs ... 44
- III. Front Suspension Service ... 46

Chapter 3. Rear Suspension Systems ... 49
- I. Hotchkiss Drive ... 50
- II. Torque Tube Drive ... 51
- III. Rear Independent Suspension System ... 53
- IV. Rear Axle Housings ... 55
- V. Rear Suspension Alignment ... 56

Chapter 4. Springs and Shock Absorbers ... 62
- I. Springs ... 62
- II. Shock Absorbers ... 80

Chapter 5. Steering Gears and Linkages ... 89
- I. Manual Steering Gear Construction and Types ... 89
- II. Power Steering ... 94
- III. Steering Linkages ... 111
- IV. Servicing the Steering Gear and Linkage ... 118

Chapter 6. Wheels and Tires ... 130
- I. Operation of Wheel and Tire Assembly ... 131
- II. Static and Dynamic Balance ... 133
- III. Corrections and Adjustments ... 136
- IV. Construction of Wheel and Tire Assembly ... 140
- V. Servicing the Wheel Assembly ... 145

Chapter 7. Wheel Alignment Factors ... 153
- I. Caster ... 155
- II. Steering Knuckle Inclination (Angle) ... 162
- III. Camber Angle ... 165
- IV. Point of Intersection ... 168
- V. Toe-In ... 170
- VI. Toe-Out on Turns ... 172

PAGE

Chapter 8. Customized Vehicle Alignment **186**
I. Pre-Alignment Visual Inspection 186
II. Pre-Alignment Road Test 191
III. Vehicle Repair 192
IV. Checking Wheel Alignment Equipment 192
V. Vehicle Alignment 193

Chapter 9. Brakes **213**
I. Purpose of Brakes 213
II. Factors Controlling the Stop 214
III. How Brakes Stop the Vehicle 216
IV. Construction of Brakes 216
V. Self-Energization of Brake Shoes 221
VI. Brake Shoe Actuating Mechanisms 224
VII. Construction of Hydraulic Brake System 232
VIII. Hand Brakes 238
IX. Power Brakes 240

Chapter 10. Brake Service **254**
I. Common Brake Troubles 254
II. Adjustment of Brakes 259
III. Flushing Hydraulic Brakes 264
IV. Bleeding Hydraulic Brakes 266
V. Brake Relining 268
VI. Brake Drum Service 273
VII. Master Cylinder and Wheel Cylinder Repair 274

(*John Bean Corp.*)

PORTABLE ALIGNMENT MACHINE

This portable alignment machine employs a beam of light to measure camber, caster, steering geometry, and toe. By means of a light projector mounted in the projector panel, a beam of light, triple reflected indicates the measurements required.

CHAPTER 1

THE FRAME

		PAGE
I.	General Description of Frame	1
II.	Types of Frames	2
III.	General Principles of Frame Repair	5
IV.	Analysis of Kinds of Frame Damage	6
V.	Correction Sequence of Frame Repair	14
VI.	Estimating	29

For all practical purposes the frame of an automotive vehicle is the foundation on which the car or truck is built. The purpose of the frame is to provide a strong and rigid structure which will support the engine, transmission, drive shaft, springs, axles, wheels, tires, and the body mounted on the frame.

Proper alignment of the frame must be maintained at all times. Should misalignment of the frame result due to collision, it is almost certain to affect alignment of body doors, to place undue strain on other body parts, and, generally, to promote rapid body deterioration. If, for example, one side of the frame should be forced back farther than the other side as a result of a collision, the wheels of the vehicle would no longer be in alignment. The vehicle would then be unsafe for operation.

The major portion of this chapter explains the practices and procedures applied in correcting and removing misalignment from an automotive vehicle frame. To achieve full understanding of frame correction and alignment it is necessary that you first become familiar with the various types of automotive vehicle frames and the differences in the construction of these frames.

I. GENERAL DESCRIPTION OF FRAME

Frame side members, which are the basis of frame construction, are usually made of U-shaped channel sections as shown in Fig. 1, or box-shaped sections. Cross members of the same material reinforce the frame and provide support for the engine, wheels, and suspension systems. Various brackets and openings are provided to permit installation of the many parts which make up the automotive chassis.

The box channel type of construction is composed of two U-shaped channel sections fitted as shown in Fig. 2. The box construction is obtained by overlapping the free edges of two U channel sections and either bolting, riveting, or welding them together.

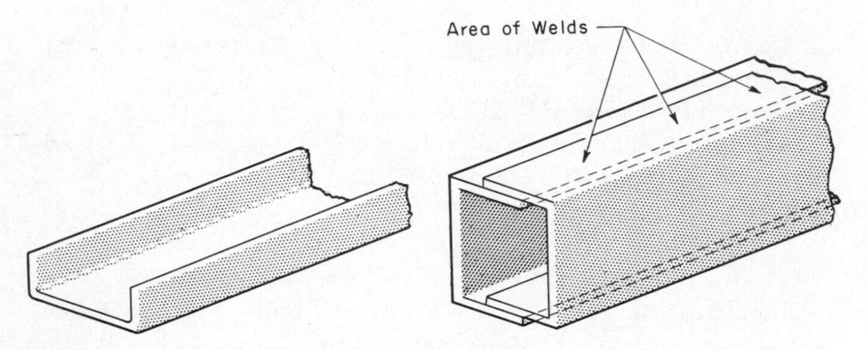

Fig. 1. U channel frame section.

Fig. 2. Box channel frame section.

The various brackets, cross members, and braces are welded, riveted, or both, to the frame side rails.

Most frames are wide at the rear and narrow at the front. The narrow front construction enables the vehicle to make a shorter turn. A wide frame at the rear provides better support of the body.

II. TYPES OF FRAMES

a. X-Type Frames. Frames vary in size and shape to accommodate the particular units they are intended to receive. Fig. 3 illustrates an X-type frame construction with a tubular center section. The propeller shaft is enclosed in this tubular center section. The side members or rails are of the box channel type construction. A heavy front cross member is used to support the upper and lower suspension control arms and coil springs. The "kick-up" at the rear (that portion of the frame raised above the center section) is to accommodate the rear axle assembly and permit flexing of the rear springs. By using a "kick-up" at both front and rear wheels the center of the frame can be kept lower. Extended brackets welded to the frame side members provide for the mounting of the body.

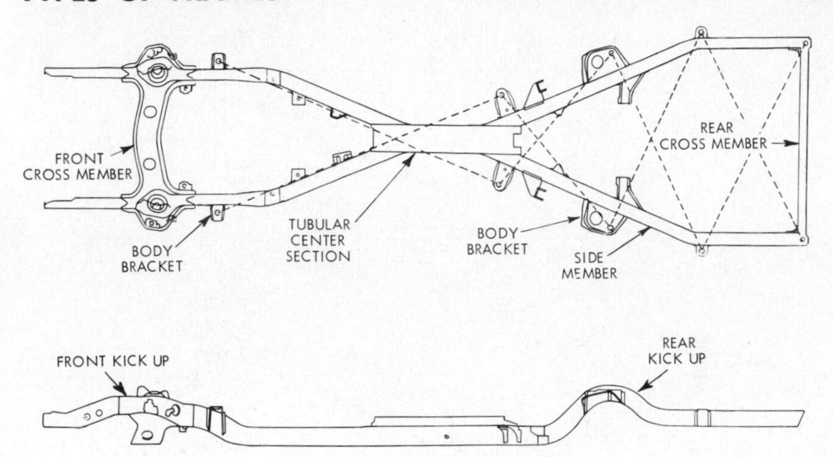

Fig. 3. X type of frame construction.
(Chevrolet Motor Div.—General Motors Corp.)

b. Box-Type Frames. A box-type frame is illustrated in Fig. 4. No center bracing is provided in this frame. However, additional cross members provide the necessary bracing for rigidity. The side members are of the box channel type construction.

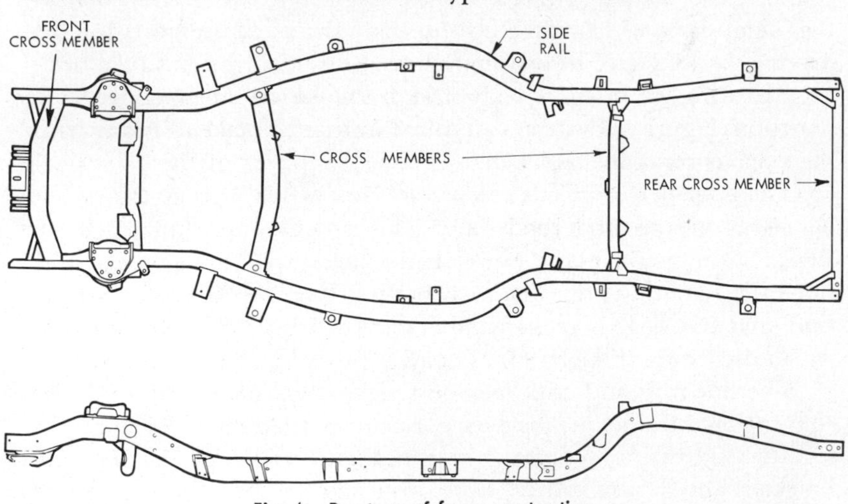

Fig. 4. Box type of frame construction.
(Ford Div.—Ford Motor Co.)

c. Box-Type with Bracing. A box-type frame with X bracing is illustrated in Fig. 5. This additional bracing is used by some manufacturers in the construction of convertible coupes and station

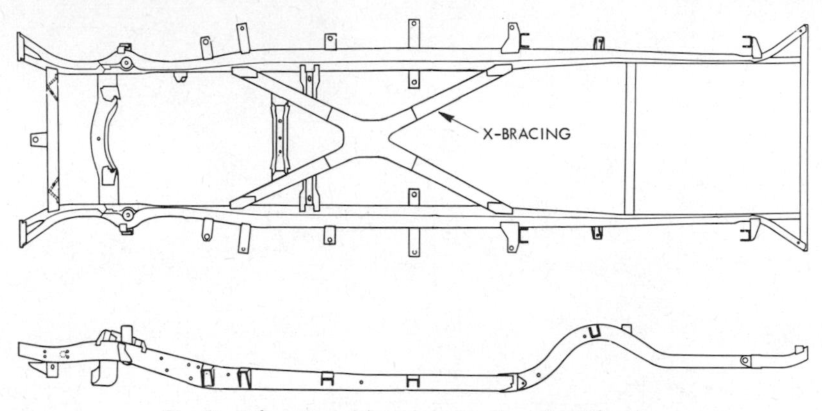

Fig. 5. A box type of frame construction using X bracing.
(Plymouth Div.—Chrysler Corp.)

wagons. Numerous variations and combinations of the described types of frames are used by the different automotive manufacturers to fit specific weight, stress and design requirements.

d. Unitized Body and Frame Construction. Some manufacturers combine the body and frame into a single unitized section. All of the metal parts which make up the body shell and supports for the driving, braking and suspension loads are welded into a single unit, thus creating an integral body and frame of all steel welded construction. Figure 6 illustrates a typical unitized body and frame with the various components labeled.

The floor pans and side rail assemblies, which include the rocker panels form the underbody area, incorporate attachment provisions for the power plant, power train and suspension systems. The side rails, sometimes referred to as body sills on this type of construction, and the various cross members are of heavy box type sections which distribute the load over broad areas of the body structure.

The side rails and cross members serve the same functions as the conventional frame members except that by welding all of the units together (unitizing) weight is reduced and many of the separate brackets and braces which were attached by bolts or rivets are eliminated.

The front suspension member assembly which supports the engine and front suspension is structurally similar to the front end of a conventional frame. The rear suspension member assembly which supports the rear suspension is also similar to the rear end of a con-

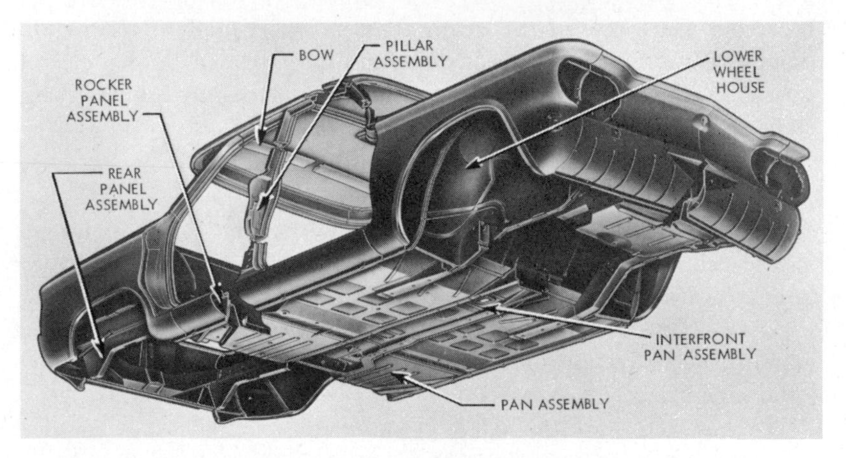

Fig. 6. Unitized type of body and frame construction. In this type of construction the frame structure is built into the body.
(Chevrolet Motor Div.—General Motors Corp.)

ventional frame; however, the assemblies are integrated into the rest of the body assembly.

Above the side rails the body structure is comparable to that of a vehicle with a separate body and frame construction.

Care must be exercised when using a jack or hoist to lift a vehicle with this type of construction. Unless the jack or hoist makes contact on rigid members, damage to the underbody may result.

III. GENERAL PRINCIPLES OF FRAME REPAIR

Ordinarily the only service required on frames is the result of an accident which has twisted, bent, or broken the frame. Generally it is possible to repair such damage by straightening the twisted or bent member. Those parts that cannot be repaired must be replaced. Each year more and more car manufacturers are employing unitized body and frame constructions. With unitized design becoming increasingly popular, body and frame repair are no longer distinct and separate operations.

a. Importance of Correct Alignment. As body damage corrections are made, it is absolutely essential that underbody alignment also be corrected as part of the entire operation. Correct frame alignment is very important in order to maintain correct steering, wheel alignment, and proper tire wear patterns.

b. Three Basic Steps. In frame straightening, the principles of reversing the forces of the original impact are used to restore the damaged frame and body sections. Frame repair can be made without the removal of the body, engine, or drive train. Three basic steps to follow are:

(1) *ANALYSIS.* Make a complete analysis to determine the amount of body-frame damage and misalignment.

(2) *CORRECTION SEQUENCE.* Reverse the forces of impact in the proper sequence through the correct usage of essential tools and hook-ups.

(3) *GAGING.* Check all dimensional planes with the correct gages to make certain measurements are within the manufacturer's specifications.

In the following discussion of these three basic points *analysis* and *correction* sequence will be treated as separate operations. *Gaging* will be explained as it applies to each separate operation.

IV. ANALYSIS OF KINDS OF FRAME DAMAGE

Frame damage usually results from a collision. However, a collision does not always produce frame damage. The direction of impact usually indicates the type of frame damage to look for. Over a period of years, the manufacturers of body straightening equipment, shop owners, and collision experts, have established a fundamental approach or collision pattern for estimating frame damage. Generally speaking, an average collision pattern would be 50% of the collision (damage) to the front of the vehicle, 40% to the rear of the vehicle, and 10% to the center of the vehicle.

a. Center Section Damage. Since the center of the vehicle frame is the least likely to be damaged in a collision, it is logical that the center section is the first to be checked. If the center section of the frame proves to be undamaged, it will then serve as a starting point so as to analyze the remainder of the frame.

Two types of damage may exist in the center section of the frame although the side rails may not be damaged; these are the *diamond* and the *twist.*

(1) *DIAMOND.* Diamond damage is a misalignment that has occurred when the impact of a collision has forced one side member of the frame further back than the other, causing the body to shift on the frame. As a result of an impact on either front corner of the car, a diamond frame will be noticed by an unequal spacing be-

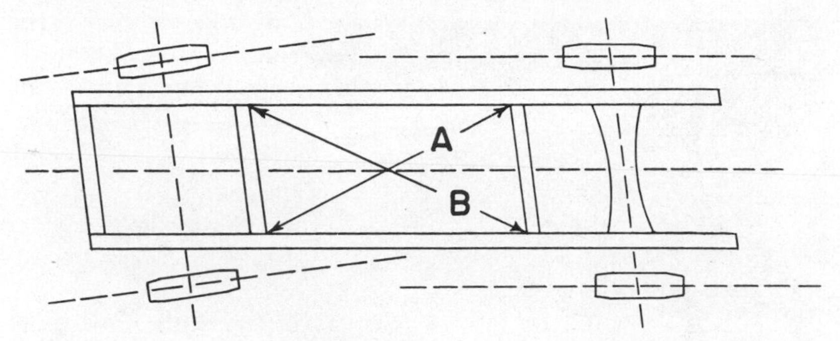

Fig. 7. Diamond type of frame damage which is usually the result of a front collision. (*John Bean Corp.*)

tween the rear bumper and the rear end of the body. Looking underneath the car, a diamond frame will be evidenced by the body bolts having been wrenched (shifted) on the body brackets on one side of the damaged car. Also note that the road film (dirt, etc.) will be cracked at the junction of the cross-members and side rails. Usually the box type frame is more susceptible to diamond damage than other types of frames.

Look at Fig. 7 and note that dimension A should be equal to dimension B if the frame is free from diamond damage. If dimension B were one inch longer than dimension A, the right rail would then be 1/2 inch behind the left rail. The frame would, therefore, have a one inch diamond. If the difference between the right and left rail were 1/2 inch or less, then this condition would not normally warrant straightening, since one rail would be only 1/4 inch behind the other. The bumper bracket holes are slotted on the frame to make up for this difference.

The simplest way to determine the exact amount of diamond damage would be to cross check (measurements A and B, Fig. 7) with a tape measure. These measurements should be taken between the jig holes in the frame rails, since jig holes found in one rail have matching holes in the other rail. Rivets may be used to measure from, but recognize the fact that the rivet head may not be directly over the center of the hole and could cause an error in measurement. If the muffler is in the way, a two point tram (gage used for aligning) may be used to make the measurements as shown in Fig. 8. The use of a diamond sight gage is another method that reveals a diamond frame very quickly. This gage is mounted 90 degrees to a

Fig. 8. Cross checking a vehicle with a unitized body and frame by means of a two-point tram or gage.
(John Bean Corp.)

self-centering gage and the pins of all the gages should align if the frame is free from diamond damage. See Fig. 9.

(2) *TWIST*. A twist in the frame is usually the result of a collision in which a vehicle that is carrying a heavy load has been

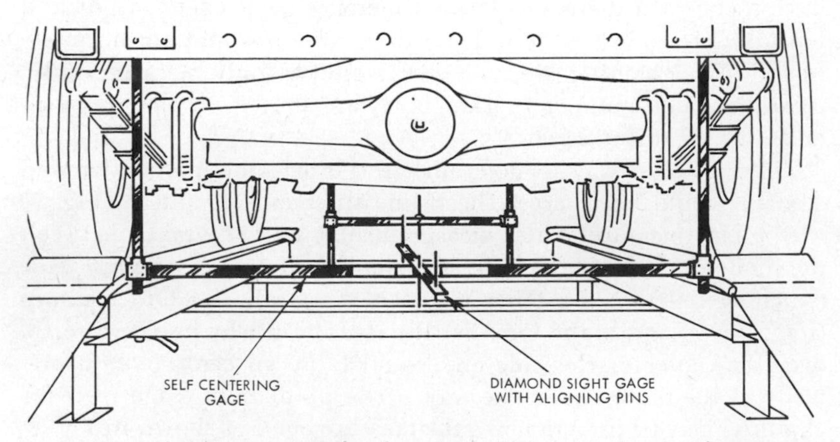

Fig. 9. Diamond sight gage. Note that the vertical aligning pins of each sight gage must be in direct alignment if the vehicle is free of diamond damage. See Fig. 11 opposite.
(John Bean Corp.)

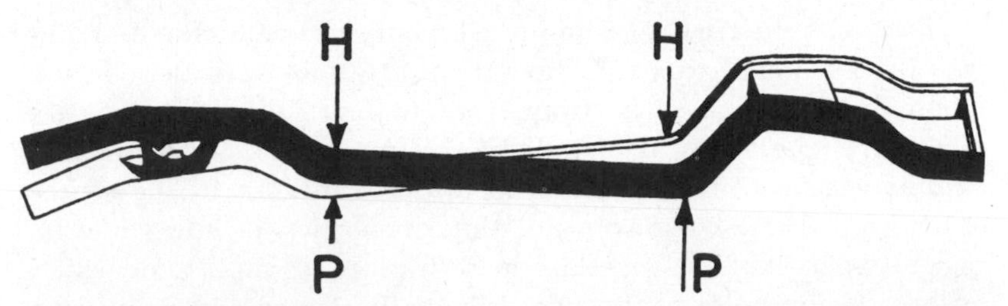

Fig. 10. A twisted frame as the result of a collision. The points marked H denote where the frame is to be held during the straightening process while the points marked P denote where the correcting force or ***pull*** is to be applied.
(John Bean Corp.)

overturned. This action raises one rail of the frame higher than the opposite rail, as shown in Fig. 10.

A vehicle that has a twisted frame will not set level to the ground. However, this may not be true in all cars that do not set level to the ground, since a weak or broken spring will give the same effect. One way of determining if the frame is twisted is to jack up the frame between the front wheels and observe if the car sets level. If the car sets level, then jack up the rear of the frame with the front wheels on the ground (jack in center of frame) and observe if the car then sets level. If at both ends of the car, the car sets level, the uneven trim height when all four wheels are on the ground is due to a twisted frame and not to bad springs. The body may also be twisted and usually the glass in front or rear will not remain in the body intact.

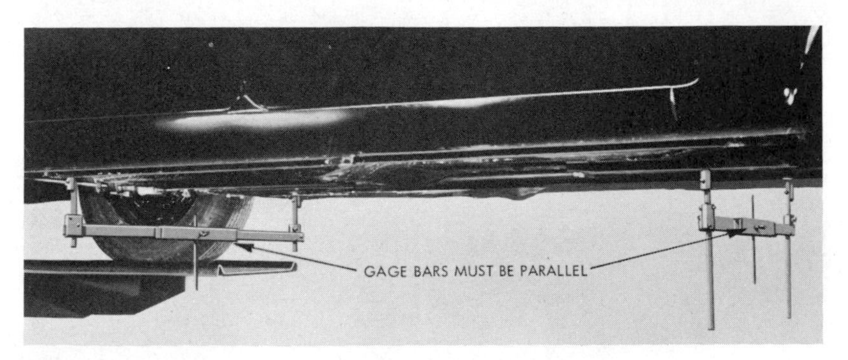

Fig. 11. Two self-centering gages mounted under a unitized body and frame construction to determine whether the body and frame are twisted. If the gage bars are not parallel when mounted, the body and frame then has a twisted condition which is referred to as twist damage.
(John Bean Corp.)

Two self-centering gages mounted on the frame at the extremities of the center section will show the exact amount of twist in the frame. Sight the gage bars from front to rear. The gage bars, as shown in Fig. 11, must be parallel if the frame is free from twist.

The gage is called self-centering because the pin in the center of the gage always remains in the center regardless of how wide the gage is expanded. The gages are held in place by small pins which fit into the jig holes in the side rails of the frame. On a unitized body, however, the gages are mounted by means of C clamps, magnetic adaptors, or special studs screwed into the bottom of the body. A mounted self-centering gage is shown in Fig. 12.

(3) *SAG AND RAISE.* Diamond and twist are the only types of damage that may exist in the center section of the frame in which the frame side rails have not been deformed.

The bottom edges of most side rails are flat underneath the body of the car. Sag is misalignment of the frame when one or both

Fig. 12. A self-centering gage mounted under a vehicle to determine the extent and type of vehicle damage due to a collision. The gage is called self-centering because no matter where the gage is placed, the center pointer will always be in the center of the gage.

(*John Bean Corp.*)

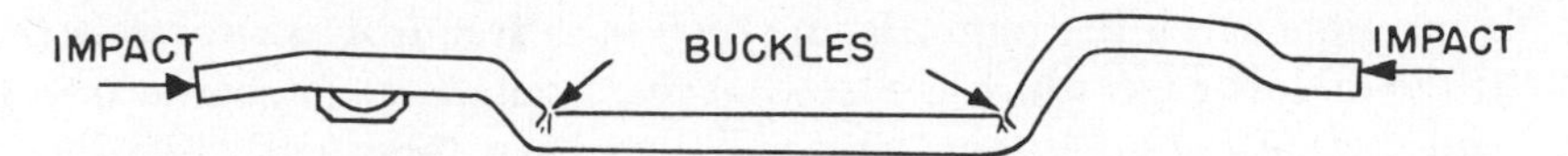

Fig. 13. A sag in the center section of a frame side rail. During a front or rear collision, the force of impact will cause one or both side rails to bend at its lowest point of construction, that is, the dip in the center area. This condition, if the buckles are on top of the frame side rail, is known as **sag**.

(*John Bean Corp.*)

rails are bent downward upon impact. Raise frame damage occurs when one or both side rails are bent upward.

Visually, sag or raise damage to the side rails may be determined by a poor fit of the doors and a buckle in the roof. The rail itself will be buckled on top if the misalignment condition is sag, whereas a rail that has raise damage will be buckled on the bottom. Buckles in the rail, as shown in Fig. 13, are the result of one side of the rail shortening while the opposite side of the same rail stretches.

Sag or raise in the center frame section can be determined by the use of three self-centering gages, as shown in Fig. 14. If all three

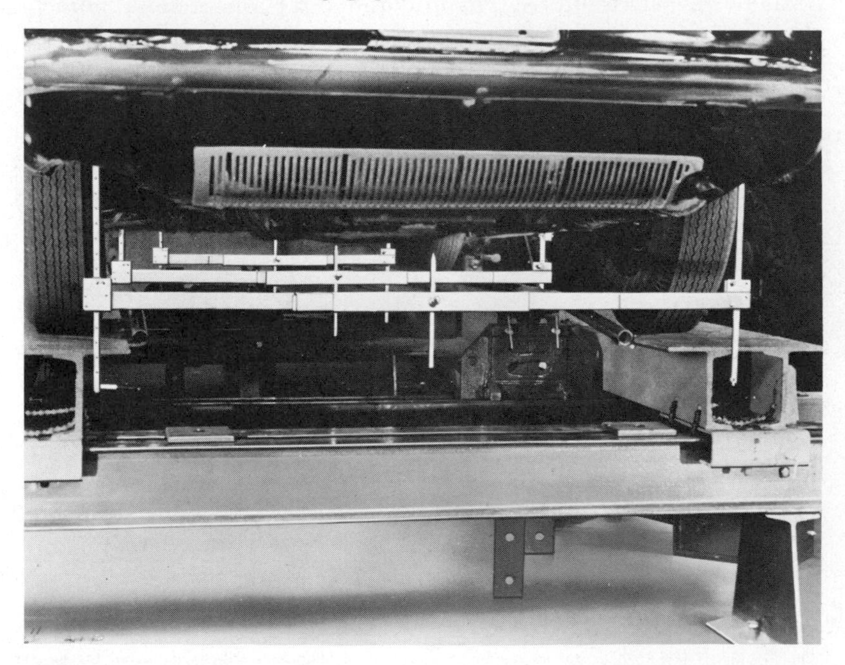

Fig. 14. Using three self-centering gages to check for frame sag. Note that all three gages must be in horizontal alignment if the frame is free from sag damage.

(*John Bean Corp.*)

gages sight level, the center frame section is free from sag or raise. If the middle gage, which is placed at the cowl area, is higher at one end than at the other, one rail may have a sag condition while the opposite rail may have a raise condition.

Since most side rails in the center section of the frame are level on the bottom, a straight edge may be used across the bottom of both rails to determine which rail is damaged. Usually a side rail will sag downward rather than raise upward as the result of a collision.

(4) *SWAY.* Sway occurs when one or both side rails are bent either inward or outward, depending upon the direction of impact. Sway is a lateral misalignment of the frame due to a collision. The side rails of the frame will show evidence of sway by being buckled. The buckles will appear in the side of the rail, as shown in Fig. 15. An X-type frame with tubular center will usually bend at either end of the tubular center should sway damage occur.

Three self-centering gages placed in the center section of the frame will determine the amount and direction of misalignment. If the pins of all three gages as sighted from front to rear are in exact alignment, the center section is then free from sway. Refer to Fig. 14.

b. Rear Section Damage. If the tests made on the center section of the frame indicate that it is undamaged, then either the front or rear section should be checked. If the front of the vehicle obviously has been damaged then the rear section should be checked first.

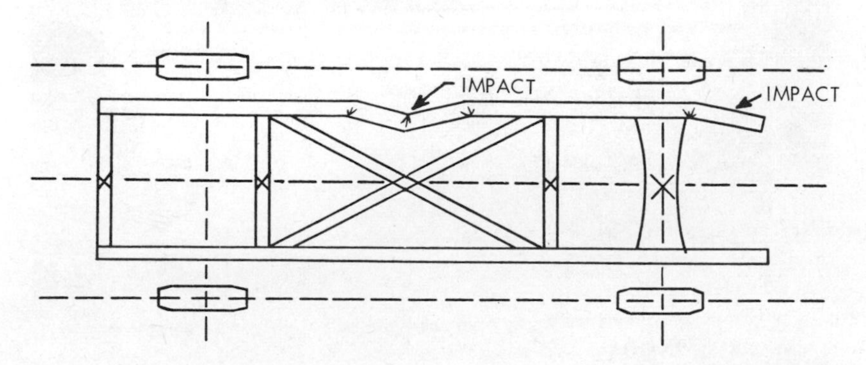

Fig. 15. A frame with center sway. When the force of impact during a collision forces one frame side rail inward toward the center of the vehicle, this condition is known as *sway*. The vehicle will lean *away* from the point of damage.

(*John Bean Corp.*)

Fig. 16. Tru-way gages are installed on the frame, one at the front of the center section, one at the rear of the center section, and one at the rear of the vehicle side rail, to determine whether sag or raise damage is present in the frame. The two center gages are set as sighting pins to determine the location of the rear pin. If the rear pin is above the sight level, the frame rail is too high (raise damage). If the rear pin is below the sight level, the frame rail is too low (sag damage).

(*John Bean Corp.*)

This may easily be done by taking the middle self-centering gage from under the center of the frame and placing it on the rear of the frame. The bars of all three gages will be parallel in the absence of sag or raise in the rear section of the frame. However, both rails may have the same amount of sag or raise damage. To determine the extent of rear frame damage, if any, a set of three side rail height gages may also be used. A manufacturer's dimension manual for each make of car will give the height of the side rail at various points of the frame.

Usually the rear section buckles at the top of the rail in front of the rear kick-up and under the rail over the rear axle housing.

The height or tru-way gages, as shown in Fig. 16, will determine which side rail is out of alignment and which rail is the correct height.

The pin of the rear-self-centering gage will, when it is sighted with the pins of the other two self-centering gages, reveal any sway damage that may exist in the rear section of the frame. See Fig. 14.

c. Front Section Damage. The front section of the vehicle may now be checked for damage and repairs begun. Follow the same general procedure that was used to diagnose the damage to the rear section. A self-centering gage is placed on the front part of the frame, as shown in Fig. 14, to determine the extent and nature of damage. If the bar of the self-centering gage does not align with the two gages underneath the center section of the vehicle, the front frame section probably has a sag at the cowl area (in line with the windshield). A buckle will be visible at the top of the damaged rail underneath the cowl area and there will be a raise at the front suspension pocket. The front suspension pocket will be egg shaped rather than round. Place the height gages on the side rail having the least amount of damage and check it out for height. The rail should meet height specifications within a tolerance of 1/8 inch. If it does, the self-centering gages can then be used to determine when the other rail is straightened to the correct height. A complete analysis of the frame must take place before the frame straightening procedure begins.

V. CORRECTION SEQUENCE OF FRAME REPAIR

In general, the basic principle to follow when straightening a frame is to reverse the force that caused the damage, both in direction and amount. If heat is applied properly, the amount of force needed will be considerably less than the initial impact force. The energy that was consumed by the collision must be expended to straighten the frame and body back to its original condition.

The usual procedure that is followed is to straighten the side rails to their correct height and length. The side rails and frame can then be corrected for sway. After the sway misalignment has been corrected, the twist and diamond conditions are removed from the frame. As these corrections are made, the body must be brought along with the frame. Therefore, unitized body and frame construction will still entail the same basic frame straightening procedures as have been used for conventional frame straightening. Equipment used to straighten conventional type frames may be used on unitized body and frame construction if this equipment is brought up to date with modern body tools and gages. After the frame and body have been straightened, the front and rear suspensions must be completely repaired and aligned. Then the body shop may finish and paint the vehicle.

a. Using Straightening Equipment. The most simple tool used in straightening a damaged frame is the hydraulic ram, which is shown in Fig. 17. This tool can often be used directly against the frame to reverse the impact force of a collision. However, the ram is sometimes limited in its use since it can not always be brought against the work at the correct angle. Often other vehicle parts such as the engine, exhaust pipe, etc., interfere with its use.

Fig. 17. The hydraulic ram is one method of applying the push which is necessary in frame and body straightening to correct any damage inflicted on the vehicle as the result of a collision.

(Ford Div.—Ford Motor Co.)

A body and frame aligner of the type shown in Fig. 18, uses the same type hydraulic ram as shown in Fig. 17. However, this ram is designed to apply the correcting force at any angle on all sections of the body or frame.

A frame straightener and body press, as shown in Fig. 19, is a more complete tool than the body and frame aligner. It often proves a faster method because more than one hook-up or correction may be made at the same time.

b. Repairing Frames. An analysis of the damage to a frame must be made before the condition can be corrected. The method used to straighten a frame usually depends upon the equipment available.

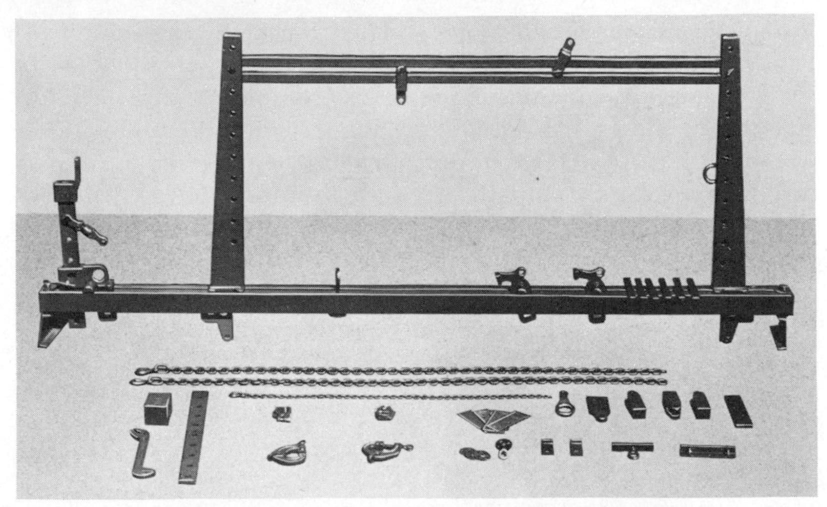

Fig. 18. The rack type of frame and body aligner, with its various clamps, chains and pull plates shown in the foreground.
(*John Bean Corp.*)

In general, the body and frame aligner will use the same general method of hook-ups that the frame and body press would employ.

(1) *SAG AND STRETCH HOOK-UPS.* These are the most

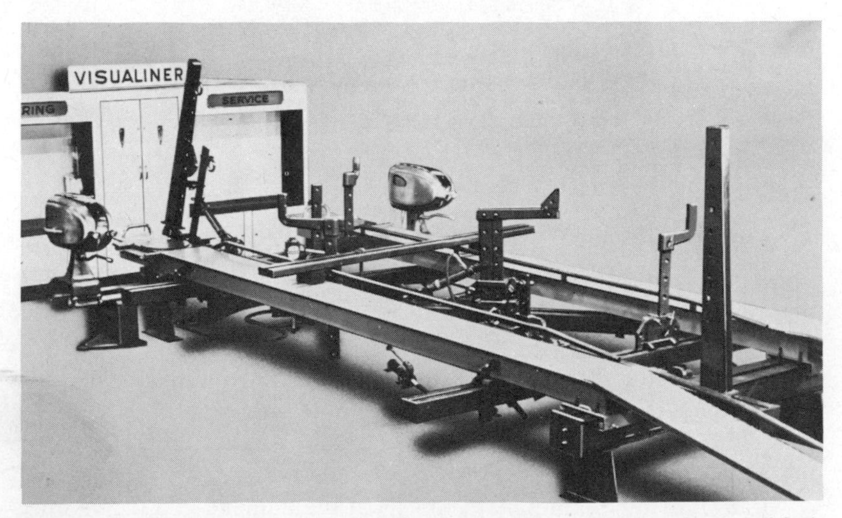

Fig. 19. The frame and body press on which wheel balancing as well as frame and body straightening may be done. This type of construction is known as the ***Visualiner***.
(*John Bean Corp.*)

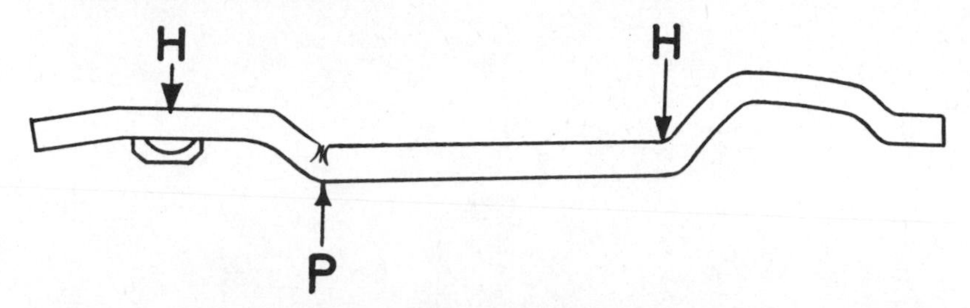

Fig. 20. A minor type of sag damage which exists in the frame side rail. Note that the buckle is on the top of the rail, causing the rail to sag downward. The points marked H indicate where the rail is to be held, while the points marked P indicate where the push or correcting force is to be applied.

(*John Bean Corp.*)

common hook-ups used and usually the first hook-ups made on a frame. A side rail that has a slight buckle at the top, as shown in Fig. 20, may be straightened by means of a chain hook-up attached to an aligner at the H positions. A corrective force in the form of a lift or push is applied by a hydraulic jack at the P position. This will straighten the side rail if the buckle is slight.

If the buckle is quite severe, a stretch and pull method must also be applied to the side rail. Figure 21 illustrates this method. The position marked P2, as shown in Fig. 21, is the point of applied pressure or pull and the H2 position the point of rear hook-up or hold. The buckle must be heated while pressure is applied to the rail or the buckle will tear. An oxygen-acetylene welding unit, as shown in Fig. 22, is used to provide the heat. During correction height gages are used to determine when the side rail has been straightened to its correct shape.

Figures 23 and 24 illustrate the methods of hook-up for the

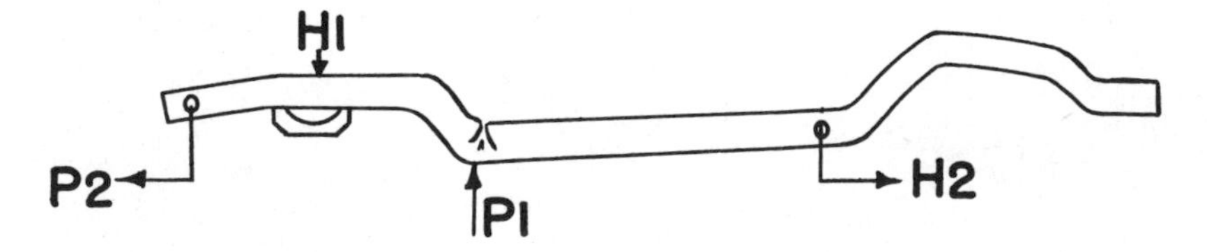

Fig. 21. The points marked H-1 and H-2 indicate where the frame side rail is to be held while the points marked P-1 and P-2 indicate where the correcting force is to be applied. This type of damage is similar to a compound fracture in a human bone, since the buckle is severe and more than one break may exist at that point. Therefore, this type of damage is known as a major sag.

(*John Bean Corp.*)

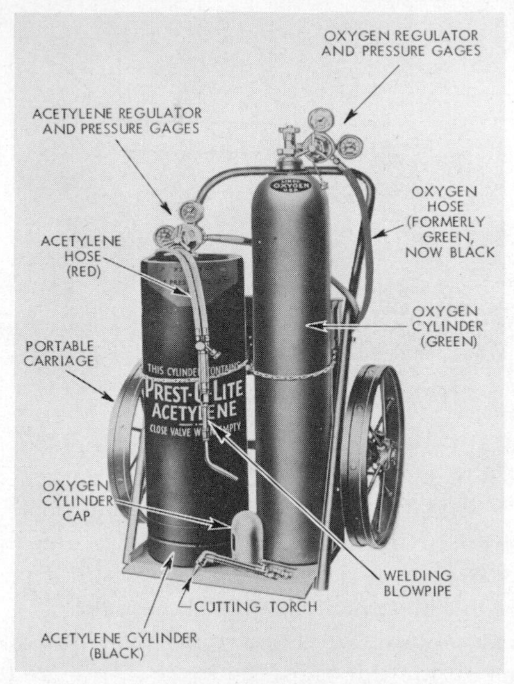

Fig. 22. Oxygen-acetylene welding unit. Note that each part of the unit is color coded for easy identification.
(Linde Air Products Co.)

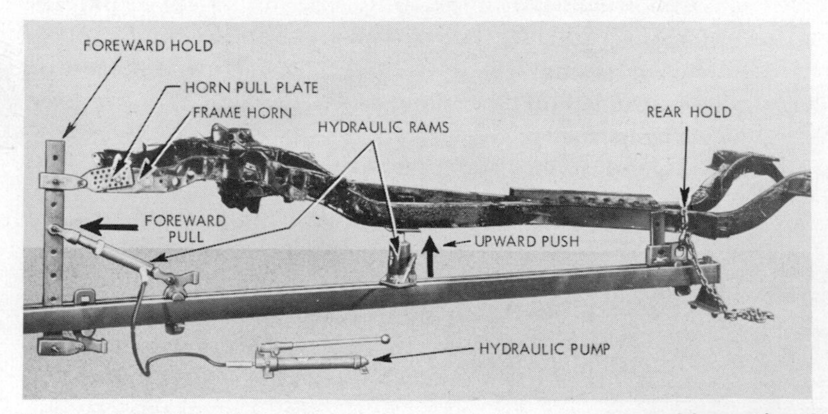

Fig. 23. The body and frame aligner in the process of correcting a sagged frame side rail. Pressure is supplied to the hydraulic rams by the hydraulic pump, the hydraulic rams applying an upward push at the center section of the rail and at the same time, a forward pull on front section of the rail, thereby pushing and pulling the damaged rail into alignment. Note the position of the rear hold which allows only the damaged section to be moved.
(John Bean Corp.)

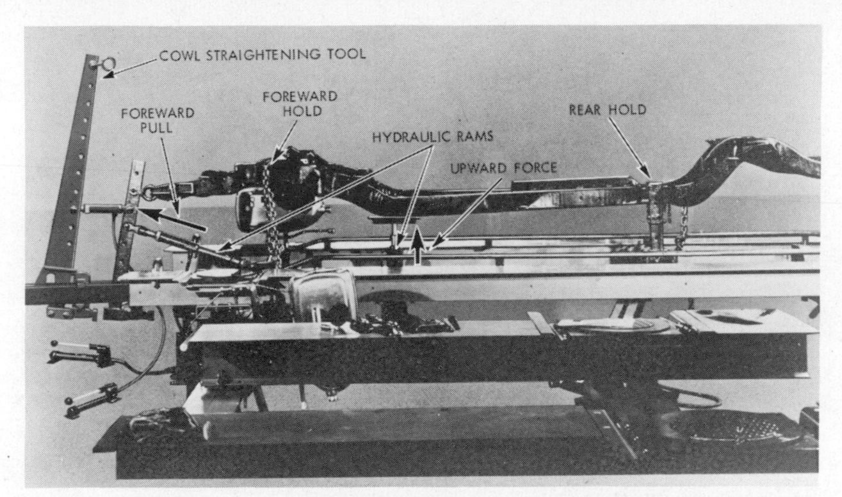

Fig. 24. The frame straightener and body press in the process of correcting a sagged frame side rail. Note the various hook-ups for applying the correcting force plus the body upright tool for correcting damage in the cowl area of the body. Note also the position of the forward and rear holds.

(*John Bean Corp.*)

body and frame aligner and the frame straightener and body press, which are used to correct a major sag condition.

(2) *SWAY CORRECTION*. Sway is the next most common type of damage that exists in the frame. As with the stretch and sag method of hook-ups, heat must be applied. Caution should be taken not to overheat the frame, since metal heated to a dull cherry red color is hot enough for straightening purposes. If the metal should tear because heat was not applied at the right place, immediately *stop the pulling action.* Then weld the tear with either an oxygen-acetylene welding torch or an arc welder. Figures

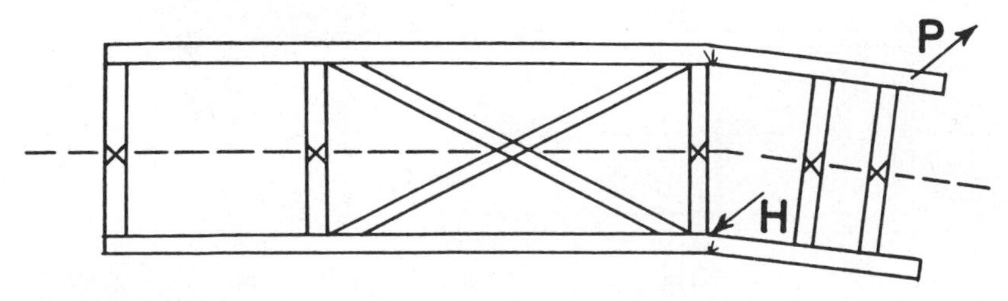

Fig. 25. A vehicle frame having side sway damage. The letter H is the point of hold, either against a frame crossmember, or if desired, a chain may be wrapped around the side rail at that point. The letter P indicates where the pull is to be applied.

(*John Bean Corp.*)

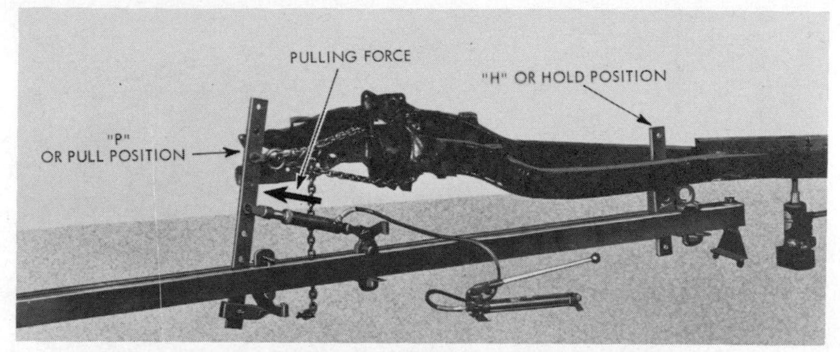

Fig. 26. The body and frame aligner correcting a frame side rail for sway. A chain is wrapped around the rail at point "P" and a tool bar is placed against the tube of the X member frame to provide the "H" or hold position.
(John Bean Corp.)

25 through 29 illustrate several methods of removing sway from a frame.

Another method that may be used to correct side sway is to hold the outer ends of the rail at the H positions and apply pressure on both rails at the P position. See Fig. 27. This will straighten the buckles in both rails and correct the sway in the frame.

On a frame straightener, a method known as a "sliding beam" setup is used to apply pressure at points P as illustrated in Fig. 27. A beam which is moved by means of a hydraulic ram is free to slide under the run-ways of the frame, therefore applying pressure to the frame. The sliding beam method is illustrated in Fig. 29. The hold or H positions are uprights (tool bars) which are locked to beams. These beams (called carriage beams) run crosswise or 90 degrees to

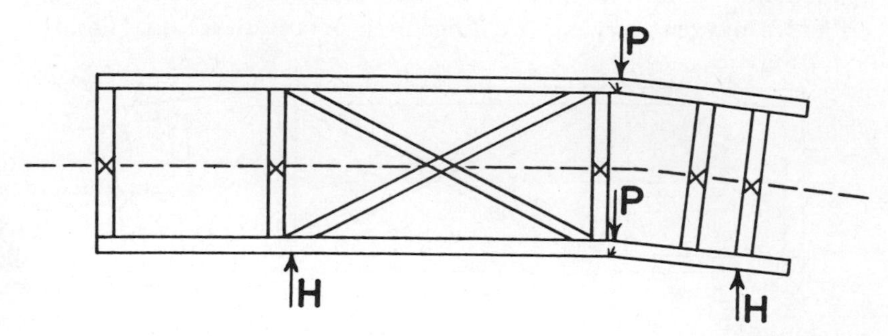

Fig. 27. Vehicle side sway in which the correcting force is applied to both side rails, "H" marking the points of hold and "P" the points of push.
(John Bean Corp.)

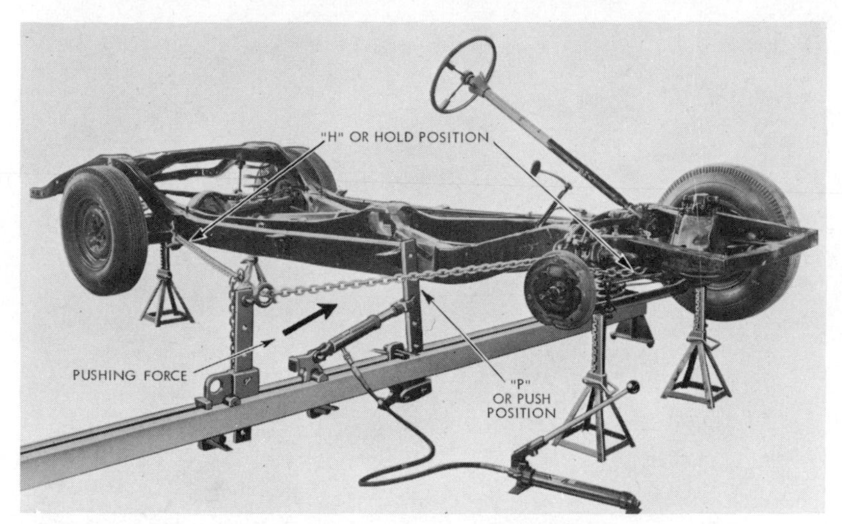

Fig. 28. The body and frame aligner in the process of correcting vehicle side sway. This method of alignment is often referred to as the bow string method. Push is applied against only one frame side rail and the vehicle body transmits the force of this push to the other rail. Therefore, the correcting force is applied to both rails through only one hook-up.
(John Bean Corp.)

Fig. 29. The sliding beam method as used with the frame straightener and body press. The tool bars and carriage are in position to correct a vehicle frame with sway damage.
(John Bean Corp.)

Fig. 30. "H" or hold positions used to anchor the sliding beams to the runway of the frame straightener and body press.
(*John Bean Corp.*)

the run-ways. The carriage beams are locked to the run-ways, as shown in Fig. 30. Therefore they provide the H or hold position against which the pressure or push may be applied so as to restore the frame to its original shape.

(3) *TWIST CORRECTION.* After the sway condition has been corrected, any twist misalignment that may exist should next be removed from the frame. The side rails must be straight, and have the correct height, otherwise, the self-centering gages will not

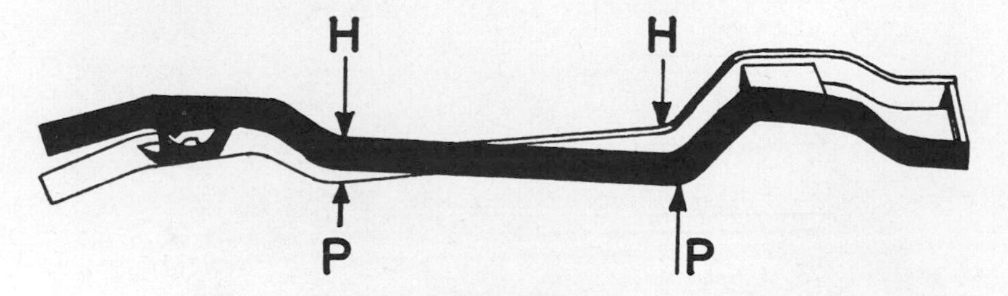

Fig. 31. The hold and push positions for correcting a vehicle with a twisted frame. The H positions are on the high points of the vehicle frame while the correcting force will be applied at the low points of the damaged frame area.
(*John Bean Corp.*)

Fig. 32. Correcting a twisted frame with the frame straightener and body aligner. Chains are used to hold the carriage beams at the H position while the hydraulic jacks apply a pushing force at the P position. The hydraulic jacks are used to lift the frame until all the self-centering gages are in parallel alignment. Usually, the frame must be corrected past the misalignment, and in the opposite direction of the damage, in order to bring the frame to the correct position.

(John Bean Corp.)

align after the twist condition has been removed. Figures 31 and 32 illustrate the hook-up methods and the pressures that are to be applied in removing a twist from the frame.

(4) *DIAMOND CORRECTION.* A diamond is the last major type of damage removed from the frame. There are two methods by which a diamond may be removed from the frame:

(a) A diagonal push may be used as shown in Fig. 33.

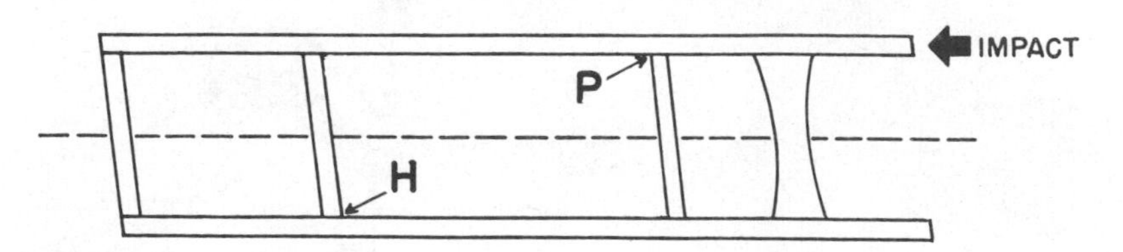

Fig. 33. The force of impact has forced one of the vehicle frame side rails slightly ahead of the other. This condition is known as diamond damage and can be removed from the frame by holding the side rail at point H while applying push in the direction opposite to that of the damage at point P. When the frame is cross measured at the center section and the distance is equal, the diamond damage has been removed.

(John Bean Corp.)

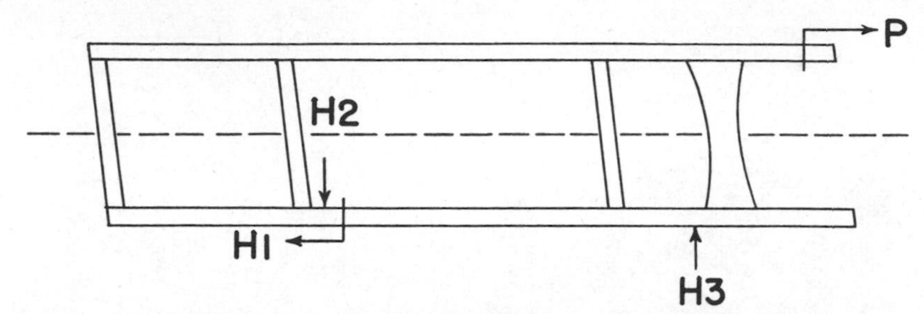

Fig. 34. The straight pull method for removing diamond frame damage. H-1 is the hold position to keep the frame from moving forward when the pull is applied at point P. H-2 and H-3 are the holds which are used to keep the frame from shifting off of the frame rack. Note that all of the hold positions are on the vehicle frame side rail opposite to that which the pulling force is applied.

(John Bean Corp.)

(b) A straight pull may be used to correct the diamond condition as shown in Fig. 34.

The portable frame and body aligner may be used to apply pressures to diagonally opposite corners of the frame, as shown in

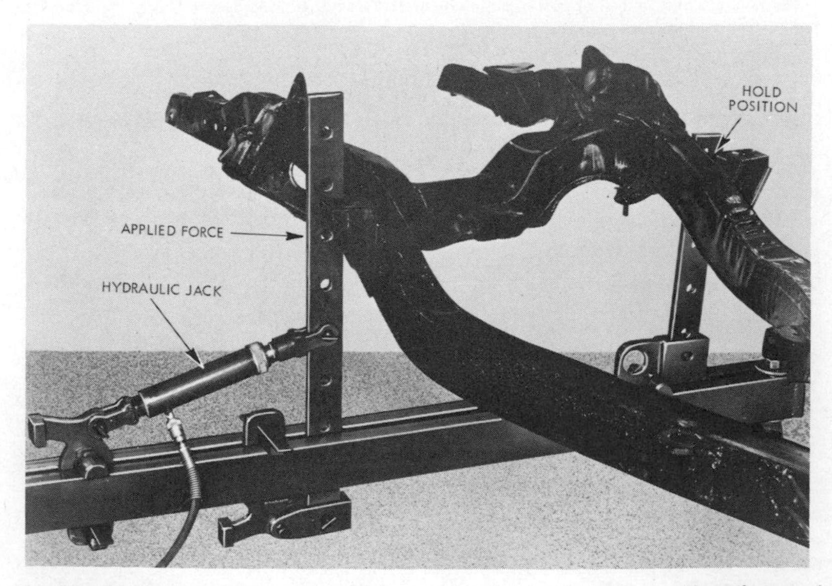

Fig. 35. The body and frame aligner being used to force the two frame side rails inward toward the vehicle center. The tool bar on the right frame rail provides the hold position, while the tool bar on the left frame rail provides the squeezing action when the hydraulic ram is expanded.

(John Bean Corp.)

Fig. 33. The straight pull method of correcting a diamond frame, as shown in Fig. 34, is used only on a frame straightener.

(5) *OTHER FRAME HOOK-UPS.* At times a frame may be too narrow or too wide at various places for conventional hook-up methods. Figure 35 illustrates a squeezing action that may be applied to a frame to decrease the width. Figure 36 illustrates a spreading action that may be applied to a frame to increase its width.

In order to correct the front suspension cross members after a collision, it is necessary to apply pressure to the cross member from its center with the outer ends chained down. A cross member that sags causes the top of the wheels to lean inward, often to the extent that the normal adjusting procedures will not correct wheel camber to specifications. Figure 37 shows how this operation may be performed on a frame straightener.

In some types of collision the front cross member may be pushed rearward at the bottom. This causes a condition known as a rolled

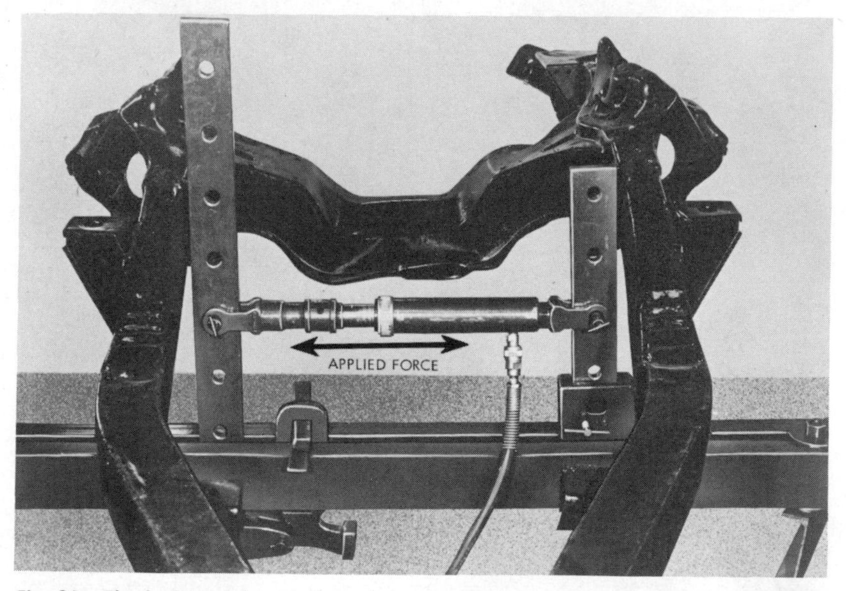

Fig. 36. The body and frame aligner being used to force the two frame side rails away from the vehicle center. The hydraulic ram is placed between the hold and the push position, and when the ram is expanded, equal pressure is applied to both frame side rails, spreading the damaged portion of the frame back to the correct position. If the front end of the frame has been damaged so that the side rails are squeezed together, this hook-up may be used without removing the engine.

(*John Bean Corp.*)

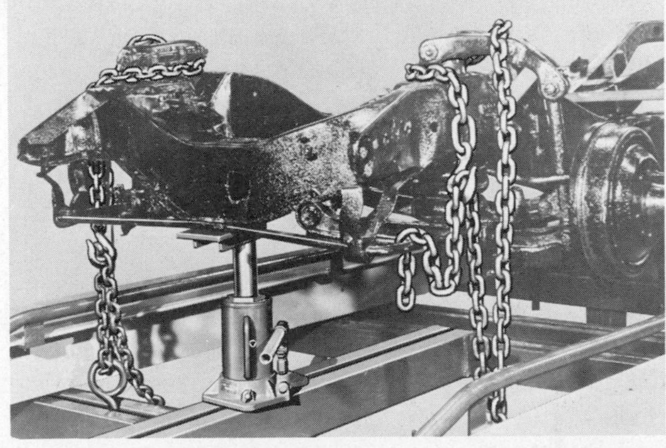

Fig. 37. Correcting a front crossmember for sag. Chains are used to hold the ends of the crossmember from moving upward as the hydraulic jack pushes upward against a plate which distributes the correcting force evenly to the bottom of the crossmember.
(*John Bean Corp.*)

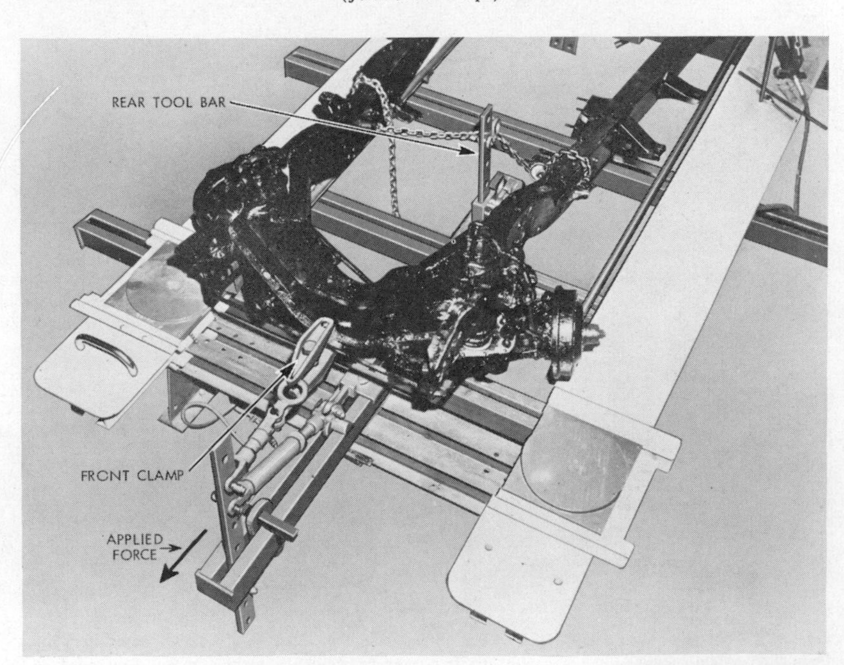

Fig. 38. Hook-up used to correct the crossmember for roll damage. A frame clamp is attached to the front of the crossmember to provide the pulling force needed to straighten the crossmember. A chain is mounted between the two frame side rails, the tool bar resting against the chain provides the hold position as the crossmember is pulled forward.
(*John Bean Corp.*)

Fig. 39. Box frame clamp. This clamp, through the use of rasps which dig into the frame side rail, forms an excellent hold on the boxed inside rail. However, care must be taken since damage to the side rail will result if the clamp is not installed correctly.
(*John Bean Corp.*)

cross member which affects the caster of the front wheels. To straighten the cross member back to a satisfactory position, the method shown in Fig. 38 would be applied.

(6) *GOOD HOLD POSITIONS.* In order that a pulling force may be applied to a side rail, the hold position must be strong, secure, and not cause further damage to the frame through slippage at the point of pull. One type of frame clamp that can be attached to a box type of frame side rail is shown in Fig. 39.

When it is necessary to apply a pulling action to the front of the frame, a horn pull plate may be bolted to the frame horn by using the bumper bracket bolt holes as shown in Fig. 40.

If the horn pull plate cannot be bolted to the frame, another tool, the horn pull clamp, may be used instead. This clamp employs a short piece of rasp which enables it to bite into the side rail. The horn pull clamp, as illustrated in Fig. 41, is attached to a tool bar by means of a clevis. Since chains are not used in this type of hook-up, the connection is considered to be trouble free.

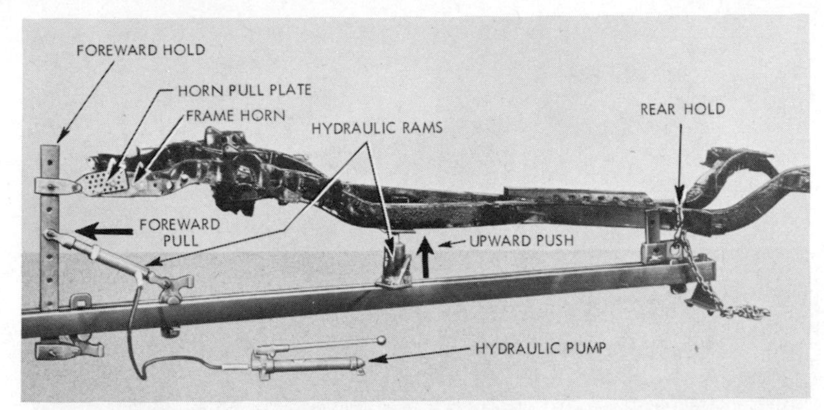

Fig. 40. The horn pull plate, which is bolted to the frame horn, is used to correct frames having sag and diamond damage by providing a means of holding the section of the frame to which the correcting force is applied.

(John Bean Corp.)

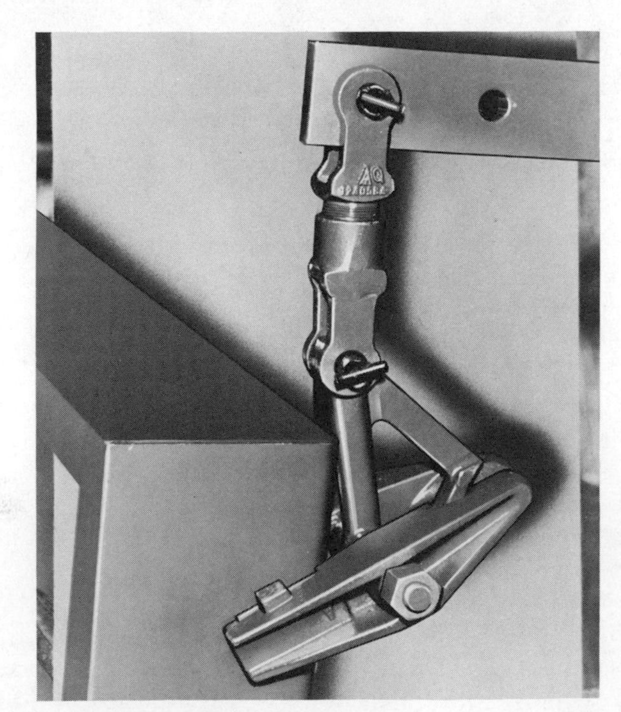

Fig. 41. The horn pull clamp is used for the same purpose as the horn pull plate and may be used in conjunction with the horn pull plate.

(John Bean Corp.)

Fig. 42. Body tools mounted on the frame straightener. The lateral beam, which is supported on two uprights, may go through either the car door openings or through the window openings to provide the correcting force necessary to bring the body and frame into alignment.

(John Bean Corp.)

c. Body Tools. A frame straightening machine must have provisions so that body and frame corrections can be made in one operation. Figure 42 illustrates two body uprights mounted to a beam on the frame straightener. The uprights support another beam from which corrections can be made on the roof or the side panels of the body. This method is time saving since the seats do not have to be removed from the body.

The portable body and frame aligner is designed for use in the shop as an aid to the body man. For corrections to be made on a unitized body and frame, both the portable aligner and frame straightener would be employed. Figure 43 shows the portable type aligner pulling on a damaged cowl.

VI. FRAME AND BODY ESTIMATING

The methods used to estimate the cost of body and frame repair

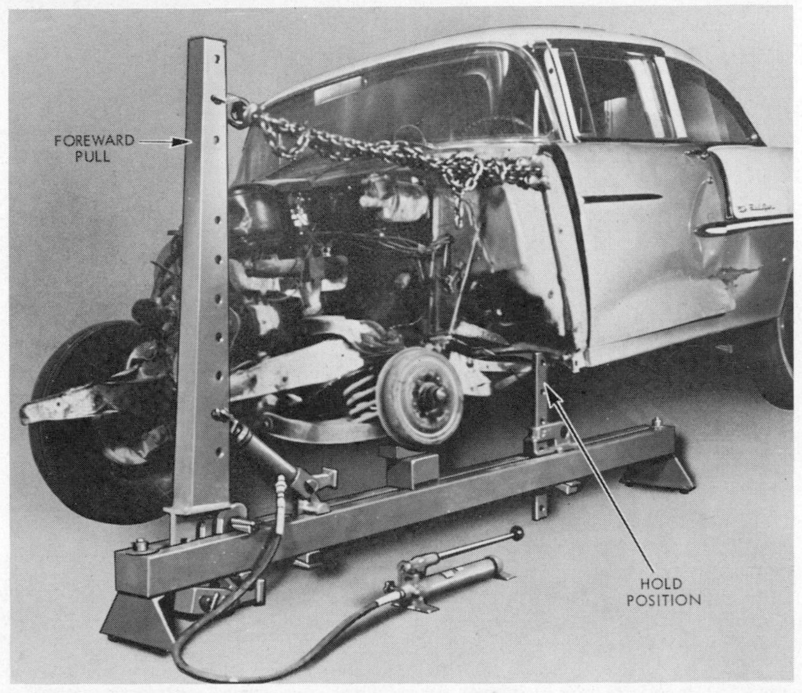

Fig. 43. Body and frame aligner in the process of pulling a damaged cowl into alignment. Clamps are used to provide the hook-up to the cowl. Note the hold position as provided by the tool bar against the frame body bracket.

(John Bean Corp.)

would depend largely upon the extent of the damage and the equipment available to make such repairs. In some localities, repairmen charge a flat fee when a car is placed on their rack regardless of the extent of the frame damage.

The lack of frame straightening equipment and the production of more cars with unitized body and frame construction emphasizes the need for the portable type of frame and body equipment. This has also changed to a certain extent the method by which the cost of frame work is estimated. The hourly rate system now seems to be used in some frame and body shops.

The hourly rate system sets up a certain time in which to make a correction. A twist, for instance, may take three hours to be removed from the frame. The current average rate is about $8.00 an hour for frame straightening. To correct a twist with a body and frame aligner would cost the customer $24.00. The body and frame aligner is popular with body shops since it allows repairmen to do frame work in their own shops.

In some localities, when a vehicle is estimated for the cost of the repair, the frame repair estimate is left open, and the cost is determined after the frame is straightened. Of course, this practice is frowned upon by the customer since he likes to know in advance what the job will cost him.

The ability of the frame repair man to know his equipment and estimate the time needed to do a certain repair is a matter of experience. It is hoped that this chapter has given the beginning frame man an insight into the problems of frame straightening and a knowledge of the methods and equipment used in the trade.

TRADE COMPETENCY TEST

1. What are the purposes of a frame? (p. 1)
2. What are the most common results of a misaligned frame? (p. 1)
3. How does a unitized body and frame construction differ from the conventional body and frame? (p. 4)
4. What are the basic steps in frame repair? (pp. 5, 6)
5. Why is the center section of the frame usually checked first when analyzing frame damage? (p. 6)
6. How can you recognize diamond damage to a frame without using special tools? (pp. 6, 7)
7. What are the usual results of a twisted frame? (pp. 8, 9)
8. How do the effects of a sagging frame show up? (pp. 10, 11)
9. What is the general basic principle to follow in straightening a frame? (p. 14)
10. What is the sequence that is usually followed in frame straightening? (p. 14)
11. What is probably the most essential tool needed for frame straightening? (pp. 16,17)
12. What type of alignment equipment is needed for unitized body and frame straightening? (pp. 14, 15)

CHAPTER 2

FRONT SUSPENSION SYSTEMS

	PAGE
I. Independent Front Wheel Suspension Systems	32
II. Axle Suspension with Leaf Springs	44
III. Front Suspension Service	46

An automotive suspension system consists of the arrangement of springs, shock absorbers, axles, or long and short arm linkages which connect the wheels to the vehicle frame.

The front suspension system carries the weight of the forward part of the vehicle, including the weight of the parts that go to make up the system. In addition, it must be so designed that the front wheels are free to pivot at various angles to permit steering and to move up and down to allow for springing.

Each wheel in a front suspension system is supported on a spindle which is part of the steering knuckle assembly. This arrangement permits the wheels to swing from side to side and enables the vehicle operator to steer. Leaf springs, coil springs, torsion bars, and air bellows absorb road shock and permit the wheels to move up and down.

This chapter deals with the construction, identification, location, and functioning of suspension parts, so that the student can intelligently analyze failures and plan necessary repairs. This chapter also discusses the repairs required to restore clearances, caused by wear, back to their original specifications. Other chapters will deal in detail with the adjustments and repairs required to restore proper alignment.

I. INDEPENDENT FRONT WHEEL SUSPENSION SYSTEMS

The term independent suspension refers to the system of springing a vehicle so that each wheel is free to move up and down without directly affecting the other. No axle as such is used in the independent suspension system; the wheels are attached to a cross member of the frame of the vehicle by individual linkages.

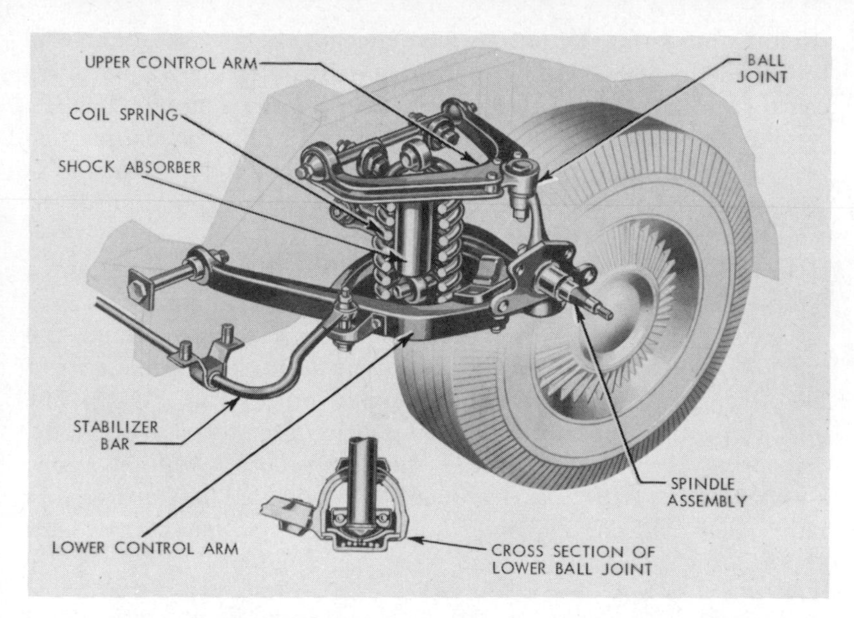

Fig. 1. Independent front suspension system using ball joints. This is a typical type of front suspension used on present vehicles, employing a direct acting shock absorber mounted between the lower control arm and the vehicle frame. The shock absorber is mounted inside a coil spring, the spring and the shock absorber working together to reduce road shocks. (*Lincoln Div.–Ford Motor Co.*)

All present passenger vehicles use the independent type of front end suspension in which each front wheel is independently supported by a coil spring, torsion bar, or air bellows. The coil spring arrangement is the most common; however, all forms of springs can be made to behave similarly.

The linkages used in the construction of the front end unit comprise the basic features of the suspension. All independent front suspensions used on passenger vehicles now manufactured are of the short-long arm type with spherical type ball joints connecting the control arms and steering knuckles. Previous models used kingpins to attach the steering knuckles to the control arms.

a. Independent Suspension System with Ball Joints. On the short-long arm type of independent front end suspension two control arms are used on each side of the vehicle, an upper control arm (short) and a lower control arm (long). The arms are shaped like a chicken wishbone, or like the letter V. The arms are attached to the vehicle frame cross member by the open ends, extend sidewise from the mounting points and have the closed ends out beyond the frame side members. One arm is mounted under the frame (lower control arm), while the other (upper control arm) is mounted above. Both arms are attached to the frame by means of pivot shafts which permit free movement of the linkage in the up-and-down directions. The other ends of the arms are spaced by the steering knuckle assembly which connects them. This steering knuckle assembly is attached to the control arms by means of ball joints. Fig. 1 shows a typical short-long arm suspension system using ball joints.

A coil spring, if used, is generally located between the frame and the lower control arm (Fig. 1). On some front suspension systems the coil spring is located above the upper control arm (Fig. 2). The operating principles and basic components are the same as if the coil spring were located between the lower control arm and frame cross member. When the front end is suspended by torsion bars rather than coil springs the basic construction remains the same

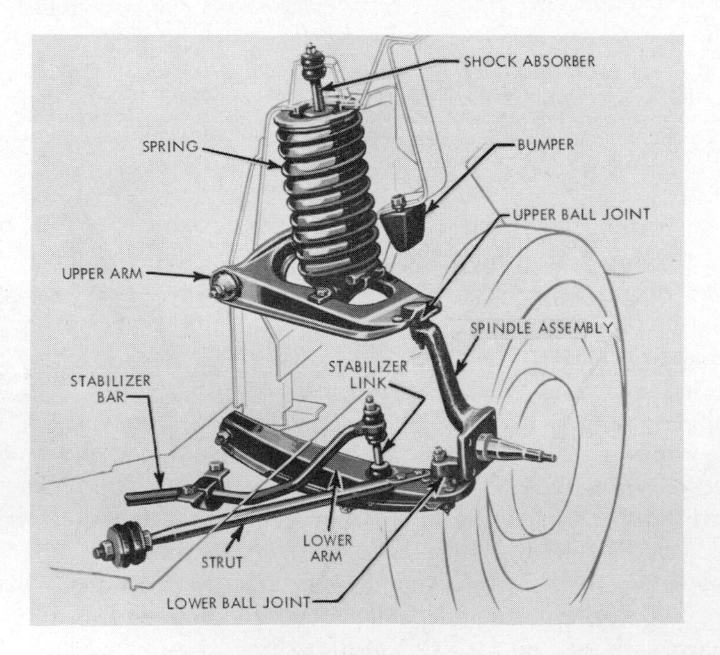

Fig. 2. An independent front suspension with the coil spring mounted between the upper control arm and the vehicle frame. The coil spring and the shock absorber still operate in the same manner no matter where they are mounted or whether they are mounted together or not.

(Ford Div.—Ford Motor Co.)

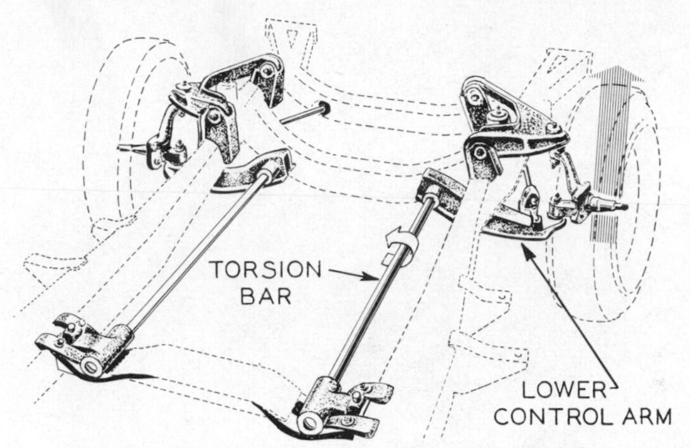

Fig. 3. Typical front end construction using torsion bars.

(Fig. 3). The torsion bar replaces the pivot shaft of the lower control arm.

When the vehicle is in a normal position the frame rests on the spring and the spring rests on either the lower control arm, Fig. 1, or the upper control arm (Fig. 2). When the wheel goes up due to a change in the surface of the road, the control arms swing up at the outer end and the spring is compressed. The spring then proceeds to rebound and raise the weight of the vehicle. The same reaction takes place on torsion bar suspension with the twisting of the bar.

b. Component Parts of the Suspension. The same general types of parts are used in all short-long arm suspensions regardless of whether coil springs, torsion bars, or air bellows are used to suspend the weight. Figure 4 gives the names of the component parts of a disassembled front suspension unit using ball joints.

(1) *CONTROL ARMS.* The control arms are attached to the vehicle frame cross member. They extend sidewise from the frame and are attached at the outer end to the support. Two control arms are used on each side of the vehicle. These are called the upper and lower control arms. The upper control arm is always shorter than the lower control arm. Control arms are sometimes called wishbones or A frames.

(2) *PIVOT SHAFTS.* The inner end of the control arm is mounted on the frame cross member by means of the pivot shaft. Some manufacturers refer to this as the pivot bar or control arm shaft. The control arm is free to move up and down on the outer

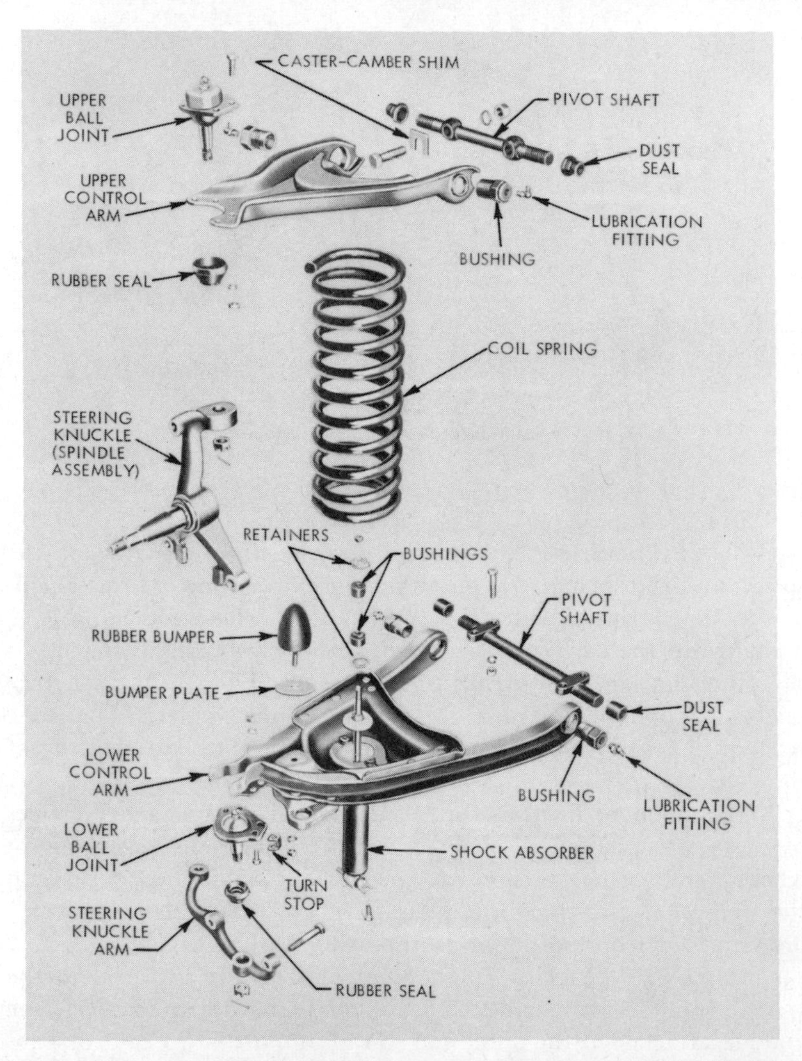

Fig. 4. Exploded view of a ball joint front suspension unit using a coil spring. Note that the ball joints serve the same purpose as the kingpin of earlier vehicles, that is, to attach the steering knuckle to the upper and lower control arms.
(*Cadillac Div.—General Motors Corp.*)

ends of the pivot bar. Shims are generally located between the pivot shaft and frame cross member to permit caster and camber adjustment. On torsion bar suspension the torsion bar replaces the lower inner pivot shaft.

(3) *BALL JOINTS.* Ball joints attach the outer ends of the control arms to the steering knuckle assembly. Ball joints permit the knuckle to be turned for steering and also permit up and down movement when the wheel goes over an irregularity in the road surface.

(4) *STEERING KNUCKLE.* The steering knuckle has an elongated yoke which is attached directly to the upper and lower control arms by means of ball joints. The steering knuckle also consists of a spindle for mounting the wheel. A steering knuckle arm is incorporated for holding the knuckle in any desired position in its swing or travel. The arm may be part of the knuckle forging or it may be a separate piece attached by bolts or by securing a tapered end into a corresponding hole in the knuckle by means of a nut.

(5) *OPERATING CHARACTERISTICS.* The short-long arm suspension is designed so that the front wheels always track. This is done by making the upper control arm shorter than the lower one. Under normal load, the arms are practically horizontal. Due to the fact that each arm pivots at the frame, the outer end swings in a circular path. This means that when the outer end moves up or down, it moves closer to the center of the car as shown in Fig. 5.

If the wheel were permitted to move in toward and out from

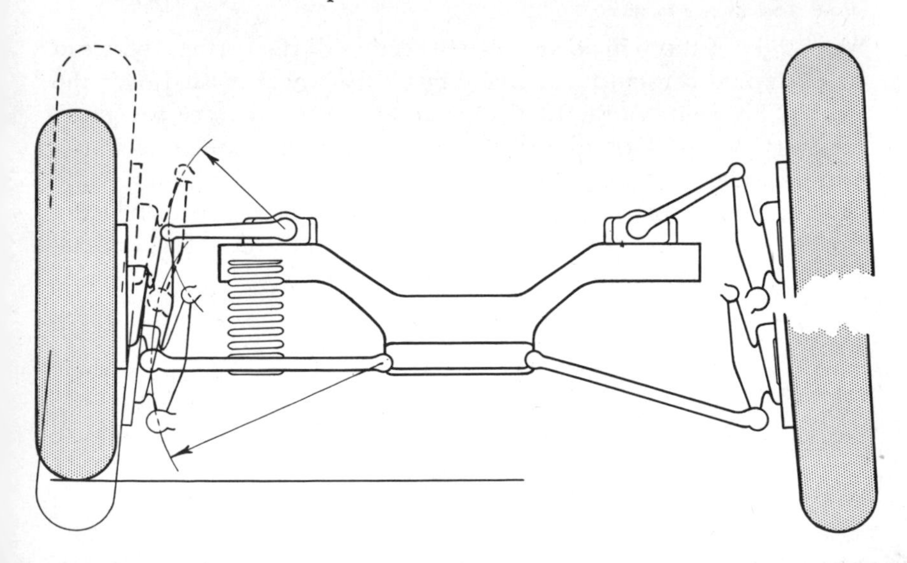

Fig. 5. Front wheels always track. When the outer end moves up or down, it moves closer to the center of the car.

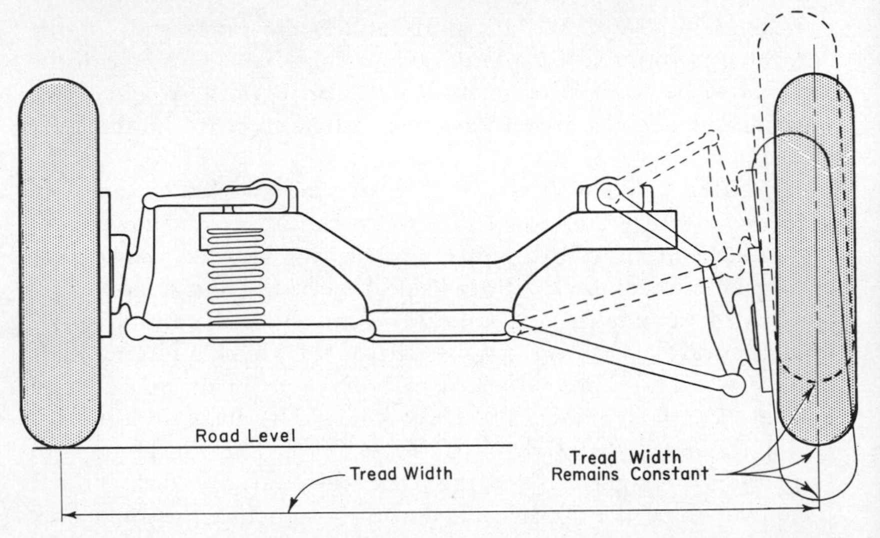

Fig. 6. When the spring deflects and the outer end of the lower control arm moves inward toward the center of the vehicle, the outer end of the upper control arm moves farther inward toward the vehicle center because it is much shorter than the lower control arm. The steering knuckle leans inward at the top as it is brought toward the frame by the motion of the control arms. The spindle points slightly upward causing the wheel to lean inward at the top. However, the portion of the tire that contacts the road remains the same distance from the vehicle while the wheel hub moves inward and therefore, the vehicle tread remains almost constant.

the center of the vehicle at every deflection of the spring, the tread width would constantly be changing as the wheels passed over the road. This would cause the tires to scrub sidewise on the pavement at every bump. This difficulty is overcome by making the upper arm considerably shorter than the lower one. The outer end of the shorter arm swings in a shorter arc as shown in Fig. 6. When the spring deflects and the outer end of the lower arm moves in, the

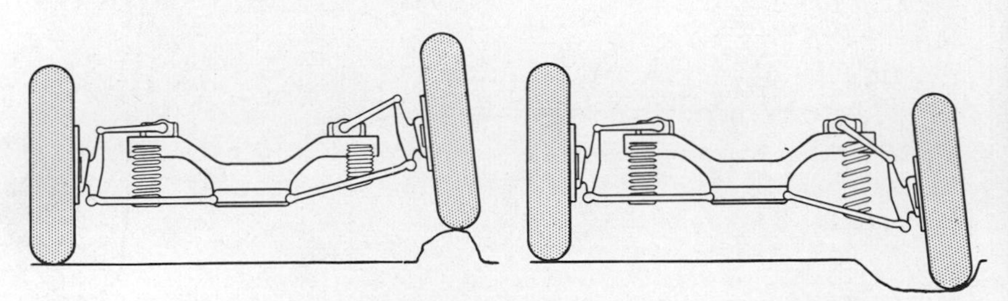

Fig. 7. Linkage action as the spring is compressed on the upward movement of the wheel.

Fig. 8. Action of the linkage as the spring rebounds on the downward movement of the wheel.

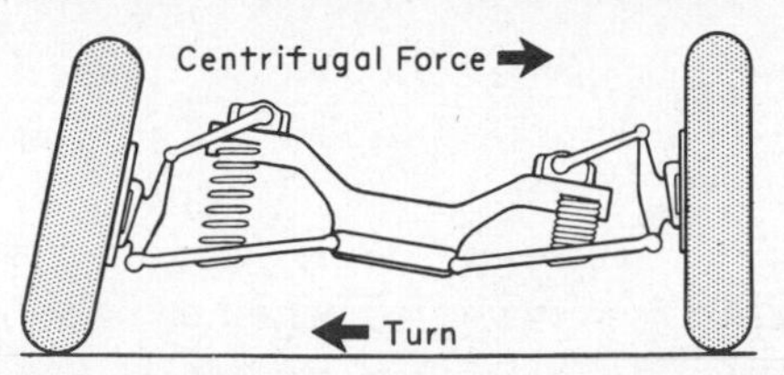

Fig. 9. Linkage action of the front suspension as the vehicle makes a right turn. This action would be the same on a left turn, but in the opposite direction.

outer end of the upper arm moves in farther, due to the sharper arc. The steering knuckle leans in at the top as it is brought in toward the frame by the swinging arms. The spindle points slightly upward, and the wheel leans in at the top. The bottom of the wheel in contact with the road stays at the same distance from the other wheel, while the hub moves in toward the car. The vehicle tread, therefore, remains practically constant. These conditions come into effect regardless of whether the arms swing upward or downward (Figs. 7 and 8).

On a severe turn where the vehicle heels over, these characteristics cause the outside wheel to bank against the turn (Fig. 9). This puts the best tractive action at the point of the greatest load. The inside wheel leans away from the turn, but carries the smaller portion of the load.

c. Independent Suspension System with Kingpins. Previous designs of front suspension systems used an additional linkage member

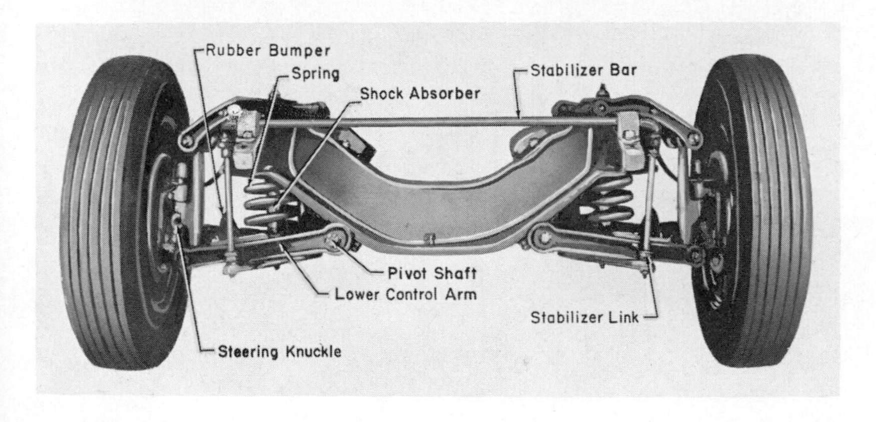

Fig. 10. Front suspension consisting of the steering knuckle and support assembly mounted together by means of the kingpin. This type of assembly is known as the Reverse Elliot steering knuckle and support assembly.

to attach the outer ends of the control arms. This additional member is known as a steering knuckle support and is attached to the steering knuckle assembly by means of a kingpin. Fig. 10 illustrates a typical independent suspension using kingpins. Basically the suspension construction is very similar whether ball joints or kingpins are used; however, additional units are used with kingpins.

(1) *STEERING KNUCKLE.* The steering knuckle is constructed in the same manner as the steering knuckle with ball joints except that the yoke is shorter and built with a hole on the top and bottom to receive the kingpin, Fig. 10. The opening which the kingpin passes through is larger than the kingpin to permit the installation of removable bushings. The bushings reduce friction and prevent wear on the knuckle.

(2) *SUPPORT.* The support carries the steering knuckle. It is affixed to the vehicle by means of control arms through pivot pins at the top and bottom. The support may also be called the support arm or the steering knuckle support. Fig. 11 illustrates a front suspension unit which uses a kingpin.

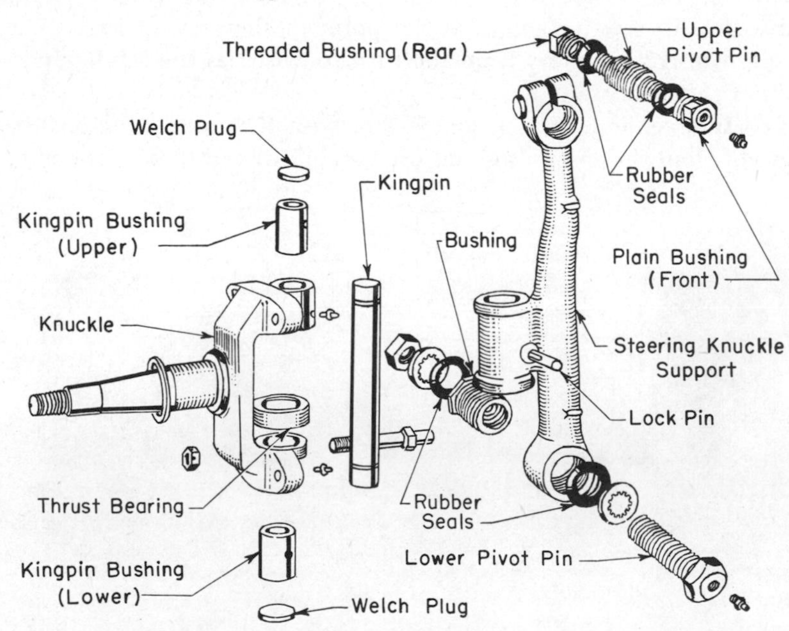

Fig. 11. The independent coil spring type of front suspension using kingpins. In this type of installation, the steering knuckle is mounted on its support by means of the kingpins, one kingpin for each front wheel.

(3) *PIVOT PINS.* The pivot pin (Fig. 11) attaches the outer end of the support at both top and bottom. Generally, the pins are threaded to permit adjustment for alignment. The top pin is generally in the form of an eccentric to facilitate camber adjustment.

(4) *KINGPIN.* The kingpin is used to attach the support to the steering knuckle and also is the pivot upon which the steering knuckle turns. The kingpin is locked in the support arm. A thrust bearing is installed between the lower yoke of the steering knuckle and the bottom of the support. The bearing may be a sealed ball bearing or roller bearing. This bearing actually supports the weight of the vehicle. (Note: A *thrust bearing* is a shaft bearing designed to take an axial load. It consists of either a plain or modified bearing pad—or, in instances where the axial load is extremely heavy—a ball or roller bearing provided with lateral races).

d. Elongated Kingpin. A somewhat different type of coil spring

Fig. 12. Front suspension system using an elongated kingpin to attach the steering knuckle assembly to the upper and lower arms.
(*Studebaker Corp.*)

front suspension is illustrated in Fig. 12. An elongated kingpin extends above and below the steering knuckle. The upper end of the kingpin is attached to the outer end of the upper control arm by an eccentric pin. A kingpin support attached by a pin to the lower control arm receives the lower end of the kingpin. A thrust bearing located on the kingpin between the top of the steering knuckle and a shoulder on the kingpin supports the weight of the vehicle.

e. Transverse Leaf Service. One type of suspension used a transverse leaf spring instead of a lower control arm (Fig. 13). The link-

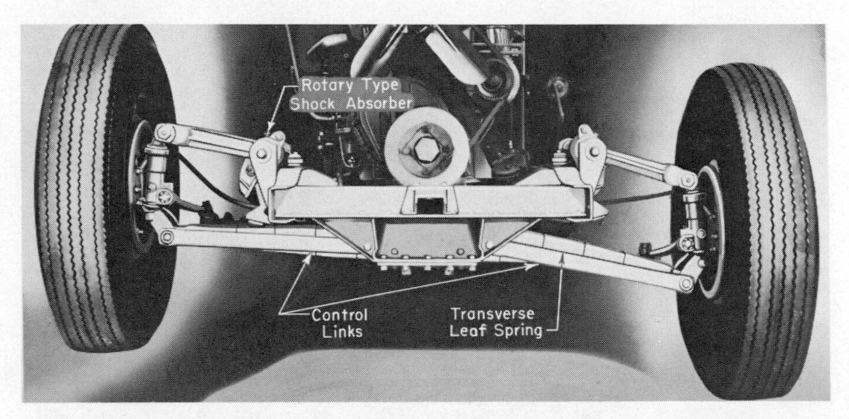

Fig. 13. Independent front suspension system using transverse leaf spring. (*Studebaker Corp.*)

age consisted of an upper control arm, a support arm, a steering knuckle and a leaf spring. The spring served two functions: that of holding the lower end of the support arm and of providing the spring action. One spring was used, extending between the supports on both sides of the vehicle. The basic construction was similar to the regular suspension system used today with the exception that no lower control arm is used.

f. Parallelogram. One of the early types of suspension systems was known as the parallelogram linkage system. The basic construction of this unit was very similar to the present day suspension system except that the upper and lower control arms were of equal length. By having control arms of equal length the wheels remain upright as they are moved up and down by irregularities in the surface of the road. The only time the wheels would tilt was when

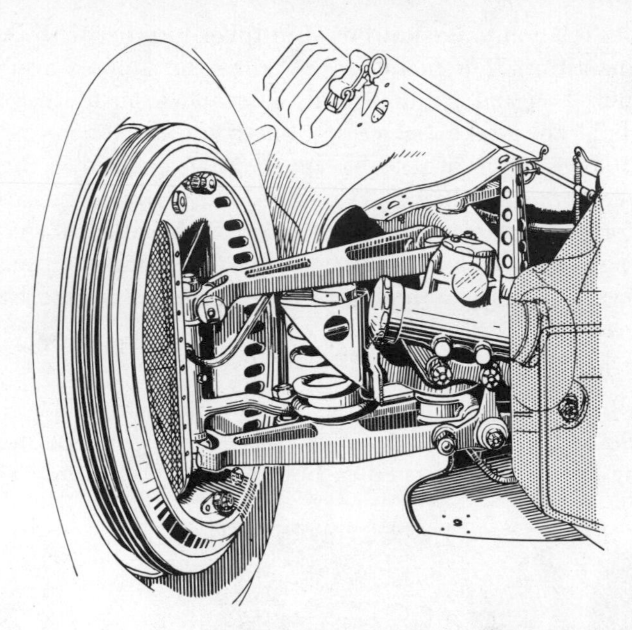

Fig. 14. Characteristics of a parallelogram system.

the entire vehicle tilted. Fig. 14 illustrates the characteristics of a parallelogram system.

The trailing link or Dubonnet type of suspension used on some previous models had parallelogram linkages paralleling the frame side members. The entire suspension unit was mounted on the kingpin and swiveled as the wheels were steered. The unit was enclosed in a sealed housing which contained the shock absorber as well as the coil type suspension spring (Fig. 15). The wheel springs up and

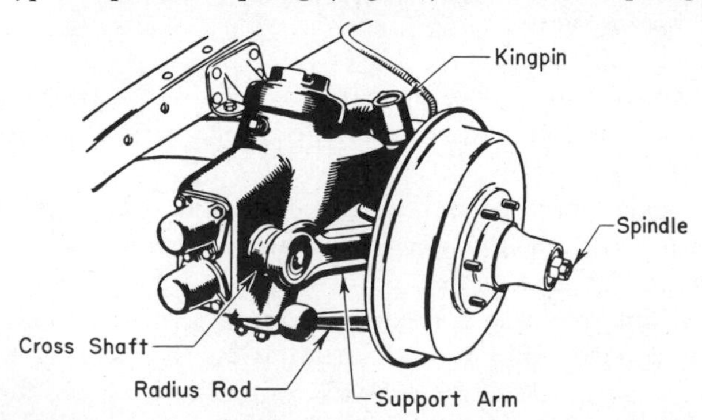

Fig. 15. Sealed housing containing shock absorber and coil spring.

down with relation to the housing, but turns together with the housing during a turn. The main link is called the support arm. Below the support arm and parallel to it, a second arm, the radius rod, acts to hold the brake assembly from rotating. When the wheel moves up, the support arm swings on the shaft and moves the spring lever to compress the spring. The large, soft, main coil spring compresses for about two inches, whereupon the small, stiff, secondary coil spring is engaged and compresses. As the spring compresses, the spring lever also engages the upper unit of the shock absorber.

II. AXLE SUSPENSION WITH LEAF SPRINGS

The front axle consists of a beam which extends across the underside of the vehicle for almost the entire width of the tread. Swiveling devices are attached to both ends of this beam. The axle

Fig. 16. Axle type of front suspension using parallel leaf springs. This type of installation is no longer used on present automobiles, having been replaced by independent front suspensions using coil springs.

beam is attached to the vehicle frame by means of leaf springs, either of the transverse type (crosswise to the frame) or of the type parallel to the frame (Fig. 16).

Front axles have been built according to either of two basic designs for attaching the steering knuckle to the beam. These are known as the Elliot type axle and the Reverse Elliot type axle. The Reverse Elliot type axle is used on most present day trucks.

On a Reverse Elliot type of installation the steering knuckle is constructed with a "C" shaped yoke for mounting on the ends of the axle beam (Fig. 17). The steering knuckle is attached to the

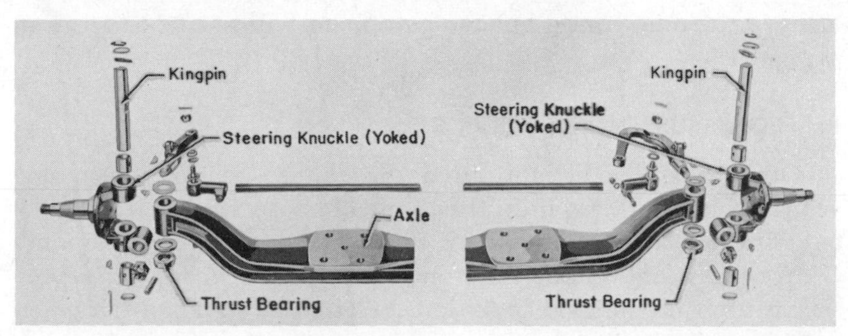

Fig. 17. Reverse Elliot type of front axle suspension system using kingpins. In modern independent front suspension systems, the kingpin has been replaced by ball joints.

beam by means of a kingpin or steering knuckle pivot pin. The steering knuckle is a heavy forging which includes the spindle on which the road wheel revolves. The kingpin extends through the upper arm of the steering knuckle yoke, through the axle beam, and into the lower arm of the yoke. The kingpin is secured in the axle beam so that the knuckle swivels on the kingpin.

The holes in the steering knuckle yoke which receive the ends of the kingpin are fitted with bushings, called kingpin bushings, so that the knuckle can turn freely. In some vehicles roller bearings are used instead of bushings. A thrust bearing is installed between the axle and the lower arm of the yoke on the knuckle. On most vehicles either a sealed ball or roller bearing is used. The steering knuckle thrust bearing actually supports the weight of the front part of the vehicle.

The Elliot type axle was basically the same as the Reverse Elliot except that each end of the axle beam is constructed to form a "C" shaped yoke. The steering knuckle fits between the upper and lower arms of this yoke.

The spindles, steering knuckles, steering knuckle arms and steering linkage used with the solid beam axle have the same general characteristics and functions as the comparable components used with the independent front wheel suspension system.

When wheels are mounted on a rigid axle and one wheel passes over an obstacle in the road, the axle executes an angular movement in a vertical plane and both of the wheels simultaneously perform angular movement in exactly the same manner. By using an independent suspension system the movement of the two wheels are not interdependent. Movement of one wheel may create some movement in the other wheel but the movement will not be as great or as regular.

III. FRONT SUSPENSION SERVICE

Other than periodic lubrication, the front suspension system of a vehicle usually requires little attention. The suspension parts should be lubricated in accordance with the manufacturer's specifications. If tire wear is uniform on the front wheels of a vehicle, the suspension is probably in good condition. Erratic tire wear, on the other hand, usually indicates the suspension system has been damaged either from lack of lubrication or as the result of a collision.

a. Locating Excessive Play in Suspension. The front suspension system should be checked for wear when the vehicle is being lubricated or the front end aligned. Place a jack under the lower control arm below the spring and raise the wheel until it is completely off

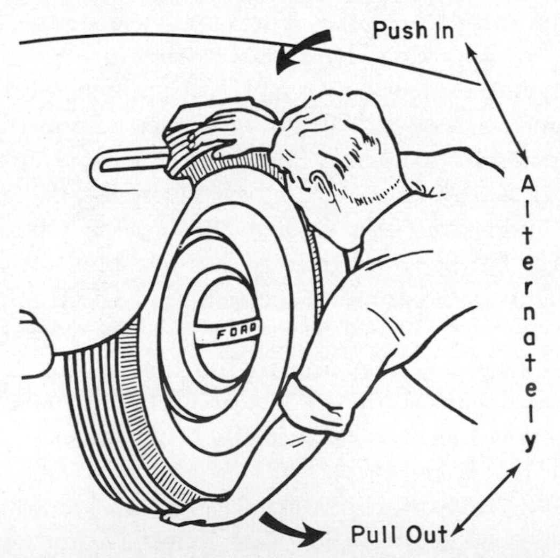

Fig. 18. Locating excessive play in suspension during lubrication.
(Ford Div.—Ford Motor Co.)

the floor. Then grasp the wheel at the top and bottom, as shown in Fig. 18, and shake it by pushing the wheel inward with one hand while pulling the wheel outward with the other. There should be no excessive looseness in the wheel although a car with kingpin suspension will have some play in the kingpin bushings. If the wheel travel (in and out) at the bottom does not exceed one-quarter inch, the kingpins and bushings are satisfactory. Movement of more than one-quarter inch at the bottom of either front wheel indicates the pins or the bushings are worn and should be replaced.

A vehicle with ball joint suspension will have about one-quarter inch of play in the load-bearing (lower) ball joint as the wheel is shaken.

On most automobiles equipped with ball joints the lower ball joint supports almost the entire weight of the vehicle. Some of the new compact cars have the coil spring bearing against the upper control arm, and therefore the upper ball joint will show some looseness.

A safe rule to follow is that any play in excess of one-quarter inch—regardless of the type of front suspension used on the vehicle—is cause for further investigation and probable replacement of worn parts.

Some of the conditions to check for excessive movement or play are listed below:

1. Loosened bolts holding the upper and lower control arm shafts to the front cross member.

2. Worn pivot points such as the bushing and shafts holding the upper and lower control arms to the frame.

3. Worn pivot pins and bushings which connect the steering knuckle support to the upper and lower control arms.

4. Rubber bushings holding the control arms to their respective shafts. (Looseness at a rubber bushing may be due to a worn bushing or to a loose cap screw which permits the inner shell of the bushing to slip on the shaft.)

5. Wheel bearings which need adjustment. (Refer to manufacturer's specifications on wheel bearing adjustments.)

If you locate looseness or play at any of these points, replace bushings or shafts that have become worn and, when required, ream them to achieve the desired fit. Replace parts when necessary if the desired tolerance cannot otherwise be obtained.

TRADE COMPETENCY TEST

1. What is the purpose of an independent front-end suspension system? (p. 32)
2. What unit in an independent suspension system serves much the same purpose as an axle? (pp. 32, 33)

3. What units are common to most independent suspension systems? (pp. 33, 34)
4. What is the difference in construction between the suspension system using kingpins and the one using ball joints? (pp. 40, 41)
5. Why are bushings used with kingpins? (p. 40)
6. What is the reason for having the upper control arm shorter than the lower control arm? (pp. 37, 38)
7. How does the steering knuckle of the Reverse Elliot type axle differ from the steering knuckle used with the Elliot type axle? (p. 45)
8. How does the torsion bar suspension differ from the coil spring suspension? (pp. 34, 35)
9. What will the wear condition of the front tires show relative to the front suspension system? (p. 46)
10. How do you check for excessive looseness in the front suspension system? (p. 46)
11. What are some of the conditions to check for excessive movement in the front end? (p. 47)

CHAPTER 3

REAR SUSPENSION SYSTEMS

		PAGE
I.	Hotchkiss Drive	50
II.	Torque Tube Drive	51
III.	Rear Independent Suspension System	53
IV.	Rear Axle Housings	55
V.	Rear Suspension Alignment	56

The rear suspension system carries the weight of the rear part of the vehicle which includes the weight of the components that make up the unit. The rear wheels must be able to move up and down with respect to the body and frame for spring action and also to assist in keeping the vehicle as near level at all times as possible.

Leaf springs, coil springs, or the air bellows employed on the air suspension system absorb road shocks and permit the wheels to flex when the vehicle encounters road irregularities.

The rear axle housing, which is designed to carry the rear vehicle weight, also serves as a means of propelling the vehicle. The springs, which make up a considerable part of the suspension system and suspends the vehicle weight, are located between the rear axle housing and the frame or body. Therefore, either the springs or some form of struts or braces must be designed to transmit the functions of the rear axle to the rest of the vehicle.

In order to overcome a fundamental law of nature which states that for every action there is an equal and opposite reaction, an additional function must be performed by the suspension system. That is, whenever power is transmitted through the power train to propel the rear wheels (driving the vehicle) the rear axle housing tries to rotate in a direction opposite to that of tire rotation. Thus, wheel rotation in one direction and the attempt of the rear axle housing to rotate in the opposite direction result in a twisting action which is called *rear-end torque*. Two different designs are used to offset this opposing torque and to transmit the wheel torque from the rear wheels to the chassis. These are the Hotchkiss type of drive and the torque-tube type of drive.

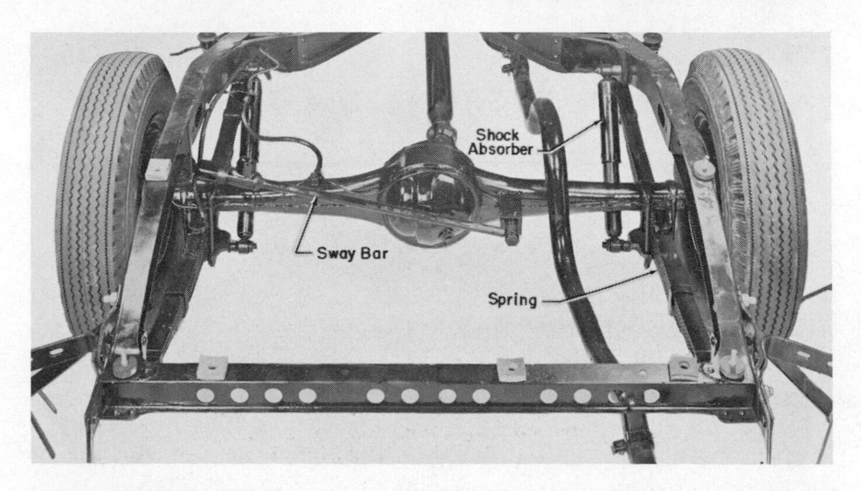

Fig. 1. Hotchkiss drive with leaf spring rear suspension. In this type of drive the rear axle torque is taken up by the leaf springs.

I. HOTCHKISS DRIVE

With a Hotchkiss type of drive using parallel leaf springs, the driving torque is transmitted by the springs. The front end of the leaf spring is mounted in a hanger so that it can pivot while the rear end of the spring is mounted by means of a shackle. This method of mounting permits the spring to lengthen and shorten as it flexes without causing a fore and aft movement of the axle housing. The center of the spring is firmly attached to the axle housing, as shown in Fig. 1.

No additional bracing is needed in this type of installation since the springs absorb both the rear-end torque and the driving torque.

When coil springs or air bellows are used between the rear axle housing and the frame or body, some form of bracing must also be used to transmit torque. Generally, a support arm, a radius rod, or a strut is attached to each outer end of the rear axle housing between the housing and the frame or body, as shown in Fig. 2. The rear end of the support arm is attached rigidly to the axle housing while the front end of the support arm is attached to a hanger. This hanger permits the axle housing to move up and down when the springs flex but prevents forward and backward movement of the axle housing. A track bar (sway bar) may be attached between one side of the frame or body and the axle housing in order to reduce the rolling

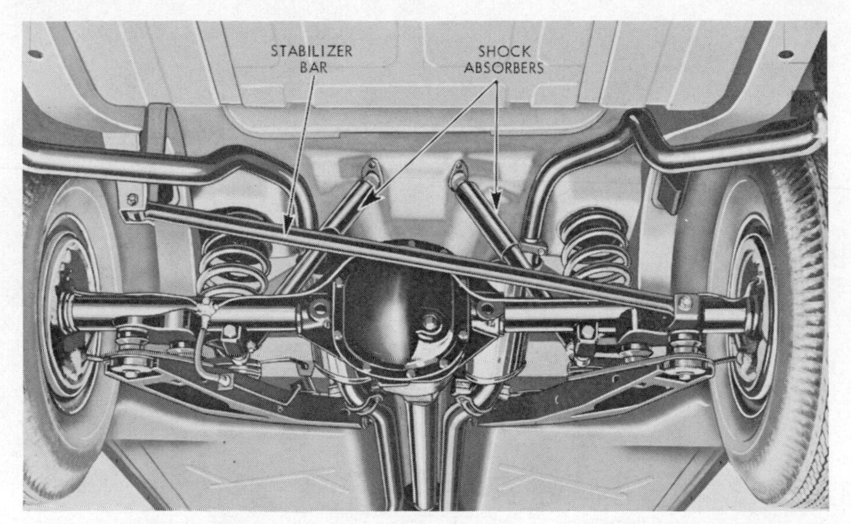

Fig. 2. Hotchkiss drive with coil spring rear suspension. Note the use of a stabilizer bar in this type of installation to provide a minimum of body roll as the vehicle makes a turn. Note support arms attached to outer ends of rear axle.

(Lincoln Div.–Ford Motor Co.)

action of the vehicle body on turns. Some installations will also use a stabilizing bar to increase body stability.

In addition to support arms at the outer ends of the axle housing, some vehicles have an upper control arm which is shaped like the letter A. The small end of the arm is attached to the center of the rear axle housing by means of a flexible connection, while the outer ends of the control arm are attached to a frame cross member by means of pivot pins. The coil spring type of installation using a control arm is illustrated in Fig. 3.

Regardless of the type of spring employed or method used in transmitting torque, shock absorbers are always used in conjunction with the springs. Shock absorbers are located between the axle housing and the frame or body. A rubber spring bumper is fastened to the axle housing, the frame, or the body to prevent bottoming. *Bottoming: Bottoming is a term used to define the condition when the spring is compressed to its limit of travel and the spring bumper is engaged.*

II. TORQUE TUBE DRIVE

In the torque tube type of installation, the propeller shaft is en-

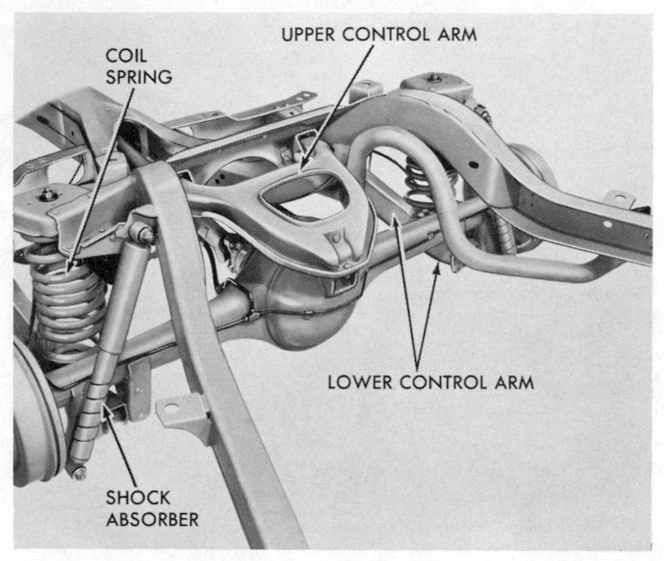

Fig. 3. Coil spring type of rear suspension using a control arm. The control arm is a means of preventing the rear axle housing from falling away from the suspension system when the vehicle encounters road irregularities.

(Pontiac Div.—General Motors Corp.)

cased within a rigid tube or housing. Engine torque is transmitted by means of the transmission to the propeller shaft which, in turn, transmits torque to the rear axle differential assembly. The rear end of the torque tube is attached to the rear axle differential housing. The front end of the torque tube is attached to the back end of the transmission and depending upon the design of the frame may or may not pass through a frame cross member. A bell type fitting (which encloses a universal joint) is mounted at the transmission to permit up and down movement of the rear axle assembly as the springs flex and at the same time to prohibit fore and aft movement of the assembly. The driving torque of the rear axle assembly is absorbed by the torque tube. Radius rods or struts are generally located between the ends of the rear axle housing and the front end of the torque tube for additional stability. The torque tube type of drive is illustrated in Fig. 4. This type of installation is used with either leaf springs, coil springs, or air bellows if the vehicle employs an air suspension system.

Shock absorbers in this type of installation are located between the rear axle housing and the frame or body.

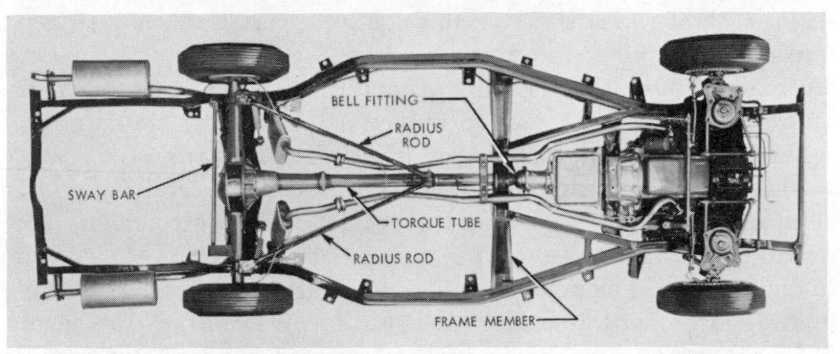

Fig. 4. Torque tube type of drive using coil spring rear suspension. The torque tube is a hollow tube enclosing the propeller shaft and absorbs the rear end torque.
(*Buick Div.—General Motors Corp.*)

III. REAR INDEPENDENT SUSPENSION SYSTEM

Independent rear suspension is used by one American manufacturer at the present time. This type of suspension employs two axle

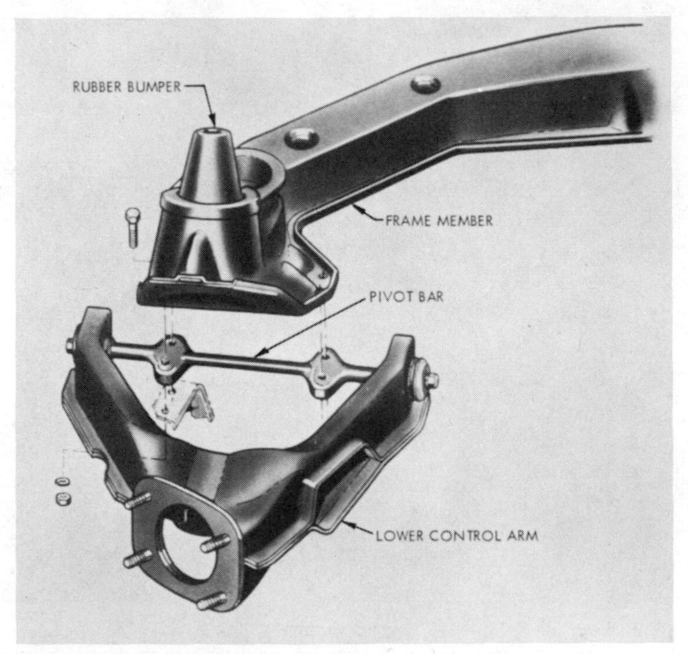

Fig. 5. Lower control arm and frame member of the independent type of rear suspension using coil springs.
(*Chevrolet Div.—General Motors Corp.*)

shafts, each of which is driven through a universal joint which permits the axle shaft to move up and down when the vehicle encounters road irregularities. The independently suspended axle shafts are attached at their inner ends to universal joints which, in turn, are splined to the differential side gears. The outer ends of the axle shafts are supported by the lower control arms. Lateral forces are absorbed by the wheel bearings mounted in the outer end of the control arm. The lower control arm is attached at its inner end to the frame cross member by a pivot bar, as shown in Fig. 5. Rubber bushings are used to insulate the control arm from the cross member. Coil springs and shock absorbers located between the control

Fig. 6. Coil spring, shock absorber, and lower control arm as used with independent rear suspension. The shock absorber used in this type of installation is on the direct acting type, mounted between the lower control arm and the vehicle frame.

(Chevrolet Div.—General Motors Corp.)

arm and the frame as shown in Fig. 6 cushion the impact of the road shock as the vehicle encounters road irregularities.

The angle which the control arm forms creates a trailing arm effect. In normal operating position, the rear axles are horizontal and the wheels vertical. When a rear wheel goes over a bump, the wheel pivots at about a 45° angle (toes in) and the axle pivots at about a 90° angle.

IV. REAR AXLE HOUSINGS

In conventional rear suspension systems, the rear axle housing supports the rear end load, and the weight, in turn, is equally distributed on the rear wheels. In addition, the axle housing contains the driving mechanism and carries the rear wheel bearings. These features have no effect upon the function of the housing as part of the vehicle's rear suspension system.

The housing in common use on today's passenger vehicles is known as the *banjo type* housing. This type of housing consists of two tubular halves joined to an enlarged, hollow, center part. The housing extends across the underside of the vehicle for the full width of the tread. The housing is suspended from the frame or body by the rear spring mechanism. Brackets are welded at the outer ends of the housing for the purpose of providing spring pads for mounting the springs, shock absorber, and radius rod (if used).

The center section in the banjo housing is a shallow cylinder situated lengthwise under the vehicle and closed at the back end. This type of housing is shown in Fig. 1. The two tubular halves which complete the housing are welded to opposite sides of the center cylinder. The welded assembly can be considered, for all

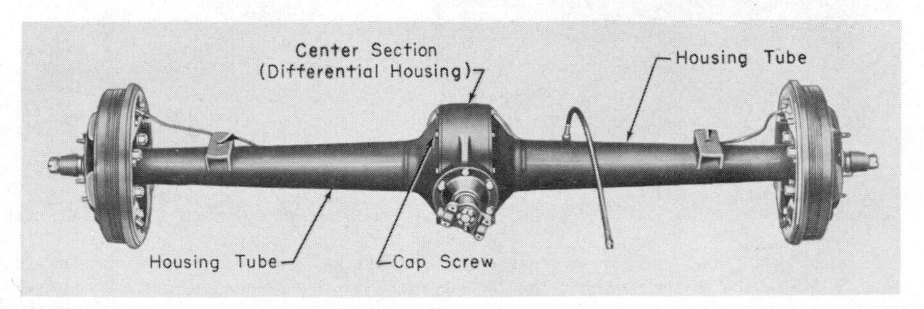

Fig. 7. Three-piece type of rear axle housing. The housing consists of a center section which is the differential housing, and two tubular sections, each of which mounts a rear wheel and tire assembly.

practical purposes, as a one-piece unit. In general appearance, it resembles an ordinary musical banjo, having two necks extending in opposite directions. The front end of the center section carries a circular flange. This flange supports the differential carrier which is attached by means of cap screws.

A divided type of housing has been used on some passenger vehicles in the past. A few makes of trucks also use this type of housing. The housing may be either of the two-piece construction or of the three-piece construction. Figure 7 illustrates a divided housing of the three-piece construction.

V. REAR SUSPENSION ALIGNMENT

The rear suspension of an automobile must be properly aligned if it is to track properly. The body of a vehicle that is not parallel to the direction of vehicle travel is the result of the rear suspension being out of track. There are a number of conditions which will cause the rear suspension of a vehicle to be out of track. A rear suspension of the Hotchkiss design (a solid rear axle suspended by leaf springs) may go out of track as the result of the rear axle's

Fig. 8. Checking the track of the rear suspension with a track bar. The bar consists of three pointers, one at the front and two at the rear. The two pointers are placed against the rim of the rear wheel while the front pointer is placed against the front wheel spindle (hub cap removed). The bar must be in alignment with all three pointers in position in order to determine the vehicle's track.

(John Bean Corp.)

slipping either forward or backward on one or both of the leaf springs which support the axle. The center tie bolt which ties the leaves of each leaf spring assembly together is used to determine the position of the rear axle housing in relation to the leaf springs. If the U bolts which hold the rear axle housing to the leaf spring become loose and the rear wheel hits an obstruction, the head of the spring center bolt mounting the loosened spring assembly may be sheared off. Should the bolt head shear off, the axle housing will move in relation to the spring causing the vehicle to be out of track. Failure of the vehicle to track properly will cause excessive tire wear.

The rear axle housing may be deflected downward at the center which would cause the top of the rear wheels to move inward. This inward movement of the top of each rear wheel would result in negative camber and cause the inside edges of the rear tires to wear. This downward bending of the axle housing at the center may result from overloading the vehicle or from imposing too much engine torque upon the rear axle during acceleration.

The rear axle housing is generally designed as a straight member and as such would have no camber, no toe-in or toe-out. However, a rear axle housing which is bent in a horizontal plane will cause the rear wheels to either toe-in or toe-out.

Should the vehicle become involved in a head-on collision, the rear axle housing may be so bent as to produce a toe-in effect in the rear wheels. The force of impact in such a collision would move the engine, drive line, and the center of the rear axle housing somewhat rearward, thereby causing the rear wheels to toe-in. Some vehicles are so designed that the rear axle produces a slight positive camber and a small amount of toe-in or toe-out on the rear tires so as to reduce tire wear.

a. Check Vehicle Track. A three-point gage called a track bar is used to determine the track of the rear suspension, as shown in Fig. 8. Before using this gage, amount of rear wheel run-out should be determined. The rear axle housing is lifted from the floor by means of a jack or alignment rack until the rear wheels are free to revolve. Place a runout gage against the rim of the wheel as the tire is rotated, marking with chalk the position on the rim where the runout gage touched the rim wheel. Then, lower the rear wheels to the floor, with the chalk mark at the bottom. Follow this procedure for both rear wheels. Sight along the sides of both front wheels, moving the wheels by hand until they are directly in front of or

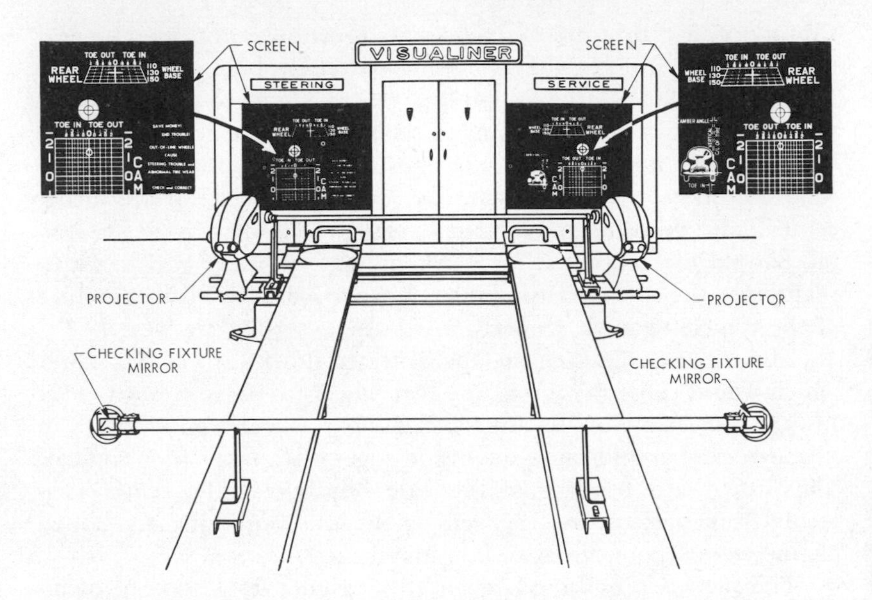

Fig. 9. The Visualiner with calibrating fixtures in position to determine the calibration of the machine. The alignment machine must be checked for calibration before it can be used to check the track of the vehicle. Always remove the error from any alignment equipment before its use on a vehicle.

(*John Bean Corp.*)

in line with the rear wheels. This represents the relation of all four wheels when the vehicle is traveling along a straight road. Next, place the three-point track bar against one of the front and one rear wheel of the vehicle. Place the single point of the track bar against the end of the spindle of the front wheel. Then, place the two pointers of the gage against the rim of the rear wheel. Adjust the relation to the bar, carry the bar over to the other side of the vehicle, and check the track of front and rear wheels.

The front pointer will now indicate whether the vehicle is out of track and whether the distance between the front and rear wheels on both sides of the vehicle is the same.

With the two pointers of the track bar on the rim of the rear wheel, the front pointer should rest on the spindle of the front wheel (hub cap removed). If the front pointer is away from the spindle, the rear wheel on which the pointers are resting has a toe-out condition and the rear wheel on the other side of the vehicle has a toe-in condition. The front pointer also shows if the vehicle's wheel base is either too long or too short. However, realize that the front suspension may also alter the wheel base. If the front suspension lower control arm has been driven backward due to the vehicle's being in a collision, the wheel base will be too short.

b. Check Rear Suspension for Camber, Toe-in or Toe-out. The camber and toe-out or toe-in of the rear wheels may be determined in the same fashion as camber and toe-in of the front wheels. Camber is the tilting of the wheel from the vertical.

The vehicle is backed on an alignment rack and the readings taken. Notice that since the vehicle has been backed on the alignment rack a reading of toe-in on an alignment machine actually represents a condition in which the wheels are toed out. The Visualiner, as shown in Fig. 9, may be used to check the track and the rear wheels without backing the vehicle on to the rack. If the vehicle has abnormal rear wheel tire wear, the wheel alignment operator can determine the cause of this tire wear while checking front wheel alignment.

c. Check Rear Suspension with the Visualiner. To determine the condition of the rear suspension, first place a mirror like the one shown in Fig. 10 on each rear wheel. Then jack up each rear wheel and check the wheel for run-out. This is done by rotating the wheel and holding the rear wheel mirror to keep the illuminated cross on

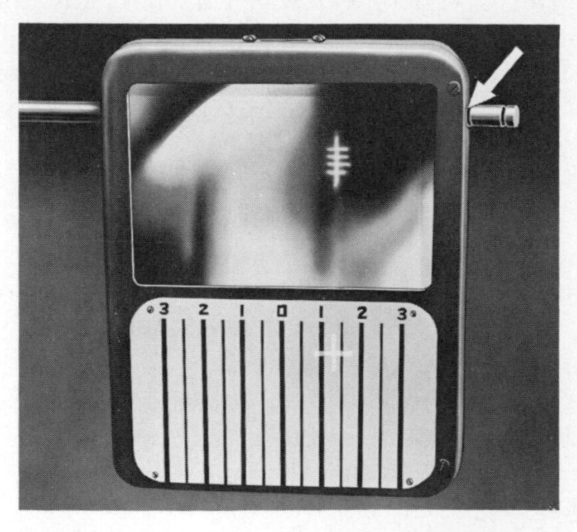

Fig. 10. Rear mirror as mounted on the vehicle's rear wheel. Two mirrors, calibrated in degrees of plus or minus, are used, one for each rear wheel. The arrow shows the adjusting screw by which the mirror may be locked in any given position.

(John Bean Corp.)

the rear wheel toe chart. As the wheel rotates, determine the maximum travel that the illuminated cross makes from side to side on the rear wheel toe chart. Stop rotating the wheel when the illuminated cross on the rear wheel toe chart is in the center of its travel. Lower the wheel to the machine.

This same procedure is used on the other rear wheel. Caution must be taken so that the wheel whose run-out has been determined does not rotate when the opposite wheel's run-out is determined.

Figure 10 illustrates the mirror as mounted on a rear wheel showing the lower cross on the numbered spaces of the mirror chart. The rear of the vehicle must be centered until both crosses fall on the same position on the lower portion of the rear wheel mirror. Most alignment racks have runways on roller chains that allow the car to be pushed at either the front or rear to center the crosses on the rear mirror chart. Then pivot the mirror about its shaft until the cross (projected forward to the screen) falls on the rear wheel toe chart on the projector screen. The set up of the Visualiner can be seen in Fig. 9. The cross will now indicate the toe-in or toe-out of that rear wheel. The other wheel's rear mirror will tell the condition of the toe of the other rear wheel.

If both rear wheels read zero toe on the rear wheel chart, then the vehicle is in perfect track and the rear axle is straight as far as toe is concerned. If the left rear wheel has a 1/4 inch of toe-in, the rear axle would then be out of track. However, if the right wheel has a 1/2 inch of toe-in and the left wheel has a 1/4 inch of toe out not only would the rear axle be out of track but the axle housing would also have a 1/4 inch of toe-in.

Vehicles with independent rear wheel suspensions must now have the rear suspension checked for toe and tracking. Refer to the manufacturer's specifications before making any corrections.

d. Straighten Rear Axle Housing. When making corrections in suspension parts with any type of equipment, it is necessary to observe certain common-sense precautions.

First, it is not wise to attempt a correction on any unit that is out of alignment more than three degrees. Any unit bent more than three degrees indicates that the unit has suffered severe damage and, therefore, should be replaced rather than straightened. In addition, any part that has been straightened should be examined minutely immediately after the operation to determine whether cracks, nicks, or looseness exists. Nicks and small surface cracks in the corrected unit should be filed out smooth to prevent the nicks or cracks from enlarging which would result in the unit's eventual breakage. Parts which bear any evidence of deep cracks (that cannot be filed out smooth without weakening the part) should be replaced. A final precaution is to examine the suspension parts for evidence of their having been straightened previously. Bulges in the metal indicate the beginning of fatigue which would result in the early failure of the unit. Likewise, a unit which has been bent at a sharp angle should not be straightened; install a new part.

To straighten a bent rear axle housing, the same equipment used to straighten a solid type truck front axle is generally employed. The axle housing can be straightened while on the vehicle or after the housing has been removed from the vehicle. Corrections that necessitate the bending of the axle housing should be made with the axle shafts and wheels installed complete. This will prevent distortion at the bearings. However, the results cannot be guaranteed since the correction may cause the rear axle to become noisy.

TRADE COMPETENCY TEST

1. What is the purpose of the rear suspension? (p. 49)
2. What is rear-end torque and what problems does it create? (p. 49)
3. What is meant by a Hotchkiss drive? (pp. 50, 51)
4. What must be added to the rear suspension if coil springs are used rather than leaf springs? (p. 50)
5. What is the purpose of a track bar? (p. 57)
6. Trace the flow of torque from the transmission to the chassis when a torque tube drive is used. (pp. 51, 52)
7. Why is a bell type fitting used at the rear of the transmission with a torque tube drive? (p. 52)
8. When an independent suspension system is used at the rear of a vehicle what must be used between the wheels and differential? (pp. 53, 54)
9. How is a banjo type rear axle housing constructed? (p. 55)
10. What will cause a rear suspension to be out of track? (pp. 56, 57)
11. If the U bolts which clamp the rear springs to the axle housing are loose what may happen? (p. 57)
12. When is it necessary to replace rear axle housing parts? (pp. 60, 61)

CHAPTER 4

SPRINGS AND SHOCK ABSORBERS

	PAGE
I. Springs	62
II. Shock Absorbers	80

The purpose of the springs and the shock absorbers in the automotive vehicle suspension system is to support the weight of the vehicle and to reduce or eliminate the effect of jarring or shocks which are transferred to the frame, the body, and to the passengers as the wheels of the vehicle move up and down due to irregularities in the road surface.

In this chapter you will learn the types and locations of the various springs now in use. You will learn how they are mounted and how to service and replace them.

The same information regarding shock absorbers is contained in the last half of this chapter.

I. SPRINGS

A spring is an elastic device that yields under stress, or pressure, but returns to its original state or position when the stress or pressure is removed.

a. Types of Springs. Five types of springs are in use in automotive suspensions. These are multiple leaf springs, single leaf springs, coil springs, torsion bars, and air cylinders. Multiple leaf springs and coil springs are characteristic of automobiles manufactured in the United States. Single leaf springs are an innovation on certain 1962 model passenger cars. Air cylinders are used now only on heavy vehicles such as busses. There is some use of torsion bars in this country, but their main popularity is in automobiles of European manufacture.

Leaf springs absorb shocks by bending; coil springs by compressing; torsion bars by twisting; and air cylinders by the compression of a column of air.

(1) *MULTIPLE LEAF SPRINGS.* These springs are built of long, flat strips of spring steel. Each strip is called a leaf. Several

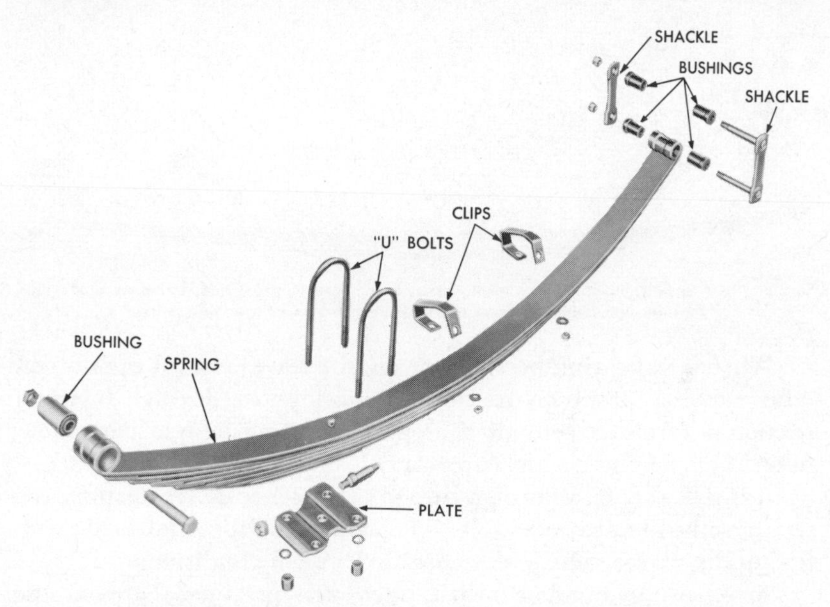

Fig. 1. Leaf spring construction and attaching parts. The leaf spring may consist of two or more leaves depending upon the design of the suspension.
(Plymouth Div.—Chrysler Corp.)

leaves, four to eight, are placed one upon the other and are held together by clamps and a bolt. The one leaf that extends the full length of the spring is known as the main leaf. The ends of the main leaf are formed into loops which are called eyes. The front of each spring is secured to a bracket on the frame by means of a spring bolt which is placed through the front eye. The rear of the spring is attached to the frame by means of a shackle. The leaf spring is assembled as shown in Fig. 1, each succeeding leaf being shorter than the preceding one. In some springs the leaves are tapered to ends thinner than the middle position.

Each leaf has a hole in the center through which a bolt—called the tie bolt—passes to hold the leaves together. Starting with the main leaf, each succeeding leaf has greater spring camber (more arch). If the leaves were placed one on top of the other, they would not touch at the center until the tie bolt was tightened. The tie bolt serves to hold the leaves together at the center under stress, preventing normal arch of the individual leaves. Spring leaf clamps (also called clips) are used to hold the outer ends of the leaves in line with each other.

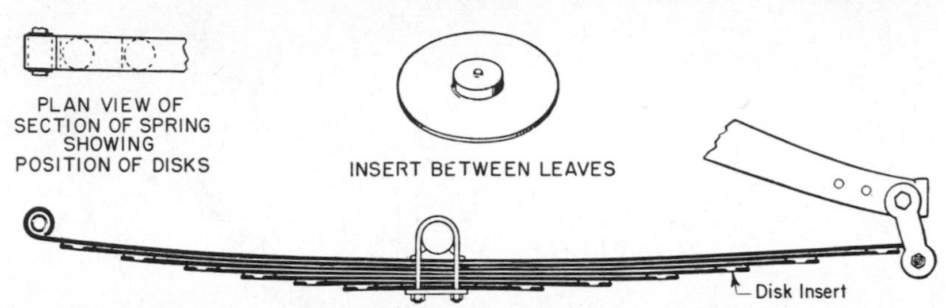

Fig. 2. Leaf spring insert of the disk type. These inserts are fitted between each leaf, thereby reducing the friction between the leaves as the springs flex.

When a leaf spring bends or flexes, the leaves rub on each other. This rubbing produces frictional resistance to flexing. Interleaf friction is carefully computed as part of spring design, dependent upon the load the spring is to carry.

If interleaf friction is high due to the absence of lubrication, the spring will stiffen considerably. The riding qualities and load-carrying ability of the vehicle decrease under such conditions.

Some springs are built with interleaves or liners between the spring leaves. A typical interleaf consists of a paper-like material impregnated with wax or a similar lubricant. The wax is not soluble in water; consequently it does not wash away. Interleaf springs do not require attention unless a leaf breaks or an interleaf insert fails. Interleaf inserts should never be lubricated.

Leaf springs may be fitted with inserts at the ends of each leaf—except the main leaf—as shown in Fig. 2. The inserts may be of rubber, waxed cloth, or oil-bronze disks (porous metal disks made of powdered metal and impregnated with oil). The spring insert eases the rubbing action between the leaves, thus aiding in retaining correct interleaf friction to insure desired spring action.

(2) *SINGLE LEAF SPRINGS.* Since 1940 there have been many experiments conducted to improve a single-leaf spring to the practical stage. In 1962 the first major breakthrough was made when certain truck manufacturers and a major producer of passenger cars brought out models with the single-leaf system.

The expectation is that the single-leaf spring will assume uniformity of performance by eliminating the interleaf elements which frequently deteriorate unevenly and are subject to unfavorable weather conditions. In addition, improvement is expected since the single leaf is always in action while conventional leaf systems lose their efficiency when the interleaf elements become worn.

(3) *COIL SPRINGS.* Coil springs used in automotive suspension systems consist of helical coils made from spring steel rods. Such springs are made from round rods between one-half and seven-eighths of one inch in thickness and from 10 to 15 feet in length. The rod is heated to a high temperature, wound on a special form, and heat-treated to obtain the desired spring resiliency. The finished coil spring has an inside diameter of from three to six inches, is about one foot high, and has ten to twelve uniform turns or loops. In most constructions the ends of the coil are flattened to provide a better seat on the supporting framework of the vehicle. Fig. 8 on page 71 illustrates a typical coil spring installation. Coil springs used on rear suspension systems generally have one or two turns at the end of the spring wound smaller than the others to provide a means of attaching the spring to the rear axle housing. See Fig. 9, page 72.

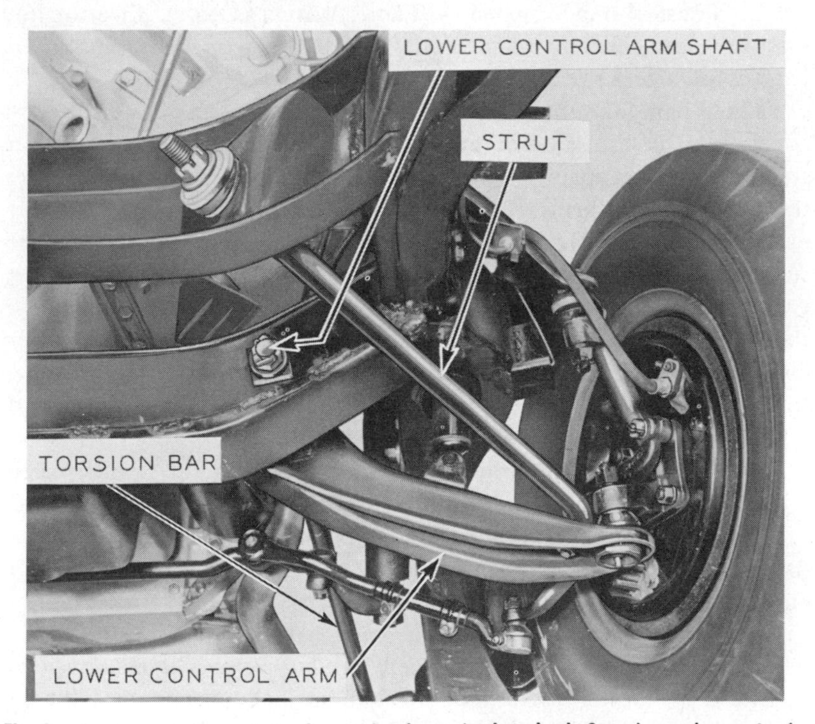

Fig. 3. Front suspension system using torsion bars. As the wheels flex, due to bumps in the road, the up and down movement of the wheels twists and untwists the torsion bars. This twisting action absorbs the road shock, thereby producing a smooth ride.

(Plymouth Div.—Chrysler Corp.)

(4) *TORSION BARS.* Some automotive vehicles use torsion bars rather than leaf or coil springs. The torsion bar (Fig. 3) is a straight bar made from round spring steel. The torsion bar mounting as shown in Fig. 3 is so arranged that movement of the wheel upward or downward causes the torsion bar to twist from its normal position. As the wheel resumes the normal position, the bar untwists. It is the resistance of the torsion bar to twisting which provides the spring action. The torsion bar is a true spring.

Two types of torsion bar installation have been used on American passenger cars. On the system in use today torsion bars are placed only on the front wheels, the rear of the frame being fitted with leaf springs.

An earlier design no longer in use employed two main torsion bars the full distance between the wheels, each bar suspending one front and one rear wheel.

(a) Torsion Bar Suspension (Front Wheels Only). Two torsion bars are used, one for each front wheel, the bars being mounted lengthwise along the frame (Fig. 3).

These bars take the place of coil springs. The suspension unit is constructed in the same manner as that used on a front suspension system using coil springs. The front ends of the torsion bars engage the lower control arms at the inner pivot points (Fig. 4). The rear ends of the bars engage adjustable anchor assemblies, which are supported by brackets welded to the frame side rails located about two feet to the rear of the front wheels. A brace (strut) attached to the front frame cross member and to the outer end of the lower control arm gives rigidity to the front end assembly and prevents fore and aft movement. As the torsion bar has a hex on each end and fits solidly into hex sockets the bar must twist and untwist as the lower arm moves up and down with the movement of the wheel. This twisting action gives the same effect as a coil or leaf spring.

An adjusting bolt on the torsion bar rear support assembly is used to increase or decrease tension on the bar. The reason for changing tension is to bring the front end to a predetermined height should it be lower or higher than specified.

(5) *AIR CYLINDERS.* Although their use today is restricted to busses and trucks, air suspension systems have been available as optional equipment on different makes of automobiles in the past. An acquaintance with them is essential.

On vehicles equipped with air springs, the front suspension system is essentially the same as that employed on vehicles using coil springs. Rear air suspension systems use radius rods (struts) or control arms between the rear axle housing and the frame to absorb the axle torque developed by driving and braking.

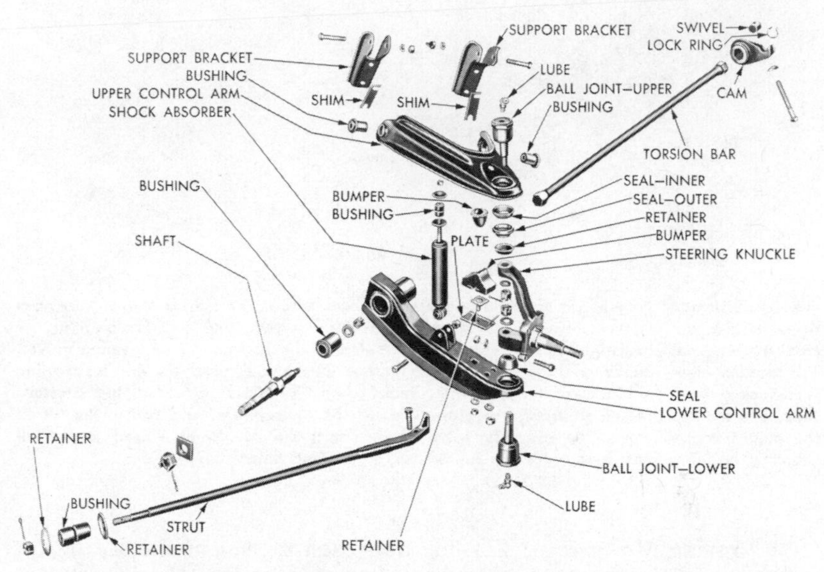

Fig. 4. Exploded view of torsion bar front suspension and all component parts.
(*Plymouth Div.—Chrysler Corp.*)

The basic components common to all four-wheel air suspension systems include an air bellows at each wheel, an air compressor driven by the engine, an air storage tank, three or four height-control or leveling valves, a pressure regulator valve, and an air filter. Figure 5 illustrates a typical air suspension system.

Compressing of the air inside the air spring as the vehicle goes over a bump provides the cushion effect necessary for a smooth ride. Fig. 6 is an exploded view of a typical air spring unit and explains its operation.

Because of high cost, liability to damage, and difficulty of maintenance, air suspensions in passenger automobiles are not in use today. Research is continuing to improve this system. Devices using air are frequently placed inside coil springs and used as part of shock absorbers to control height.

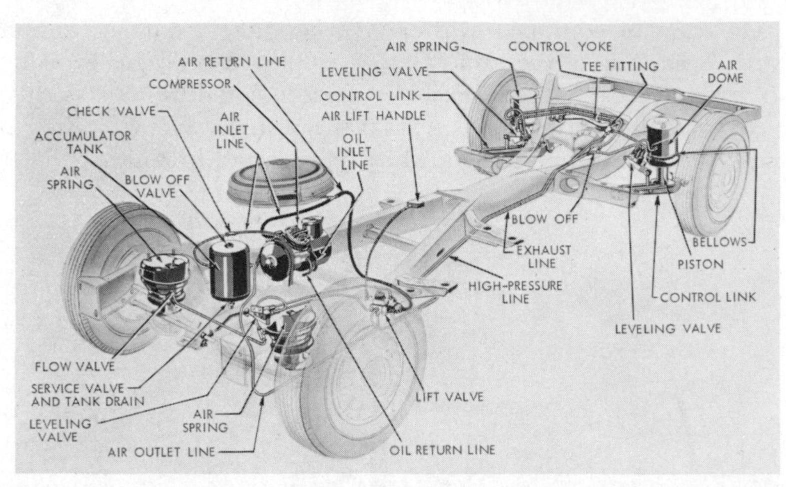

Fig. 5. Schematic view of air spring suspension. The air suspension system shown here uses three height control valves, one for each rear suspension system, and one for both of the front suspensions. The height control valves are labeled in the illustration as leveling valves. The manual over-ride valve (labeled lift valve in the illustration) used on this installation serves as a junction block for the air lines, reduces and regulates air from the pressure tank, restricts the flow of air from the return lines to the atmosphere, and routes the air to the height control valve. The override valve also permits the car to be raised to its full rebound position when it is necessary to remove a tire and wheel assembly.
(*Cadillac Div.–General Motors Corp.*)

b. Spring Mountings. The method used to mount the spring on the frame depends on whether leaf or coil springs are used.

(1) *LEAF SPRINGS.* Leaf springs are used to suspend the rear end of most passenger vehicles. The springs are mounted lengthwise along the frame. Two spring units are employed, one on either side of the vehicle. Leaf springs may be parallel to each other or they may be farther apart either at the front end or at the rear, depending on the frame design.

The ends of the main leaf are secured to the frame of the vehicle; the center of the spring unit is attached to the axle on flanges (spring pads) by means of U-bolts (spring clips). The center of the spring may either rest on the axle or pass underneath it. Fig. 7 illustrates a typical leaf spring installation. In all leaf spring mountings provision is made to prevent the center portion of the spring from sliding out of position if the U-bolt should loosen. The head of the tie bolt fits into a hole or recess in the spring pad, preventing the spring from shifting even though the U-bolts might become loose. The fitting of the tie bolt head into the recess in the spring pad also

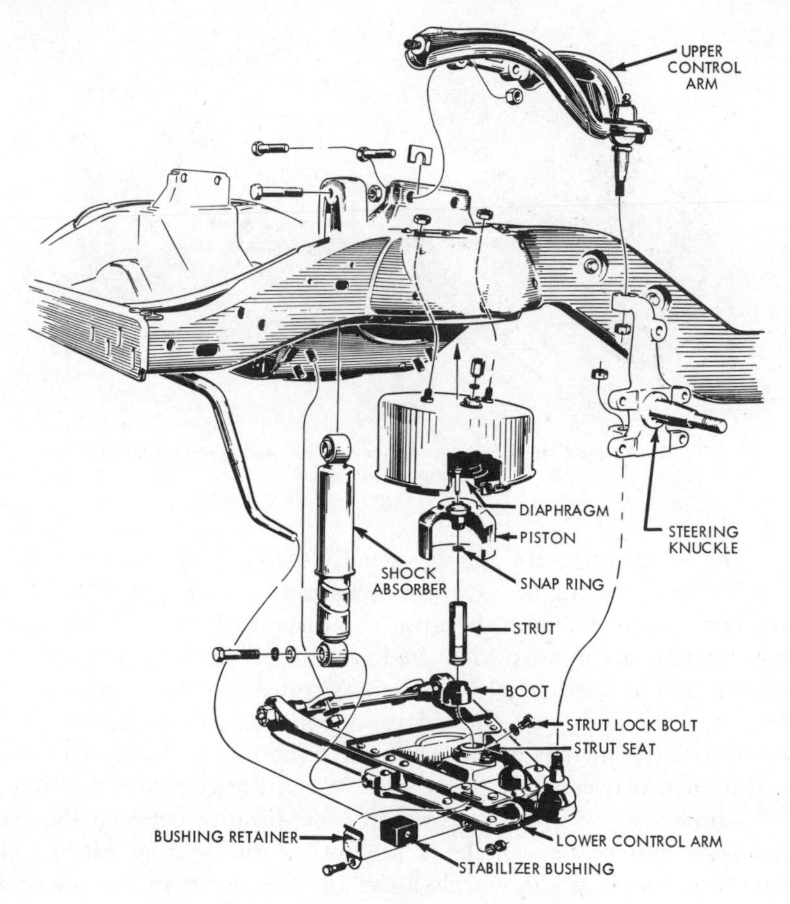

Fig. 6. Exploded view of a front air spring suspension. The air spring consists of a metal dome air chamber and a rubber diaphragm assembly which is attached to the frame and a piston assembly which is attached to the lower control arm in front suspensions and to the rear axle housing in rear suspensions.
(*Oldsmobile Div.—General Motors Corp.*)

serves as a means of properly locating the spring when installing it.

One end of the spring (usually the front end) is attached to the frame by means of a bracket or hanger which is riveted to the frame. The spring bolt, which fastens the spring to the bracket, is used with a rubber bushing which tightly surrounds the bolt and is pressed against the inside of the spring eye when the bolt is tightened. The rubber bushing provides insulation against noise and eliminates the need for lubrication.

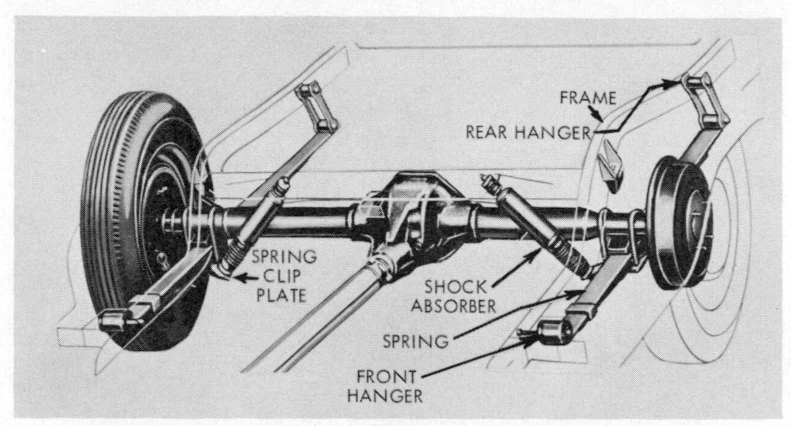

Fig. 7. A typical leaf spring installation which is used in most automotive rear suspension systems.
(Ford Div.—Ford Motor Co.)

The other end of the spring (usually the rear end) is attached to the frame by means of a swinging support called a shackle. This arrangement is necessary because the distance between the spring eyes varies in accordance with the load the vehicle is carrying. When a vehicle is at curb weight (stationary and unloaded), the normal weight of the body and chassis rests upon the springs. Under these conditions the springs have a slight arch, and a specified distance is maintained between the spring eyes. When the vehicle is bearing a load, however, the springs flatten and the distance between the eyes increases. When the vehicle is in motion, the springs alternately flatten and arch as the wheels move up and down in passing over irregularities in the road surface. This flattening and arching action causes constant variation in the distance between the spring eyes. To make this action possible shackles are used.

(2) *COIL SPRINGS.* Coil springs are mounted in either of two ways, depending on whether they are used on an independent front suspension system or on the rear axle.

In the independent front suspension, as shown in Fig. 8, the spring generally is held between the lower control arm and the frame. Circular recesses are provided at the upper and lower spring seats to receive the ends of the springs, and, once in place, the springs cannot slip. On some vehicles the spring is located between the upper control arm and the frame, but the principle remains the same.

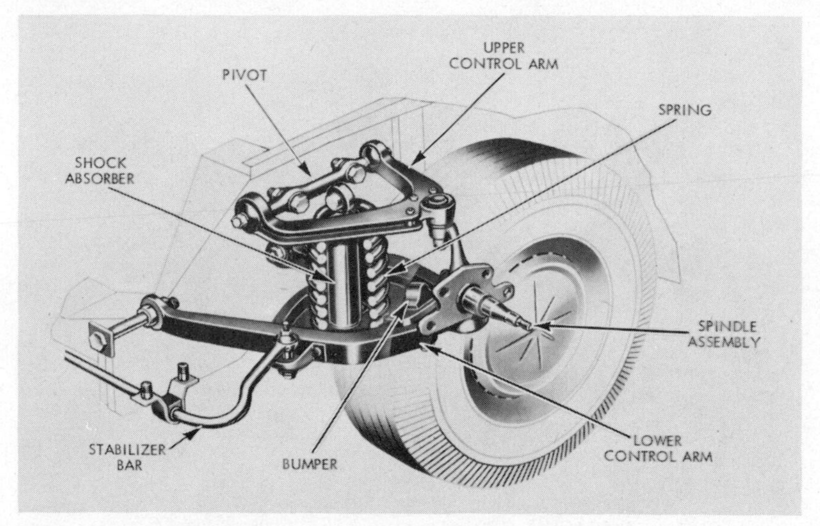

Fig. 8. Independent front suspension system employing the use of coil springs. This type of system is used on most present day vehicles having independent front suspension. *(Lincoln Div.—Ford Motor Co.)*

The upper and lower control arms swing up and down on their pivots. This action causes the coil spring to compress and expand, but it is always under load even when the control arms are at the lowest point in their swing. In other words, the spring is so constructed that its free height (unloaded or natural length) is greater than the greatest possible distance between the frame and the control arm. The spring is held in place by the load placed upon it and by the recesses into which the ends fit. A rubber insulator is generally installed in the recess between the spring and the frame.

When coil suspension is used on the rear axle, one or two turns at each end of the spring are smaller than the rest of the spring. The spring is secured to the frame and the rear axle by means of washers machined to fit the loops at both ends of the spring. A rear end coil spring assembly is shown in Fig. 9.

It is necessary in this type of installation to secure the coil spring at both ends because there is no device to limit the downward movement of the suspension. On extreme rebound the axle could fall away from the vehicle if it were not secured by the springs. Radius rods or supports (sometimes called struts) are used to attach the rear axle housing to the frame, thus preventing forward and backward movement of the axle while the vehicle is in motion. In a suspension

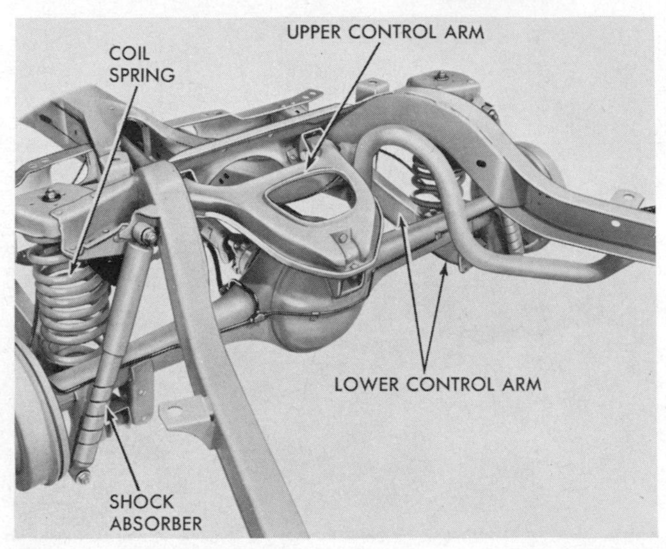

Fig. 9. Independent rear suspension system employing the use of coil springs. The coil spring rear suspension has been used on some types of vehicles, however, most vehicles use leaf springs. *(Pontiac Div.– General Motors Corp.)*

of this type the spring is subjected to tension as well as compression.

(3) *SPRING BUMPERS.* On any type of suspension rubber bumpers are used to cushion the impact should the spring "bottom." The bumper is located on the frame above the rear axle housing on rear suspensions, or, in the case of front suspensions, on the lower control arm, as shown in Fig. 8.

(4) *FRONT END STABILIZERS.* Practically all independent front end suspension systems include a stabilizer. It is another form of spring used to inter-connect the individual suspension units, either directly or by linkage. The stabilizer is a steel bar mounted transversely on (across) the frame. Arms on both ends of the stabilizer extend backward and are connected to the lower control arms. A typical stabilizer installation is shown in Fig. 8.

The stabilizer arms move up and down together when both coil springs deflect an equal amount. Under these conditions the stabilizer bar pivots in the rubber bushings by which it is mounted to the frame; hence, no spring action is in effect. When only one wheel encounters a bump, however, only the spring suspending that wheel deflects, imparting a twisting action to the stabilizer bar. Then, as the twisting force is removed, the stabilizer returns to its original state. From this explanation it is clear that the stabilizer bar is a spring resistance, in the form of a torsion bar, to the independent action of independently suspended front wheels.

The stabilizer serves to reduce heeling or tipping of the vehicle on curves. During a turn the spring on the outside tends to compress while the spring on the inside of the turn tends to expand due to centrifugal forces involved. One stabilizer arm swings downward while the other end swings upward, imparting a twist to the stabilizer bar. It is the resistance to this twist that helps to hold the vehicle level and stable.

(5) *REAR END STABILIZERS.* To provide correct tracking and proper stability of the rear axle when the rear end is mounted on coil springs or air suspension, a stabilizing device of some sort must be used. (Tracking means the following of the rear wheels directly behind, or in the tracks of, the front wheels.) A stabilizer bar, sometimes called a sway bar or radius rod, is used on some installations. Other installations use a control arm arrangement for this purpose. See Fig. 9.

The stabilizer or sway bar is designed to control lateral (sidewise) movement of the rear axle. The bar extends from the axle housing on one side to the vehicle frame on the other, as shown in Fig. 10. Rubber bushings are used at both ends to insulate the bar from the frame and the axle and thereby to reduce noise. On a severe turn the vehicle frame has a tendency to swing out on the rear wheels. This tendency is overcome by the sway bar.

c. Characteristics of Springs. Leaf springs, coil springs, and torsion bars all possess a number of characteristics which affect their operation. Usually taken into account are the deflection rate, the recoil frequency, and the fatigue point. Springs used in automotive suspension systems behave in the same manner under load, regardless of their design or type. The similarity of behavior is due to the fact that all springs are made of steel. To a certain degree steel is elastic. This means that if it is deformed (bent, squeezed, stretched, twisted) within certain limits, it will, when released, resume its original state.

(1) *DEFLECTION RATE.* Deflection rate is the amount a spring will bend under the influence of a given weight. Deflection rate is specified in terms of pounds per inch; that is, pounds of weight applied per inch of deflection. If a load of 100 pounds will deflect a spring one inch, each additional 100 pounds will deflect

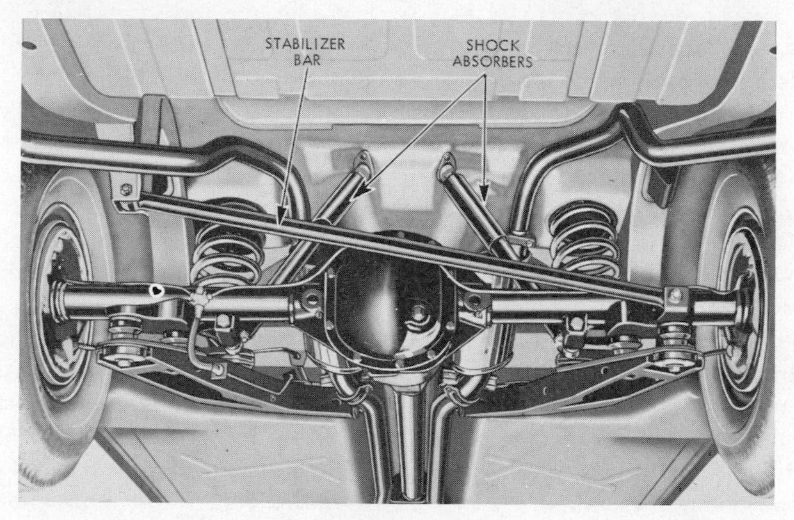

Fig. 10. The rear end stabilizer bar, also known as a track bar, reduces body roll when the vehicle makes a turn.
(Lincoln Div.—Ford Motor Co.)

it another inch. For each 100 pounds removed from the load the spring will return one inch toward its original state. The spring may be loaded at the rate of 100 pounds per inch until it is deflected beyond its capacity. This means the spring will become damaged and will not resume its original characteristics when the load is removed. This point is called the elastic limit. A spring loaded beyond the elastic limit is deformed permanently.

Deflection rate is also known as spring weight. Spring weight is given as the force required to deflect the spring to a predetermined dimension. The term spring weight is usually applied to coil springs. Deflection rate is used in connection with leaf springs. It should be noted that spring weight and deflection rate apply only within the elastic limit of any given spring.

In a leaf spring the thicker and/or wider the spring, the higher the deflection rate; that is, the greater the force required to bend the spring a given distance. The longer the spring, the lower the deflection rate. In a coil spring thickness means the diameter of the steel rod from which the spring was made, not the size of the loops. Similarly, length means the length of the rod used, not the height of the finished coil.

(2) *FREQUENCY.* Frequency is the term used to describe the number of oscillations (bounces) per minute made by a spring when it is actuated. An automotive spring, when deflected by a bump in the road bed, always tends to return to its original state. This means that a spring under a load tends to return that load to the extent that will enable the spring to rebound to its original height. But the inertia of the load as the spring flexes carries the spring beyond this point and allows it to deflect in the opposite direction. Regardless of the load or type of spring, the return motion always occupies the same amount of time for any given spring, because each spring has its own frequency. That frequency for an individual spring depends on its length, breadth, and thickness—just as these factors control the deflection rate, as well. The distance through which a spring flexes is determined by the weight of the load and the severity of the shock encountered. Distance and severity have no bearing, however, on frequency; it is a constant factor.

In selecting springs to meet specific problems frequency and its effect on the relationship between sprung weight and unsprung weight must be considered. Sprung weight is the weight of everything supported by the springs. Unsprung weight is the weight of everything between the springs and the road. In general, unsprung weight should be kept as low as possible to assure a comfortable ride. Roughness in the ride increases when unsprung weight increases.

(3) *FATIGUE AND SPRING BREAKAGE.* The most common causes of spring breakage are fatigue and overloading. Fatigue is the term used to describe spring breakage after the spring has worn out due to repeated flexings. Just as a wire or piece of metal will break after having been bent back and forth repeatedly, so will a spring break after many thousands of flexings. When fatigue sets in, the spring suddenly becomes weak and then breaks. Fatigue can even occur when the spring has never been deflected beyond its elastic limit. Nicks on the spring surface can hasten spring fatigue.

Overload, if extreme, results in spring failure and breakage. If the spring is heavily loaded and subjected to severe shocks, it will bend beyond its elastic limit and be permanently damaged.

A spring that is deformed or has broken leaves should be replaced. If the spring inserts are no longer effective, resulting in a spring squeak, the inserts can be replaced without removing the spring.

d. Spring Service. Servicing the springs on an automobile means periodic inspection of the springs and all spring components. Coil springs seldom require attention. If a coil spring becomes weak or fatigued, it may be replaced or corrected by means of spacer devices inserted either between the bottom of the spring and the lower control arm or between the coils of the spring itself. See Fig. 11. A single

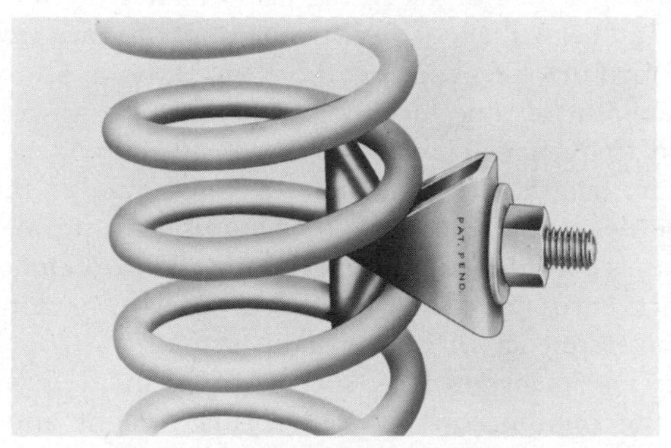

Fig. 11. Spacer device being inserted between coils of a spring. (*Turner Manufacturing Company*)

spring is never replaced alone. Both front or both rear springs must be replaced in pairs. One new and one old spring would cause the vehicle to have an uneven curb height.

Leaf springs are a different problem. They are subject to breakage—usually one leaf at a time—with the result that the car will sag on the side that has the broken leaf. In normal use leaf springs often become fatigued, causing the vehicle to ride too close to the ground. In such circumstances either the fatigued leaf springs are replaced or the spring unit is sent to a repair shop to be rebuilt. Generally, leaf springs require no lubrication since they are fitted with anti-squeak inserts beween the leaves. These inserts must be replaced when they become worn, and care must be taken to make sure the spring leaves are dry and free from oil and dirt before the new inserts are installed.

As previously described the rear leaf springs are attached to the frame by a hanger at one end and a shackle at the other by means of a spring bolt and a rubber bushing. In operating the motion between the spring bolt and the bushing is twisting. If the bushing becomes loose, a metal-to-metal contact can result, and it can cause a squeak. Under these conditions the spring bolt should be tightened to force the bushing more firmly into the eye and around the bolt. Under no circumstances should the rubber bushing be lubricated. Not only do petroleum-base lubricants cause rubber to deteriorate, but lubricants of any sort allow the rubber to slide on the metal and cause wear. If the squeak persists the bushing must be replaced.

U-bolts should be tightened periodically to prevent the axle from slipping on the spring. This condition causes the vehicle to "dog track," which means, to be out of track when driven on the straightaway.

e. Spring Replacement. Springs must be replaced when broken or weak. The vehicle must be supported on jack stands placed under

Fig. 12. Position of jack under lower suspension arm while coil spring is being compressed prior to removal.
(Ford Motor Company)

the body or frame during the operation. Be sure the correct lifting points are used on vehicles having unitized body construction.

(1) *COIL SPRING REPLACEMENT.* One method for removing a coil spring from a vehicle is stated in the following sequence of operations. First, remove the shock absorber from the inside of the spring. Place a chain over the top of the coil spring recess in the frame and tie the chain to the axle of a hydraulic floor jack. This procedure anchors the vehicle and prevents it from rising when the jack is raised. Since the vehicle cannot rise despite the pressure of the jack from beneath, the spring is compressed. With the jack in position lift the lower control arm until the upper control arm is clear of the rebound bumper. Either the lower pin or the lower ball joint may now be removed from the lower control arm. Once they are removed, the steering knuckle, hub, drum, and upper control arm may be lifted out of the way.

Spring removal is shown in Fig. 12.

A rod approximately one-half inch in diameter and at least two feet long should now be placed in the hole formerly occupied by the shock absorber. This rod will act as a safety device so that, with the chain removed, the spring will not fly out of position as the jack is lowered.

Caution: Lower the jack very slowly!

To install a new spring simply reverse the removal procedure.

(2) *LEAF SPRING REPLACEMENT.* With the car up on jack stands, the rear axle will hang down from the frame, supported only by the rear springs. To remove the springs, place a jack under the center of the rear axle housing and lift the axle just high enough to support its weight. Remove the nuts from the U-bolts. Then remove the U-bolts themselves and the spring pads. Jack stands

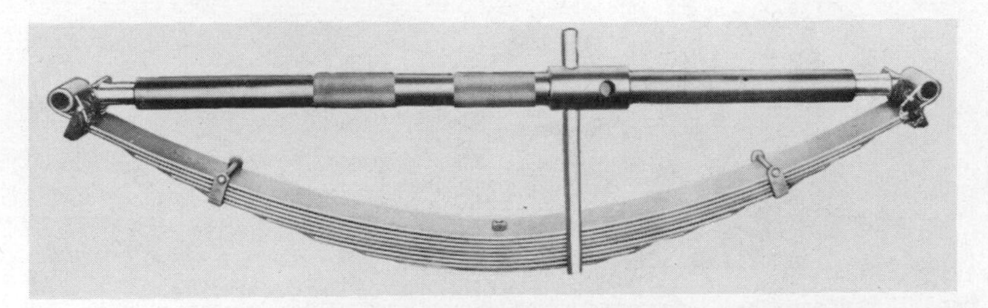

Fig. 13. In order to remove or install a leaf spring, it is necessary to spread the ends of the leaf by means of a spring jack. The above illustration shows the spring jack in use.

should be used to hold the axle in position before the springs are removed. A spring jack or hydraulic ram should now be used to spread the springs between the spring eyes as shown in Fig. 13.

Expand the spring jack or hydraulic ram until the spring is in its normal position. Remove the bushing bolts at the hanger and shackle ends of the spring and take the spring from under the car. Replace it with a new or reconditioned spring by reversing the disassembly procedure. Whenever a spring is replaced new rubber bushings should be inserted between the spring bolt and hanger or shackle.

f. Stabilizer Bar Service. The stabilizer bar requires no servicing except where it attaches to the frame and suspension parts. The attaching parts are usually made of rubber and as such should be periodically lubricated with rubber lubricant to prevent deterioration. Worn bushings are available for replacement in kit form called a stabilizer-link kit. Worn stabilizer links will cause erratic handling of the vehicle on the road.

g. Torsion Bar Service and Replacement. Front suspension torsion bars function in the same way as coil springs. To compensate for torsion bar fatigue, which permits the vehicle to sag, the torsion bar suspension system is adjustable. The front end of the torsion bar is attached to either the upper or the lower control arm. The rear end of the torsion bar is attached to the frame by an adjustable anchoring device. Adjusting this anchor will reestablish the correct height of the vehicle. When adjustment is necessary, be sure to adjust both torsion bars to equal heights. A number of manufacturers make height gages and provide specifications so that these suspensions can be easily adjusted.

To remove and replace torsion bars the vehicle frame must be supported on jack stands at a height which enables the front wheels to clear the floor. When the front suspension is resting on the upper rebound bumper, the torsion bar anchor at the rear can be loosened. When the adjusting device is completely released, the torsion bar and rear hanger may be removed. Be sure that the torsion bars are not nicked, scratched, or marred in any manner during removal or replacement.

When re-installing a torsion bar notice that the ends of the bar are marked to indicate whether the bar is for the right or left side of the suspension. The ends of the torsion bars are retained in sockets which, like the end of the bars themselves, must be thoroughly lubricated, preferably with a heavy, wheel-bearing type of grease.

After the torsion bars are installed in their sockets, tighten the adjustment part way. Then lower the vehicle to its wheels and drive it on an alignment rack or some other level surface where the torsion bars may be adjusted until the vehicle attains the proper height. See Fig. 14.

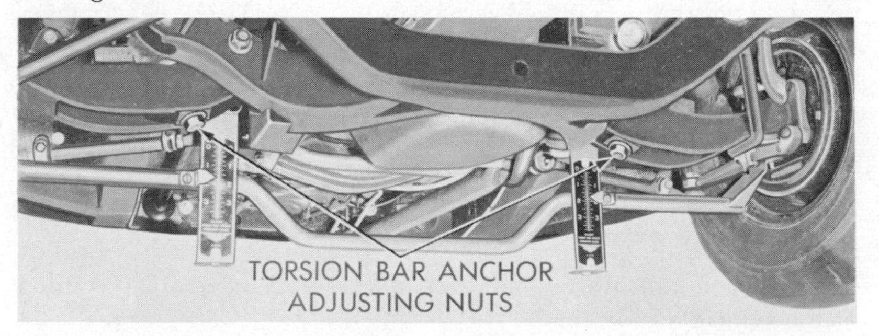

Fig. 14. Torsion bar adjusting nuts shown in position to measure front suspension height. (*Chrysler Corporation*)

h. Air Suspension Service. Service of an air suspension system is a problem too detailed to be covered in this book. The front end specialist can, however, use the adjustments provided at the leveling valves to regulate the height of the vehicle. Specifications regarding height can be obtained from manufacturers of the equipment. To aid in the aligning of a vehicle equipped with air suspension, blocks should be placed between the frame and the lower control arms to provide a constant height. If the blocks are not used, the system will automatically level itself each time a mechanic jacks up a wheel.

II. SHOCK ABSORBERS

A shock absorber is the assembly on a vehicle which checks excessively rapid spring movement and oscillation.

The ideal spring for automotive use would be one to absorb shock rapidly but return it to its original position slowly. A soft spring is too flexible and allows too much movement; at the same time, a hard spring is too stiff to provide a comfortable ride. Satisfactory riding qualities can be obained by using a fairly soft spring in combination with a shock absorber.

It is the nature of a spring to oscillate; therefore springs absorb very little energy. A load supported on springs, when displaced, continues to rise and fall as the springs deflect and rebound until the spring action dies down. The load drops until resisted by the spring, stops, and then starts to rise as the spring rebound effort comes into play. The rebound action begins slowly, increases in velocity as the spring follows its oscillation pattern, then slows down and stops due to the influence of gravity on the load. Once again, the load changes direction and begins to drop. This complete cycle repeats until the spring action ceases, each succeeding cycle being reduced in the amount of deflection. Figure 15 illustrates controlled and uncontrolled spring oscillation.

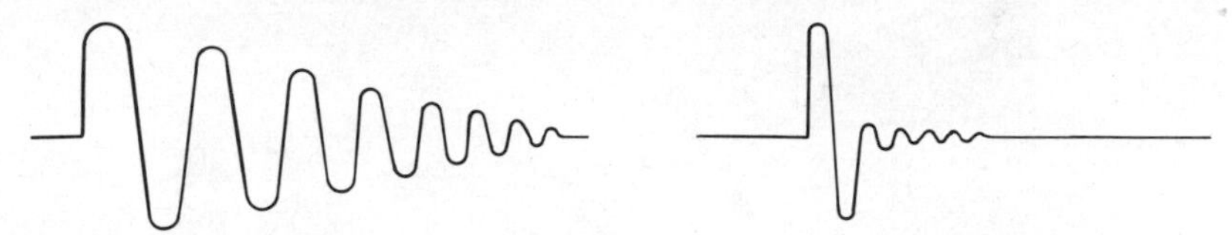

Fig. 15. Spring oscillations. The nature of a spring is to flex, and as shown in the left hand view, if the flexing of a spring or its oscillations are not controlled, the spring will not return at once to the released position. As shown in the right hand view, when the spring action is controlled by the shock absorber, it will return quickly to its released or at rest position.

Shock absorbers operate by absorbing the energy of vertical and lateral motion, converting the energy into heat and dissipating the heat into the air. The shock absorber takes in this energy and, in doing so, keeps spring oscillation to a minimum.

Shock absorbers are attached to the vehicle between the frame and the wheels. In this position they are able to control and to regulate spring action. Shock absorber mounting is shown in Fig. 16.

In many installations shock absorbers in the rear suspension are mounted on a frame cross member or floor pan. When installed in this manner both shock absorbers will lean inward at the top. This type of installation (Fig. 10) helps reduce body sway.

a. Types of Shock Absorbers. Several types of shock absorbers have been used over a period of years. Today the most widely used types on both front and rear suspensions are of direct acting, double acting, telescope design. The principle of operation is the same for all hydraulic shock absorbers regardless of the type. Spring oscillations are retarded by alternately forcing fluid through small orifices from one chamber to another.

(1) *DIRECT ACTING.* Double acting, telescope type. Double acting shock absorbers restrict spring movement in both directions.

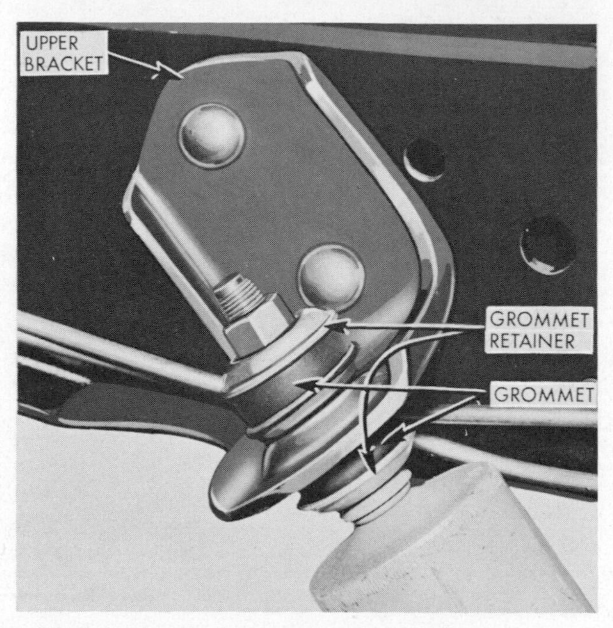

Fig. 16. Upper shock absorber mounting. In this installation the upper portion of the shock absorber is mounted to the frame side rail.
(Buick Div.–General Motors Corp.)

They reduce spring deflection on compression as well as on rebound. The double acting shock absorber makes it possible to employ a softer spring in suspension design. Since the shock absorber assists the spring in resisting up and down motion, the spring can be designed to support only the vehicle load while the vehicle is at rest. In most double acting shock absorbers the rebound stroke offers more resistance than the compression stroke.

Basically, shock absorber operation consists of forcing a fluid within a cylinder through a restricted opening. This action is accomplished by a piston whenever the vehicle springs flex. The presence of the small opening causes fluid friction which converts the absorbed energy into heat. The heat is then taken up by the shock absorber fluid and dissipated into the atmosphere.

Understanding shock absorber construction aids in understanding operating principles. Generally, the shock absorber consists of an inner cylinder filled with hydraulic fluid and divided into an upper and a lower chamber by a double acting piston. When the fluid is under pressure, it passes through a restricted orifice (open-

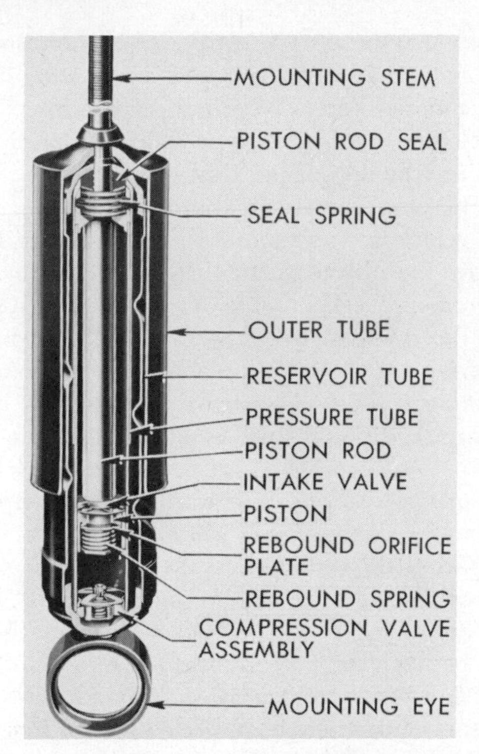

Fig. 17. Cutaway view of a typical direct acting type of shock absorber. This type of shock absorber may be mounted either between the upper and lower control arm or between the lower control arm and the vehicle frame.

(Buick Div.—General Motors Corp.)

ing), or bleeder contained in a spring-loaded valve. If fluid displacement is rapid, the valve opens against the spring and permits a faster flow. Double acting shock absorbers contain two such valves: a compression valve and a rebound valve. The valves are located on the under side of the piston (to avoid forcing fluid under pressure against the piston rod seal) and are operated by vacuum on rebound and by piston pressure on compression.

The double acting piston is moved up and down within the cylinder by means of a piston push rod. The cylinder is joined to a reservoir of hydraulic fluid at one end by a reservoir check valve. The piston rod is attached to the frame while the reservoir end of the assembly is attached to the spring plate at the rear axle housing (rear suspension) and to the lower control arm (front suspension). A typical shock absorber is illustrated in Fig. 17.

A dust cover may be affixed to the top of the piston rod around the reservoir, so that it moves up and down with the piston rod. Because of this motion, direct acting shock absorbers are sometimes known as telescopic or airplane-type shock absorbers. Other shock absorbers of this type do not use dust covers but are constructed in the same manner and operate in the same way.

When the vehicle spring rebounds, the piston is drawn upward. The fluid above the piston passes through the rebound valve (and through the rebound relief valve if the action is severe) to the lower part of the cylinder. Because of the volume occupied by the piston rod, there is not enough fluid above the piston to fill the lower chamber. Therefore, the lower part of the chamber becomes a partial vacuum, and additional fluid is sucked into the cylinder from the reservoir.

When the piston is forced downward on the compression stroke, the fluid below the piston passes through the piston intake valve to the upper part of the cylinder. As the piston rod enters the cylinder, however, it displaces its own volume in fluid. The fluid thus displaced is forced out of the cylinder through the compression valve, located between the bottom of the cylinder and the reservoir.

(2) *OTHER TYPES OF SHOCK ABSORBERS.* Single acting, direct action shock absorbers have been used on some installations. This type is constructed in the same manner as the double action shock absorber described above, but it does not contain a compression valve. It contains only a rebound valve. The compression phase of the operation serves as an intake stroke. No resistance is offered on spring compression, but it comes into play as soon as rebound begins.

Double acting, cam actuated piston types of shock absorbers have been used on some cars. One installation made the shock absorber part of the front suspension system by having its arm serve as an upper control arm.

This type of shock absorber consists of a housing which contains a fluid reservoir and two cylinders. A cam is inserted between one compression and one rebound piston, each piston being contained in a cylinder. In some designs the pistons were opposed. In others they were parallel. In either case, as the spring deflects, fluid is forced from one cylinder to the other through a small orifice. Fig. 18 illustrates a cam actuated piston shock absorber with opposed cylinders.

In both designs each piston contains an intake valve. The pistons

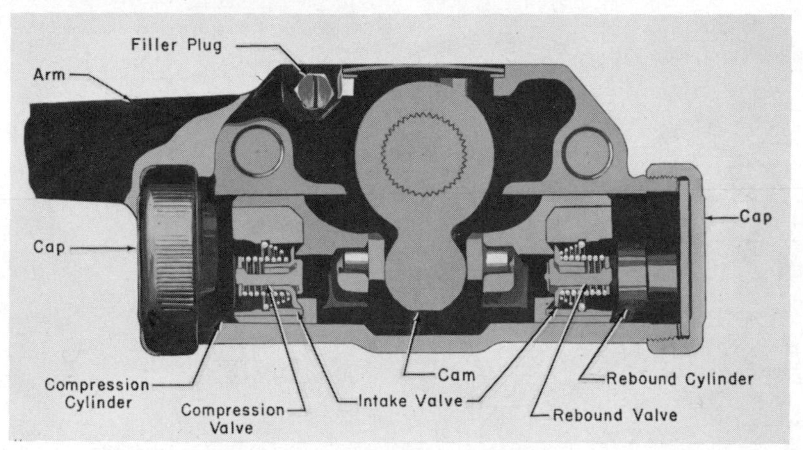

Fig. 18. The cam actuated piston type of shock absorber with opposed pistons. Since the various valves are incorporated within the piston, this installation is known as the internal valve type. The unit consists of one compression and one rebound piston; the pistons are operated by a cam connected through a shaft to an outside arm. The arm moves as the wheel flexes, thereby actuating the cam which in turn actuates the piston.

in some shock absorbers contain the compression and relief valves as well as the intake valves. An entire unit of this sort is called the interior valve type. In other types the valves are located in drilled passages in the housing and the unit is known as the external valve type.

Regardless of valve or piston arrangement, when motion is imparted to the pistons by road irregularities, the pistons force fluid through restricted openings; and the result is a dampening of spring action. The control valves in both designs are constructed to open to varying degrees, thus permitting fluid flow through the orifices and valves at varying speeds. Thus spring action can be controlled to fit any sort of road condition.

A rotary vane type shock absorber has been used to some extent on various vehicles. This type operates on the same principle as the other shock absorbers—except that vanes instead of pistons are actuated by the shock absorber shaft. Fig. 19 shows a cross sectional view of the vane type shock absorber.

When the vehicle springs flex, fluid is transferred from one compartment to the other through a valve arrangement. Small orifices and valves restrict the flow of fluid and thereby control spring oscillations.

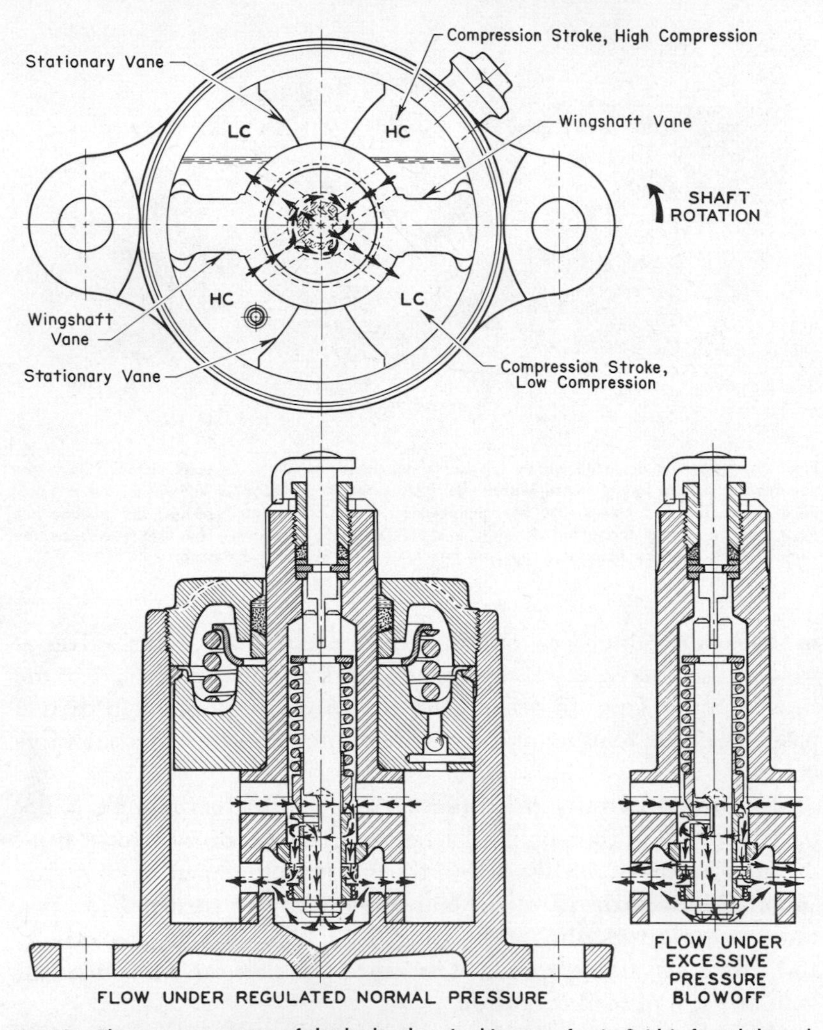

Fig. 19. The rotary vane type of shock absorber. In this type of unit, fluid is forced through restricted opening by vanes which act as pistons. The cylindrical housing, which is filled with fluid, is divided into two working chambers by stationary partitions. A vane extends into each working chamber, the vanes being operated by a shock absorber lever. The vanes oscillate with the vehicle spring when the wheel flexes and therefore, act in the same manner as pistons in the piston units.

(Ford Div.—Ford Motor Co.)

Weak or inoperative shock absorbers should be replaced to maintain maximum riding comfort and proper steering control. Shock absorbers must be kept tight on their mountings to prevent rattles and noises. This means that all worn rubber mounting bushings should be replaced.

b. Shock Absorber Service. The service garage does not repair or rebuild shock absorbers; therefore, a direct acting shock absorber must be replaced when it fails. The cam actuated piston types are rebuilt by manufacturers and sold as replacements.

To install a direct acting shock absorber on the front suspension, remove the nuts or bolts that hold the shock absorber to the cross member. Remove the bolts that secure the shock absorber to the lower control arm. Usually, the shock absorber can now be removed by pulling it out through the lower control arm. Some designs, however, make it necessary to remove the shock absorbers from the top.

Shock absorber operation may be checked on some vehicles by grasping the bumper of the vehicle and bouncing the car up and down. Almost instantly upon release of the bumper the vehicle should stop bouncing. If it does not, the shock absorbers need replacing.

If the suspension system has the shock absorber connected to the upper control arm, this test will not work. The vehicle must be road tested and the shock absorbers removed.

Another method is to check each shock absorber by itself. Hold the shock absorber in its normal operating position; then extend the shock absorber and note its resistance. Compare this resistance to that of a new shock absorber of the same height and action. Compress the shock absorber and make the comparison in the same manner. If the shock absorber is serviceable, no difference will be noted. Moisture around the push rod of the shock absorber usually means it is leaking hydraulic fluid, and it may need to be replaced. Noise coming from the front or rear suspension is often due to shock absorber mountings that are loose or worn out.

TRADE COMPETENCY TEST

1. What is the purpose of automotive springs? (p. 62)
2. Name the types of springs in use on automotive suspension systems. (pp. 62-67)
3. What is commonly used between the ends of leaf springs to prevent squeaking? (p. 64)
4. Upon what principle does a torsion bar work? (p. 56)

5. What is the purpose of a shackle used on one end of a leaf spring? (p. 63)
6. What is the difference in construction between a front coil spring and a rear coil spring? (p. 65)
7. How does a front end stabilizer operate? (pp. 72, 73)
8. What are the characteristics of all springs? (p. 73)
9. Why does a spring break? (p. 75)
10. What can be done to a coil spring if it becomes weak or fatigued? (p. 75)
11. Why shouldn't the rubber bushing and spring bolt be lubricated? (pp. 76, 77)
12. What is done to compensate for vehicle sag when a torsion bar system is used on the front end? (p. 79)
13. What is the purpose of shock absorbers? (pp. 80, 81)
14. Where are shock absorbers attached to the vehicle? (p. 81)
15. Can you describe how a double acting telescoping type of shock absorber operates? (pp. 81, 82)

CHAPTER 5

STEERING GEARS AND LINKAGES

PAGE

I. Manual Steering Gear Construction and Types 89
II. Power Steering 94
III. Steering Linkages 111
IV. Servicing the Steering Gear and Linkage 118

The steering gear is a device which converts the rotary motion of the steering wheel into side to side movement of the front wheels, permitting the driver to control the direction of vehicle travel. Various types of linkage are used to connect the steering gear to the front wheels.

The steering gear also provides the mechanical advantage necessary for the driver to maintain steering control of the vehicle. The *mechanical advantage* of a machine is the ratio of the moving force to the applied force. If a five-pound force is applied to a machine to move a twenty-pound weight, the mechanical advantage is four. The driver need only exert a small amount of physical effort at the steering wheel to change the direction of travel. This mechanical advantage is particularly helpful when the vehicle is at rest, in which case the driver must overcome the frictional resistance of the tires on the road surface in turning the wheels. When the vehicle is in motion and the front wheels strike an obstacle, only a small part of the road shock is transmitted to the steering wheel. This is due to the mechanical advantage provided by the steering gear. Manual steering gears usually have a mechanical advantage of about twenty to one, whereas in power steering the ratio varies according to manufacturer's specifications. The ratio in each case is selected to suit the needs of a particular vehicle.

I. MANUAL STEERING GEAR CONSTRUCTION AND TYPES

In most cars and trucks, the steering gear is bolted to the frame of the vehicle. The steering column extends at an angle through the fire wall or floor pan and into the driver's compartment

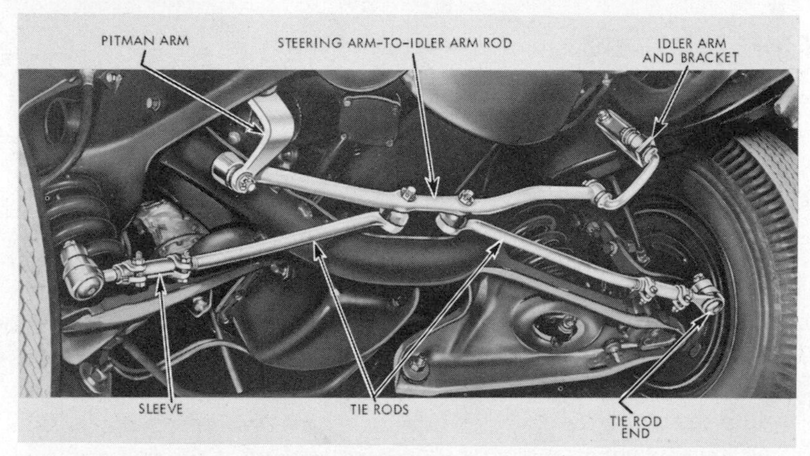

Fig. 1. Typical steering gear arrangement showing the various linkages of the steering system such as, the Pitman arm, the idler arm, the tie rods and the tie rod ends.

(Pontiac Div.—General Motors Corp.)

where the steering wheel is attached. A Pitman arm (which swings back and forth as the steering wheel is turned) is attached to the lower end of the steering gear and to the steering knuckle arm at each front wheel by means of linkages. As the steering wheel is turned the Pitman arm and its connecting linkages cause the front wheels to swing back and forth for steering purposes. Figure 1 illustrates a typical steering gear arrangement.

a. Steering Gear Construction. All steering gears are enclosed in and supported by a housing. The steering gear consists of a worm gear of some type which is contained within the housing, this worm-like device being at the bottom end of the steering column. The steering column or shaft and worm gear can, for all practical purposes, be considered as one piece. Ball bearings or roller bearings support the worm in the steering gear housing. See Fig. 2. An adjustment in the form of shims located between the housing end plate and housing or a threaded bearing adjuster nut permits the maintaining of the correct bearing pre-load on the worm. The steering wheel is mounted on the upper end of the column by splines and a nut. The steering column assembly is enclosed within a jacket, consisting of a hollow tube encircling the column assembly.

The cross shaft is located in the housing, usually at right angles to the steering column and is supported on bushings. The steering

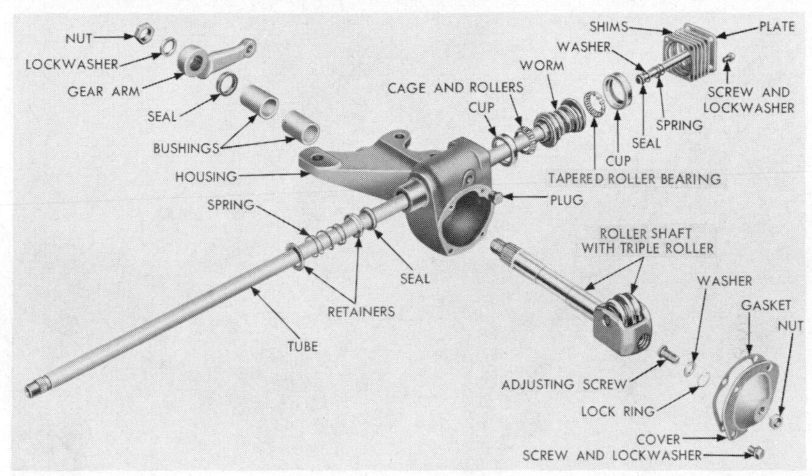

Fig. 2. Exploded view of the worm and roller type steering gear. Note that in this type of unit, the roller shaft has a triple roller.
(*Plymouth Div.—Chrysler Corp.*)

gear cross shaft incorporates a sector gear, a roller, or a lever, which meshes with the worm on the column. The outer end of the cross shaft extends through the housing, at which location the Pitman arm is attached by means of splines and held in place by a nut. The adjusting screw permits adjustment of steering gear lash or end play of the cross shaft.

b. Types of Steering Gears. Steering gears are classified according to the device used for coupling the cross shaft to the column. The types of steering gears in general use are of the worm and roller, the cam and lever, or the recirculating ball type.

(1) *WORM AND ROLLER.* The worm and roller steering gear consists of a concave (hour glass design) worm mounted on the steering column. The cross shaft is fitted with a roller which may have one or more grooves, as shown in Fig. 2. The roller fits into the worm teeth, which have the same contour as the roller, the worm being supported in the housing by tapered roller bearings. Shims located between the housing end plate and the housing provide a means of adjusting the bearing pre-load. When the worm turns, the roller threads along the worm, rolling with it and turning the cross shaft. The cross shaft is mounted within the housing by replaceable bushings, the shaft extending through the bushings which support it. The lash between the worm and roller can be reduced

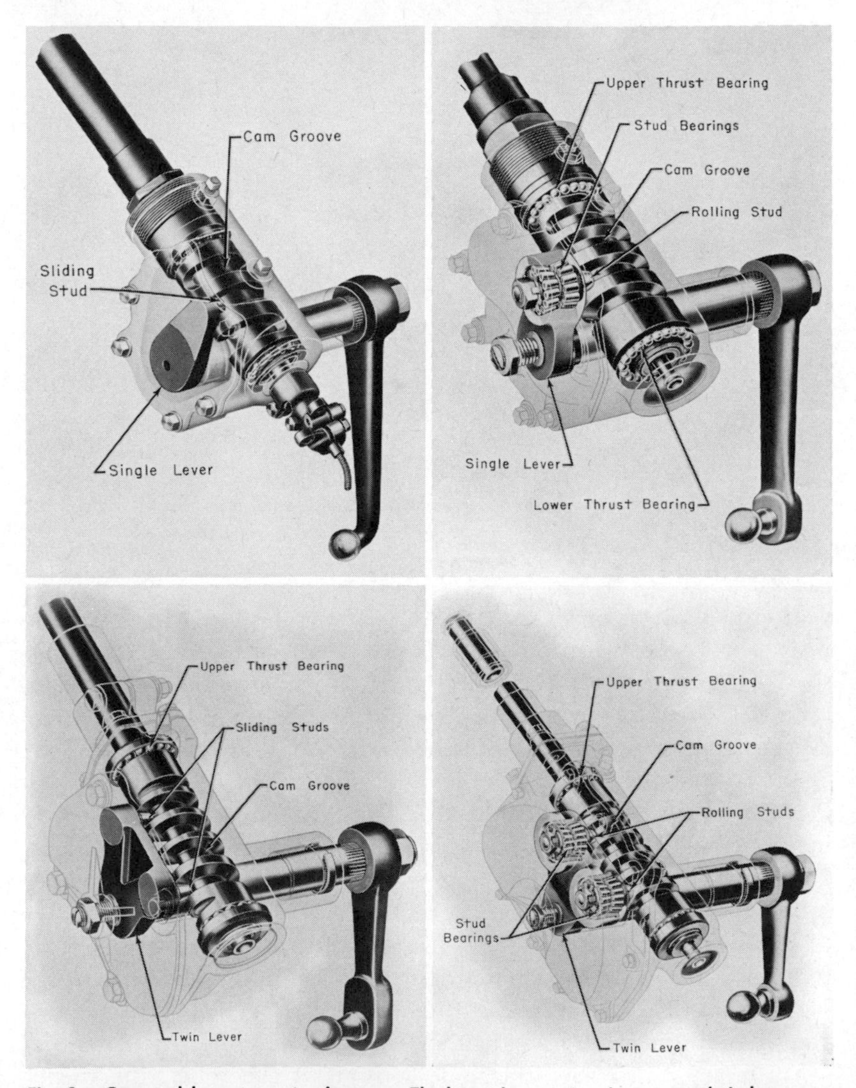

Fig. 3. Cam and lever type steering gear. The lever that carries the two studs is known as a twin lever.

(*Ross Gear and Tool Co.*)

by turning in an adjusting screw located in the housing cover. Rollers may be of the single, double, or triple type depending upon the design of the worm.

(2) *CAM AND LEVER.* In the cam and lever steering gear, the

worm is shaped in the form of a cylindrical cam (four types of steering gears with different combinations of levers and studs are shown in Fig. 3). The cam groove is tapered, being narrower at the bottom. The cam which is integral with the column is mounted in the housing on thrust type ball bearings. An adjustment in the form of shims located between the housing end plate and the housing or a threaded bearing adjuster nut is used to establish and maintain the correct bearing pre-load.

A lever is affixed to the cross shaft. This lever lies at the side of the cam and has a tapered stud projecting from it. The stud fits into the cam groove so that when the cam turns the stud moves along the cam, thereby swinging the lever and turning the cross shaft. The cross shaft is mounted within removable bushings to reduce friction and wear. An adjusting screw in the housing cover can be used to move the lever closer to the cam. As the stud is tapered, moving the lever closer to the cam reduces back lash. Figure 3, bottom, shows a lever with two studs, both of which ride the cam. The unit is known as a twin lever type steering gear.

Most cam and lever steering gears used today are of the twin lever type. The two studs may be an integral part of the lever or they may be mounted on tapered roller bearings. Those that are an integral part of the lever have a sliding contact on the cam and are known as *sliding studs.* Studs mounted in the lever on tapered roller bearings have a rolling contact and are known as *rolling studs.* Sliding or rolling studs may be used on either single or twin lever type steering gears.

(3) *RECIRCULATING BALL.* The most widely used manual steering gear at the present time is the recirculating ball type. The worm used in the recirculating ball steering gear consists of a straight cylinder with a round groove machined around the surface for the full length of the cylinder, like the thread on a bolt. A nut fits over the worm but does not mesh with it. A groove corresponding with the groove of the worm is machined on the inside of the nut. Engagement between the worm and the nut is obtained by filling the matching groove spaces with small steel balls. When the worm turns, the balls roll in the groove against the nut and cause the nut to move up or down along the worm. Each ball travels one complete loop around the worm, after which it enters a ball return guide and is pushed through the guide by the succeeding balls, over

to the opposite side of the worm where it again enters the grooves. Figure 4 shows the complete circuit. Two complete circuits or loops are needed to actuate the worm and nut.

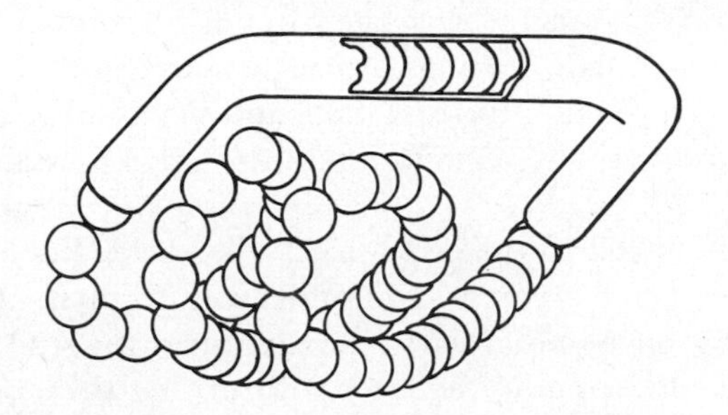

NOTE : There are two separate circuits of 33 balls each. 23 of each circuit, or a total of 46, carry the load.

Fig. 4. Recirculating ball circuit as used in the recirculating ball type of steering gear. (*Buick Div.—General Motors Corp.*)

The worm and nut are mounted on tapered roller bearings. An adjusting nut located at either the top or bottom of the housing provides a means of maintaining bearing pre-load.

The bottom outside face of the worm nut is machined in the shape of teeth forming a gear rack. A sector gear on the cross shaft acts as a pinion, meshing with the rack, thereby actuating the cross shaft when the worm nut is moved. The cross shaft is mounted within replaceable bushings. Figure 5 illustrates the circulating ball type steering gear. An adjusting screw located in the housing side cover (covering the cross shaft) is used to remove end play in the cross shaft.

II. POWER STEERING

Throughout the past few years several things have occurred that tend to make steering an automobile more difficult. The weight of the vehicle has been increased, more weight has been moved forward, wheels have become smaller, tires are wider and carry lower air pressure, and cars are capable of higher speeds. These factors have increased the effort required to turn the wheels while the vehicle is in motion. The greatest amount of effort, however, is required in parking. Parking requires that the wheels be turned while the vehicle is not moving or barely moving.

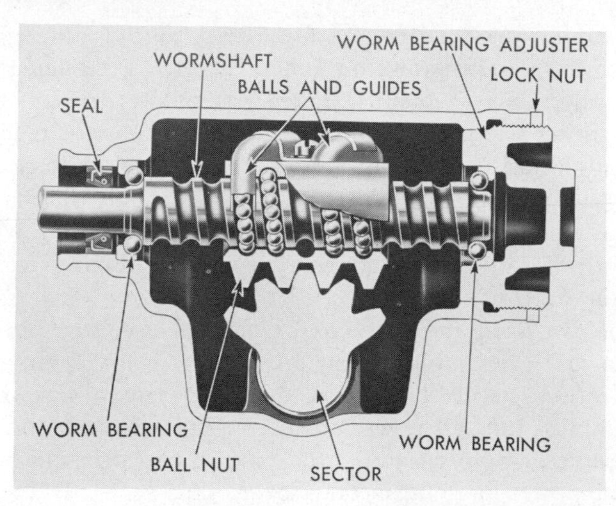

Fig. 5. Recirculating ball type of steering gear. Each ball travels one complete loop around the worm, after which it enters the ball return guide and is pushed through the guide by the succeeding balls, over to the opposite side of the worm where it again enters the grooves. There are two complete circuits or loops which are used to actuate the worm and nut assembly when the steering wheel is turned.

(*Chevrolet Div.—General Motors Corp.*)

Due to the angle of the steering knuckle, the front wheels have a tendency to remain in a straight-ahead position. When the wheels are straight ahead, the front of the car is closest to the surface of the road. This means that when the wheels are turned from the straight-ahead position the front end of the car must be lifted slightly. While the weight of the front end helps the driver to maintain a straight-ahead course, it increases the effort required to turn the wheels from the straight-ahead position. This is most noticeable as you turn the wheels when parking.

To help offset these steering difficulties, car manufacturers, by means of gears and levers, have provided more and more mechanical advantage to the driver through the steering mechanism. A practical limit, however, exists as to the steering ratio. The greater the mechanical advantage, the more the steering wheel must be turned to move the front wheels a given number of degrees. The obvious answer to this problem is to provide mechanical assistance rather than mechanical advantage. This has been accomplished by the power steering systems now available as optional equipment.

An important safety factor of the power steering system is to reduce the tendency of the front wheels to make unwanted turns.

With manual steering, if one front wheel should suddenly hit a bump, or a front tire blows out, there is often a tendency for the steering wheel to be violently jerked out of the driver's hand. In power steering systems this is reduced to a moderate tendency of the steering wheel to turn which is easy for the driver to control.

The fundamental principle behind power steering is simple. A hydraulic booster arrangement goes into operation when the steering wheel is turned with the engine running, taking over a great deal of the steering effort.

Before discussing the individual types of power steering systems, there are a few units and characteristics which are common to all power steering systems. First of all, a sense of *feel* must be retained. To accomplish this, all power steering systems have been designed so that some manual effort on the part of the driver is necessary before the power mechanism takes over. This generally amounts to from one to four pounds of pull at the steering wheel rim before power assistance is provided. Without this resistance the driver would have a feeling of uncertainty.

All power steering systems require the engine to be running in order to supply steering assistance. Therefore, if the car is being towed or pushed with the transmission in neutral, power is not available to assist in steering. Should the power steering system fail or not be brought into operation, the vehicle can be steered manually.

There are two types of power steering assemblies in use on modern vehicles. (1) The linkage type, where the power operating unit is a part of the steering linkage, and (2) the integral type, where the power operating unit is part of the steering gear. The principle of operation is the same for both. A hydraulic pump is used to supply fluid under pressure to the steering system to multiply the driver's effort at the steering wheel.

a. Hydraulic System. An engine driven hydraulic pump supplies the necessary oil pressure to the system as needed. The pump is belt driven, either as a separate unit or attached to the back of the generator. The pump delivers approximately 700 to 1000 psi pressure. Type "A" automatic transmission fluid is used in the hydraulic system. A reservoir attached to the pump is a means of storing the hydraulic fluid and a filter contained within the reservoir prevents foreign matter from entering the system. A pressure relief valve is incorporated within the pump to prevent the fluid pressure from

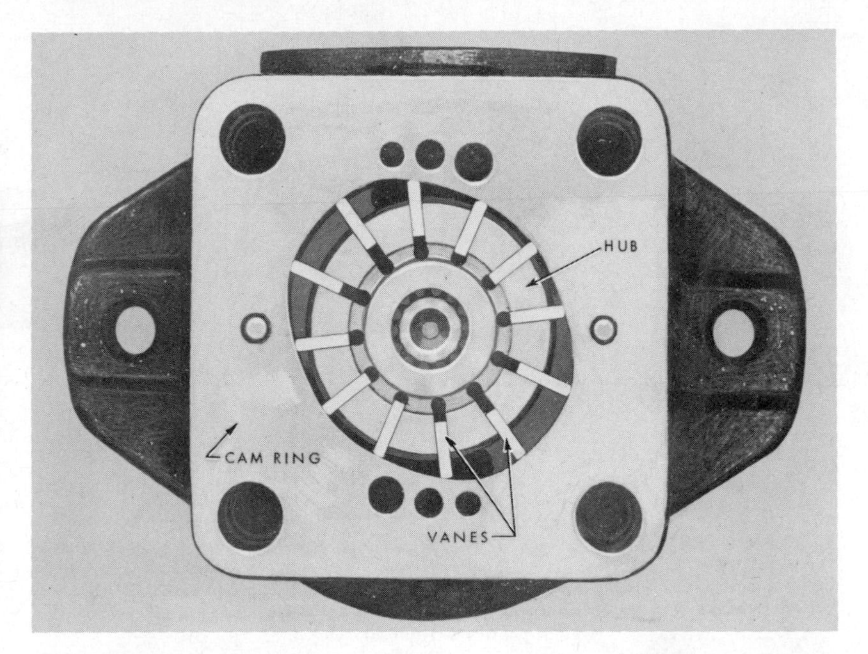

Fig. 6. Vane type of power steering hydraulic pump. There are 12 vanes assembled in the slotted driving rotor (hub), these vanes sliding outward to contact the inner face of the pump body. The inner face is oval shaped so as to provide two pumping chambers within the pump.

(Studebaker Corp.)

exceeding a predetermined maximum pressure. Without this feature, should a front wheel become jammed against a high curb so the wheel couldn't be turned the pressure could build up to a point where the steering linkage or hydraulic system might be damaged.

Flexible hoses carry the fluid from the pump to the power cylinder control valve. The control valve used in all power steering systems is of the spool type and constructed in such a manner that a small amount of steering wheel movement aligns different passageways within the system. In a straight-ahead position, fluid under pressure is equally directed to both sides of the piston. In either a right- or left-hand turn, the flow of fluid from the pump is shut off on one side of the piston, allowing the pressure to build up on the other side of the piston. After the turn has been completed, the control valve opens a return passageway which allows the fluid to return to the reservoir. The fluid then continues to circulate within the system.

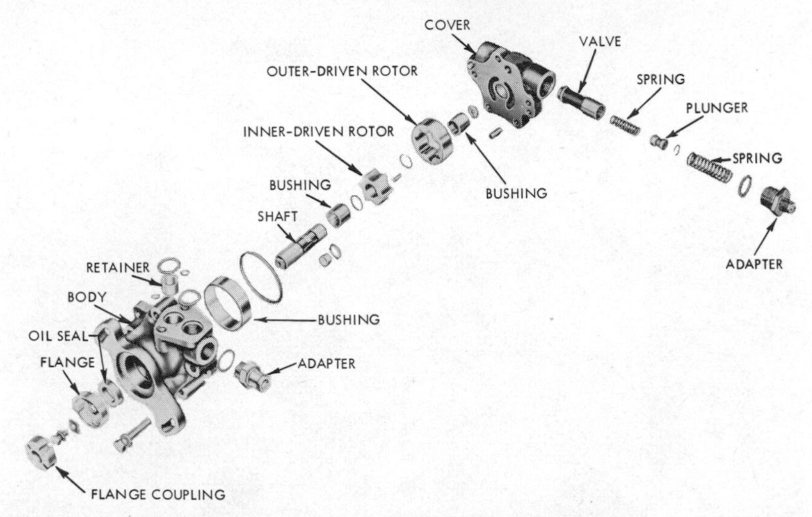

Fig. 7. Exploded view of the rotor type power steering pump, showing the inner or drive rotor and the outer or driven rotor. The inner rotor rotates on the pump shaft, driving the outer rotor, thereby forcing hydraulic fluid into and out of the pump housing. This action provides the power steering assistance as the driver turns the steering wheel.
(*Plymouth Div.—Chrysler Corp.*)

The pump may be of the vane type, the rotor type, or a variation of the vane type. Figure 6 illustrates a typical vane type of power steering pump. Variations of the same type pump are the roller and slipper types. Both pumps are similar in construction to the vane type pump except that rollers or sliding blocks (slippers) are used in place of vanes. All power steering pumps, regardless of design, are of the constant displacement type. In the vane type pump, the vanes are located either in the hub or the rotor. In operation, these vanes slide in a manner (either inward or outward, depending upon design) to contact the inner surface of the pump housing. As the rotor revolves, the vanes slide inward and then outward to increase and then decrease the space between the inner surface of the housing and the rotor. Fluid is then forced from the inlet side of the pump to the pressure check valve at the outlet side of the pump. Oil enters the pump when the vanes, rollers, or slippers are at the low side of the eccentric inside diameter of the housing and exits after being forced to the high side of the eccentric. Orifices (openings) at the valve permit fluid to flow into the system until a maximum or predetermined pressure is reached. At maximum pressure, excess fluid flows back into the reservoir.

An exploded view of the rotor type pump is shown in Fig. 7. The inner (drive) rotor is located off center within the pump housing. As the inner rotor is turned, the outer rotor turns with it. As both rotors revolve, the space between the drive rotor and the driven rotor first increases and then decreases in size. During increase, fluid flows from the reservoir and into the space between the rotors through the inlet port. During decrease this fluid is forced out of the pump through an outlet port, into the lines and back to the reservoir. The same valve arrangement is used as in the vane type pump. When maximum pressure is reached, excess fluid is bled back into the reservoir in such amounts as to maintain a working pressure.

b. Linkage Type Power Steering. The linkage type of power steering differs from the other hydraulic power steering systems in that a conventional type of steering gear is used.

The hydraulic power steering mechanism consists of an engine driven pump with check valve and reservoir, a double acting hydraulic power cylinder which assists linkage movement, and a control valve to direct the flow of fluid. The hydraulic pump, reservoir, and check valve are similar to those used with the integral type of power steering system.

In some installations, the control valve is incorporated within

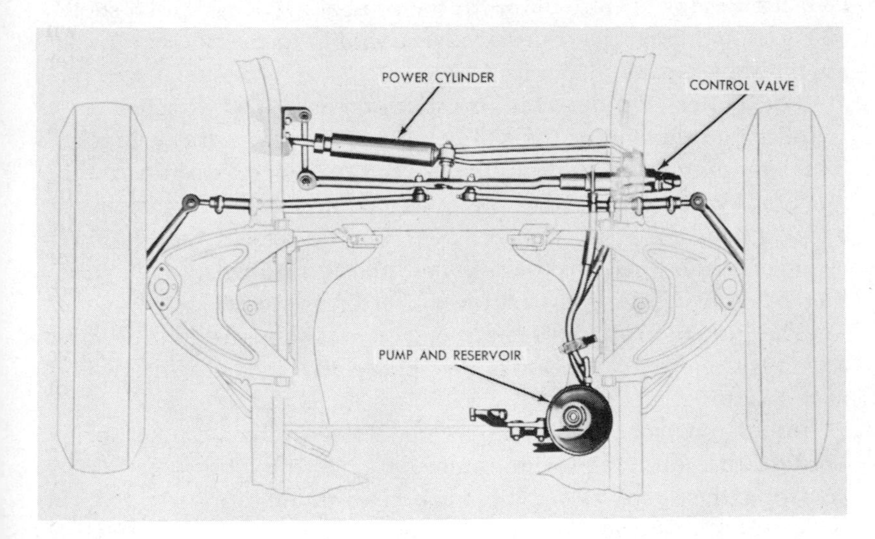

Fig. 8. Linkage type of power steering in which the power cylinder and control valve are an integral part of the steering linkage and not part of the steering gear.
(Ford Div.—Ford Motor Co.)

the power cylinder, thereby forming a single unit with an internal valve for directing fluid to the power cylinder passages. In other installations, the control valve which is shown in Fig. 8 is a separate assembly. The control valve assembly is connected to the hydraulic

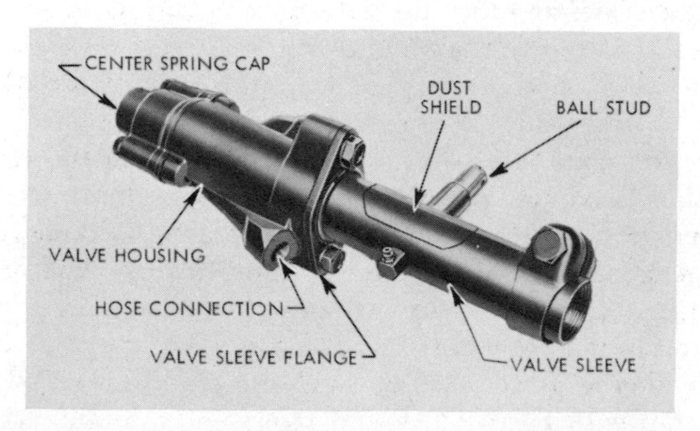

Fig. 9. Control valve assembly as used in the linkage type of power steering system. When the vehicle makes a turn, the control valve assembly directs fluid from the hydraulic pump to the power cylinder, thereby providing the power steering assistance needed.
(*Ford Div.–Ford Motor Co.*)

pump by means of two flexible hoses. Oil, under pressure, is delivered from the hydraulic pump to the control valve assembly, shown in Fig. 9, and from the control valve assembly to the power cylinder assembly by means of flexible hoses.

The power cylinder contains a piston which is attached to a cylinder rod, the end of the rod being anchored to a frame bracket. The opposite end of the cylinder is attached by a ball joint to the relay rod. When oil pressure is applied to one side of the piston, the cylinder (not the piston) is actuated. The movement of the power cylinder is transferred to the steering linkage through the relay rod, thereby reducing the effort required to steer the vehicle.

The Pitman arm actuates a spool valve within the control valve assembly. Figure 10 illustrates the spool valve used in this type of installation.

Initial movement of the steering wheel overcomes the spring pressure that holds the spool valve in a neutral position, thereby actuating the spool valve. This action shuts off the flow of fluid under pressure to one side of the power cylinder piston, directing fluid pressure to the other side. The spool valve is so constructed that the movement which closes off the fluid from the pump also lines

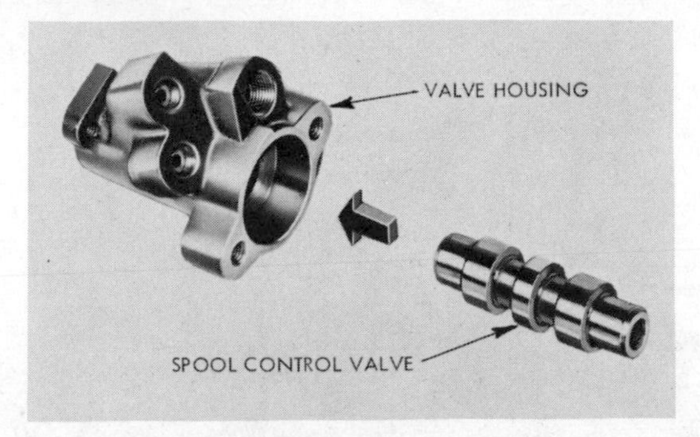

Fig. 10. Spool control valve which controls the flow of fluid within the linkage type of power steering system. The spool valve is contained within the control valve assembly.
(Ford Div.—Ford Motor Co.)

up a passage which permits fluid on that side of the piston to flow back to the reservoir.

c. Integral Type Power Steering. An integral type of power steering system is constructed in such a manner that the power operating unit is part of the steering gear.

Several different types of integral power steering units have been used by the various automobile manufacturers over a period of years. Basically, all integral types of power steering systems operate in much the same manner having the same basic components. However, construction details may vary with the different models.

The recirculating ball type steering gear is most commonly used, although the worm and roller type is used on some installations. Fundamentally, the pump, reservoir, and check valve all function in the same manner. Most systems operate at pressures of from 700 to 900 psi. All power steering systems have a double acting piston to assist in movement of the cross shaft which, in turn, moves the Pitman arm. A spool valve is used to direct the flow of fluid to the proper side of the piston. The spool valve at the same time permits fluid to return to the reservoir by allowing excess fluid to bleed out of the opposite end of the piston cylinder. The steering wheel rim pressure required to move the spool valve varies with different makes and models of automobiles. The method of moving the spool valve varies with different types of power steering installations.

(1) *CONSTANT CONTROL TYPE POWER STEERING.* The constant control power steering gear is enclosed in and supported by a housing. A cross shaft is contained within the housing at

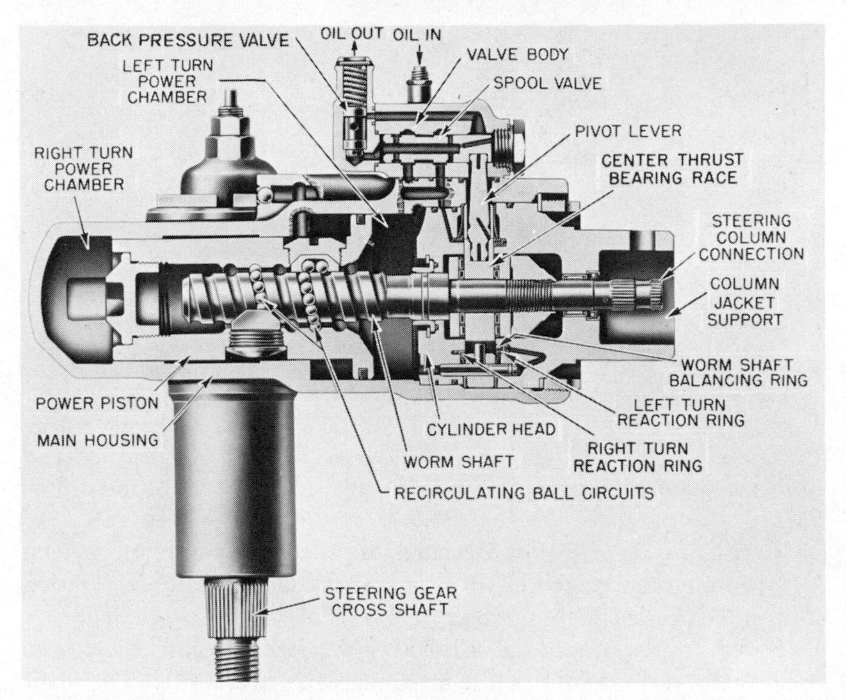

Fig. 11. Constant control type of power steering system consists of a recirculating ball-and-nut steering gear incorporated within a hydraulic power cylinder. This type of unit is sometimes referred to as the Saginaw power steering system.

(*Plymouth Div.—Chrysler Corp.*)

right angles to the steering column and a sector gear is mounted on the cross shaft. The power piston has gear teeth milled into its side enabling the piston to be in constant mesh with the cross shaft sector gear. A worm on a short shaft located inside the power piston is coupled to the steering column. The steering column extends upward into the driver's compartment where the steering wheel is mounted to the column. The worm is geared to the piston by means of a recirculating ball contact. Figure 11 illustrates the constant control type of power steering.

The upper end of a control valve (pivot) lever is fitted into the spool control valve which is enclosed in the valve body. The valve assembly is incorporated in the steering gear housing. The lower end of the lever fits into a radially drilled hole in the center thrust bearing race. The center thrust bearing race tips the valve lever which, in turn, actuates the spool control valve. The thrust bearing center race is held firmly against a shoulder on the worm shaft between two thrust bearings and bearing races. An adjusting nut is incorporated on the worm shaft to permit adjustment. The center thrust bearing race is, in effect, clamped axially to the worm shaft and must move with the worm shaft whenever the steering wheel is turned.

The spool valve is in neutral when in a straight-ahead position and fluid is delivered under equal pressure to both piston chambers. When the steering wheel is turned, the worm and shaft rotate inside the piston. Due to the resistance of the steering linkage and front wheels, the power piston does not move immediately. Instead, the worm and shaft are withdrawn from the piston a few thousandths of an inch. The center thrust bearing race moves in the same distance as the worm shaft. The center race thus tips the pivot lever which, in turn, moves the spool valve. Fluid is now directed under pressure to one of the piston chambers while a passageway at the opposite piston chamber is opened permitting fluid in that chamber to return to the reservoir. Hydraulic pressure now assists in moving the piston which, in turn, causes the cross shaft to rotate.

An adjusting screw located in the cross shaft housing permits adjustment of cross shaft end play. An adjusting nut in the steering gear housing is used to position the bearing spacer and center bearing race.

(2) *COAXIAL TYPE POWER STEERING.* The coaxial type of power steering is so called because the centerline or axis of the

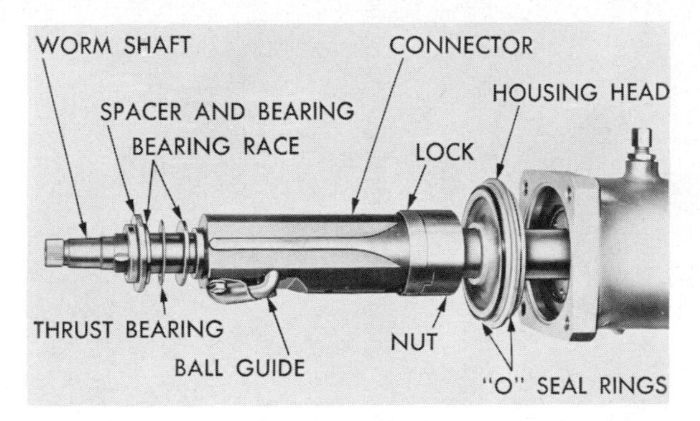

Fig. 12. Worm connector assembly as used in the coaxial type of power steering gear.
(Plymouth Div.—Chrysler Corp.)

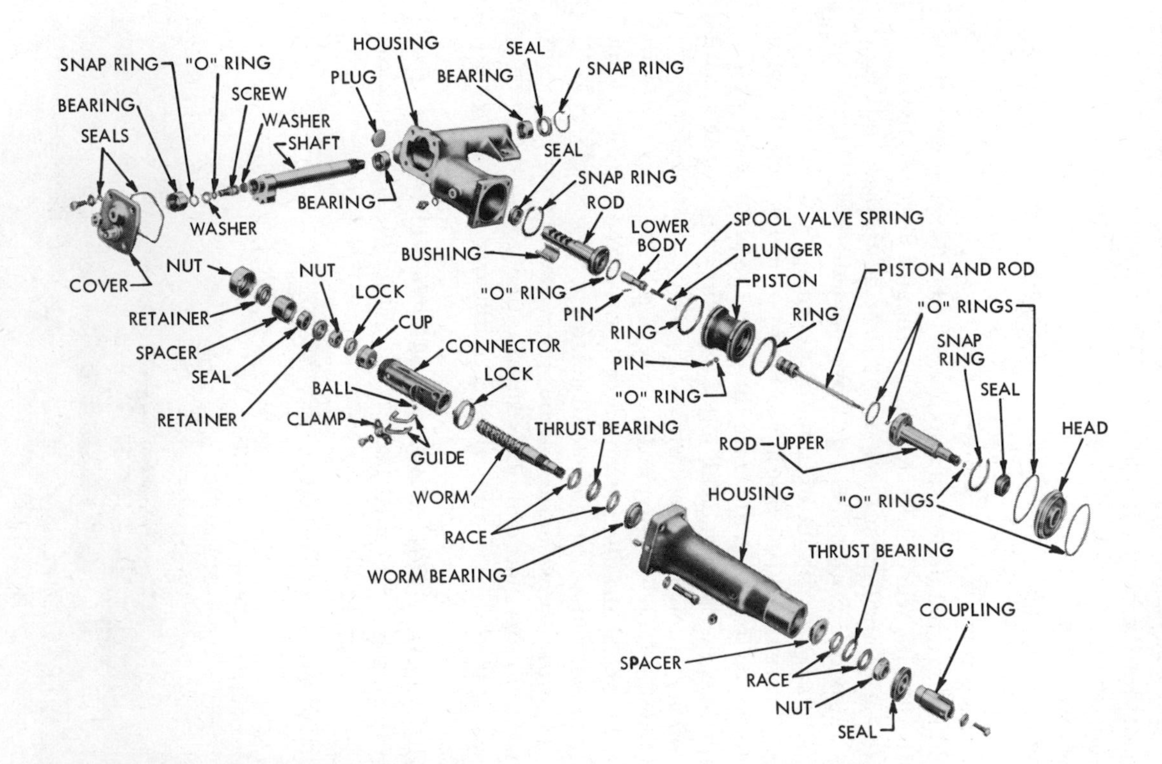

Fig. 13. Arrangement of components in a coaxial type power steering gear. Note that the steering gear consists of two basic units, an upper and a lower steering gear housing which are bolted together to form the two working chambers of the steering gear. *(Plymouth Div.—Chrysler Corp.)*

working parts all coincide. The coaxial power steering consists of two basic gear mechanisms: a worm and worm connection as shown in Fig. 12 and a rack and sector gear as shown in Fig. 13.

The worm and worm connector act in a manner similar to a bolt and nut assembly; rotation of the worm bolt causes an up and

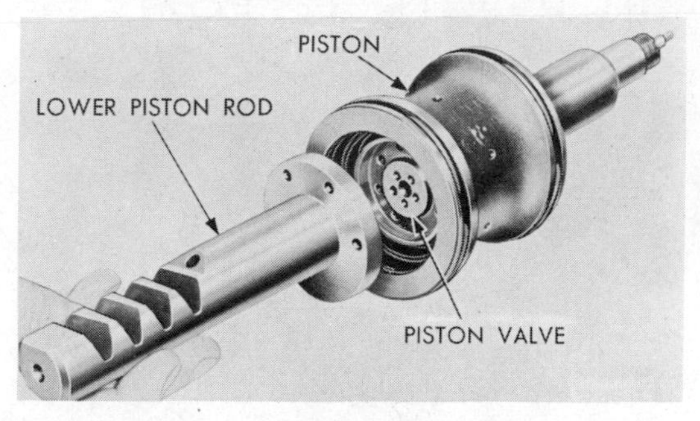

Fig. 14. Piston, sector gear rack, and control valve as used in the coaxial type of power steering gear.
(Plymouth Div.—Chrysler Corp.)

down motion of the worm connector nut. Fastened to the worm connector, in succession, are an upper piston rod, a piston, and a lower piston rod, all of which are concentric to the steering column axis. Figure 13 shows the arrangement of the various components of the coaxial power steering system. A spool type control valve located inside the piston controls the flow of hydraulic fluid to either side of the double acting piston. A sector gear rack, machined in the lower portion of the piston rod, as shown in Fig. 14, meshes with the sector gear on the cross shaft. Movement of the piston by hydraulic pressure causes the rack to move upward or downward within the housing, resulting in a back and forth rotation of the sector gear, cross shaft, and Pitman arm.

During normal straight-ahead driving, the spool valve within the power piston is centered, in a neutral position, thereby directing an equal amount of oil pressure to both ends of the piston. When the steering wheel is turned, the worm which is attached to the steering column also turns, causing the worm connector to move. The worm connector, which is attached to the spool valve by a valve operating rod, moves the valve a few thousandths of an inch. When the spool valve is moved, it cuts off the flow of fluid to one side of the piston and at the same time aligns a return passageway, allowing

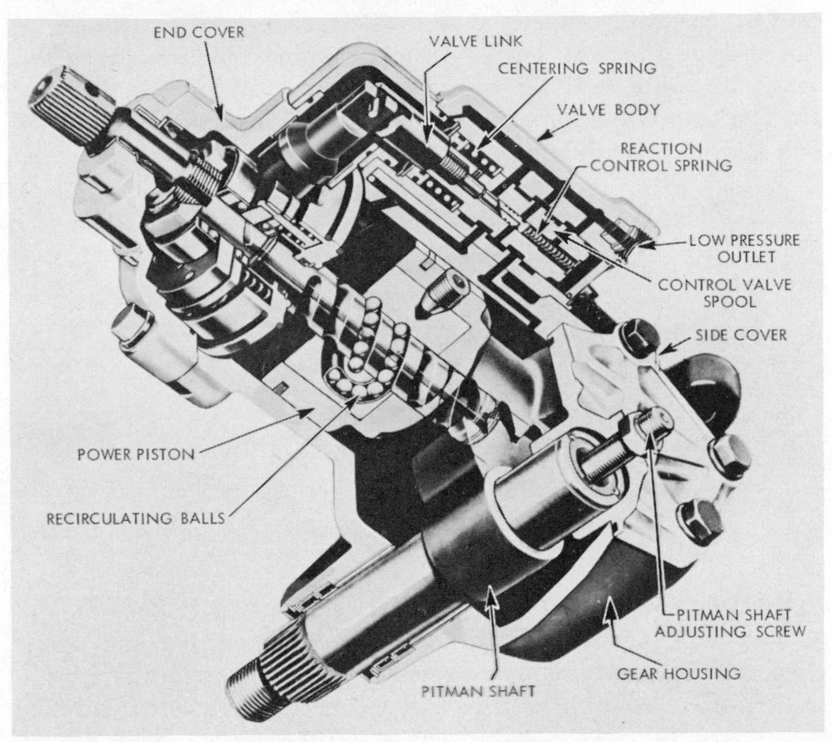

Fig. 15. Saginaw in-line type of power steering assembly. The unit consists of a recirculating ball-and-nut steering gear to which a hydraulic power cylinder has been added. The outer face of the power piston is machined in the form of teeth, thereby forming the sector gear rack.

(Buick Div.—General Motors Corp.)

the remaining fluid on that side of the piston to flow out the low pressure side of the hydraulic system. When the flow of fluid to one side of the piston is cut off, oil pressure on the other side increases, forcing the piston and gear rack to move. The movement of the piston and sector gear rack turns the sector gear and Pitman arm. As the steering wheel continues to turn, the control (spool) valve continues to move slightly ahead of the piston. Therefore, hydraulic pressure continues to be directed against the piston. As soon as the steering wheel movement stops, the control valve also stops, and the piston moves slightly ahead of the control valve so that the piston is centered with respect to the valve. This action closes the low pressure release on the opposite side of the piston and opens the low pressure channels to both sides of the piston. A reaction seal in the hydraulic reaction device applies pressure against the steering wheel in proportion to the hydraulic steering effort produced by the steering gear assembly. This reaction gives the driver a sense of steering "feel" at all times.

Three adjustments can be made to this type of steering gear assembly without removing the assembly from the car. The adjustments should be made in this sequence: worm bearing adjustment, piston valve adjustment, and gear lash adjustment.

(3) *SAGINAW IN-LINE TYPE POWER STEERING.* The Saginaw in-line type of power steering system consists of a recirculating ball steering gear, a power piston, a sector gear rack, and a power cylinder. These components are in a direct line with the steering column which is attached to the worm shaft by means of a flexible coupling. The control valve (spool type) is mounted directly on the gear housing, eliminating all external lines and hoses except the high pressure and return lines between the pump and control valve. Figure 15 shows a sectional view of the Saginaw in-line type of steering assembly. The inner end of the cross shaft has an integral sector gear which engages a sector gear rack that is part of the power piston. Any movement of the piston moves the sector gear and, therefore, the cross shaft. The Pitman arm is mounted on the outer end of the cross shaft.

The hydraulic control valve regulates the flow of fluid from the pump to the proper side of the power piston when power assistance is required. The control valve also directs equal pressure to both sides of the piston when the steering wheel is held in the straight-ahead position. A centering spring located in the valve reaction chamber, along with the thrust bearing centering springs, holds the control valve in a neutral position. The control valve also contains a second spool valve which establishes the maximum pressure that may be produced in the reaction chamber and thereby decreases the steering effort when parking. The control valve is shown in Fig. 16.

When the steering wheel is turned, the thrust bearing is moved either upward or downward along the worm shaft, thereby moving the control valve actuating lever. The movement of the actuating lever moves the spool control valve, which directs the flow of fluid under pressure to one side of the piston. The fluid on the opposite side of the piston is simultaneously forced out of the cylinder and back into the reservoir.

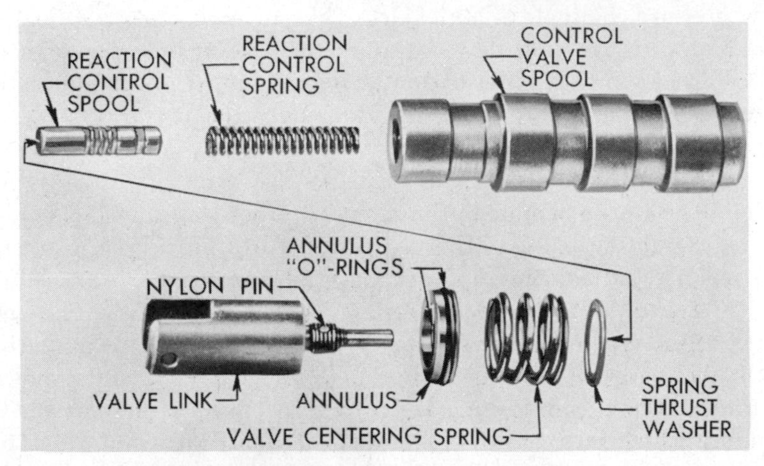

Fig. 16. Control valve spool assembly used with the Saginaw in-line power steering unit. *(Buick Div.—General Motors Corp.)*

An adjusting screw located in the steering gear housing side cover is used to control lash between the rack teeth on the piston and cross shaft sector gear.

(4) *SAGINAW ROTARY VALVE TYPE POWER STEERING.* The major components of the rotary valve type power steering assembly are: a hydraulic control valve assembly, a worm shaft, a piston one side of which is in the form of sector gear rack teeth, and a cross shaft mounting a sector gear. The pump creates hydraulic pressure to aid in movement of the steering gear components, therefore producing a steering assist action.

The steering column is attached to the worm shaft by means of a flexible coupling. The hydraulic control valve, the worm shaft, and the piston rack assembly are all in a direct line with the steering shaft. The spool valve is located directly on the steering gear housing, eliminating all external lines except the pressure and return hoses between the housing and pump.

The mechanical element is similar to the Saginaw in-line steering gear using a recirculating ball system in which steel balls act as a rolling thread between the worm and the piston. The piston rack assembly meshes with the sector gear which is mounted on the cross shaft. The hydraulic control valve is contained within the front section of the steering gear housing. Figure 17 illustrates a typical rotary valve type of power steering system.

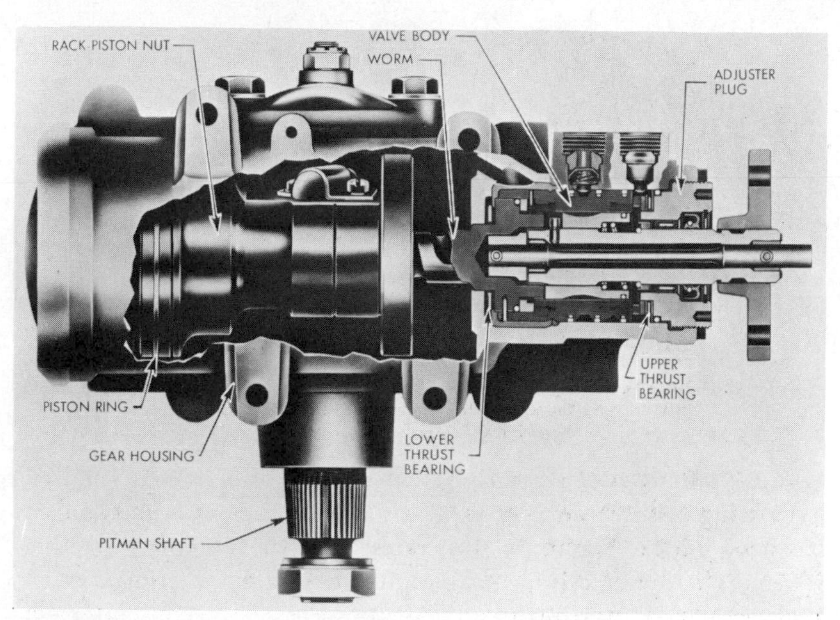

Fig. 17. Rotary valve type of power steering. The control valve encloses the valve spool and the shaft assembly on which the valve spool is mounted. When the steering wheel is turned the rotary valve assembly rotates, aligning the various passageways within the hydraulic system and applying hydraulic pressure to one side of the power piston.
(Buick Div.—General Motors Corp.)

The control valve is an open-center rotary-type, three-way valve. It contains a valve spool which is held in a neutral position by means of a torsion bar. The spool is attached to one end of the torsion bar and the valve body to the other end. When the steering wheel is turned, resistance between the front wheels and the roadbed causes the torsion bar to deflect. Deflection of the torsion bar rotates the spool valve changing the relationship between the grooves in the spool valve and the grooves in the valve body. This action directs the flow of fluid to the proper end of the piston chamber and releases the fluid in the opposite chamber. Figure 18 shows an exploded view of the rotary valve. Fluid under pressure is equally directed to both sides of the piston when the steering wheel is motionless.

A cross shaft adjusting screw is located in the housing side cover. This adjustment is provided to remove cross shaft end play and establish a pre-load between the worm and sector gear.

(5) *SAGINAW OFFSET TYPE POWER STEERING.* The

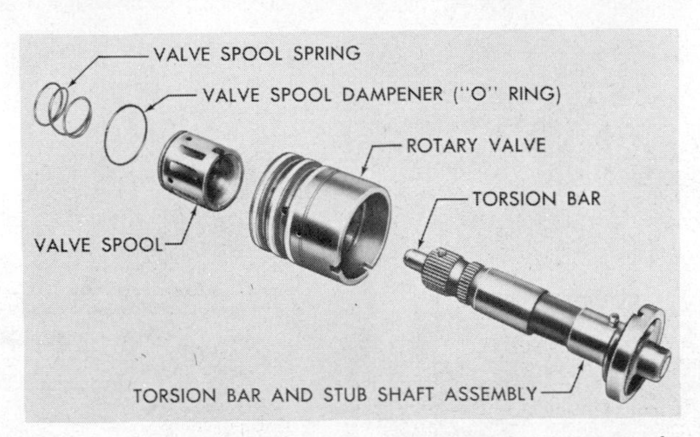

Fig. 18. Exploded view of the rotary valve assembly showing the rotary valve, valve spool, and the shaft which mounts the components.
(Pontiac Div.—General Motors Corp.)

Saginaw offset power steering system consists of a conventional recirculating ball steering gear to which a hydraulic power mechanism has been added. Figure 19 illustrates this type of power steering system. The power cylinder is mounted above the steering gear. A sector gear rack attached to the power piston is in constant mesh with the upper part of a sector gear on the cross shaft. The lower part of the sector gear is in constant mesh with the conventional steering worm nut.

Movement of the steering wheel causes a slight longitudinal movement of the steering shaft, the direction of this movement depending upon the direction the steering wheel is turned. Movement of the steering shaft shifts the spool type control valve which then directs the flow of fluid from one side of the power piston back to the intake side of the hydraulic pump, simultaneously directing fluid from the pump to the other side of the power piston. The power piston then exerts pressure upon the rack, thereby assisting the cross shaft, Pitman arm, and front wheels in turning. The front wheels turn until they assume the degree of turn called for by the amount the steering wheel is turned.

As the driver stops turning the steering wheel, a valve plunger spring moves the steering shaft longitudinally back to a neutral position, where the spool valve again directs the flow of fluid back to the intake side of the pump. In this position, as well as in the straight-ahead position, no work is being done by the power system other than maintaining equal pressure on both ends of the piston.

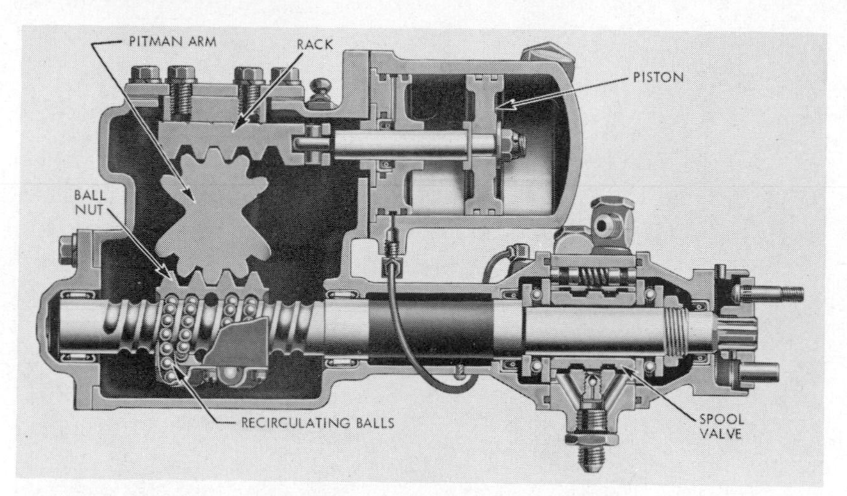

Fig. 19. Saginaw offset type of power steering employing a recirculating ball guide in conjunction with a hydraulic power cylinder.
(*Studebaker Corp.*)

An adjusting screw located in the housing side cover is provided for the adjustment of cross shaft end play and gear lash.

(6) *OTHER TYPES OF POWER STEERING SYSTEMS.* Other types of power steering units are, or have been, used on various makes of automobiles. However, in every case the basic operating principles and general construction will be the same. Variations, if any, generally occur in the relative position of the various components.

III. STEERING LINKAGES

The rods, the arms, and the levers, by which the steering knuckles are connected to the steering gear Pitman arm, are known collectively as the steering linkage. Various arrangements are used in automotive vehicles, but they all perform the same function.

The steering gear employs a Pitman arm which is attached to the end of the cross shaft that extends out of the steering gear housing. The Pitman arm on most installations generally swings from one side to the other as the steering wheel is turned. However, on some older models the Pitman arm was designed to swing forward and backward.

The steering knuckle assembly is fitted with steering knuckle

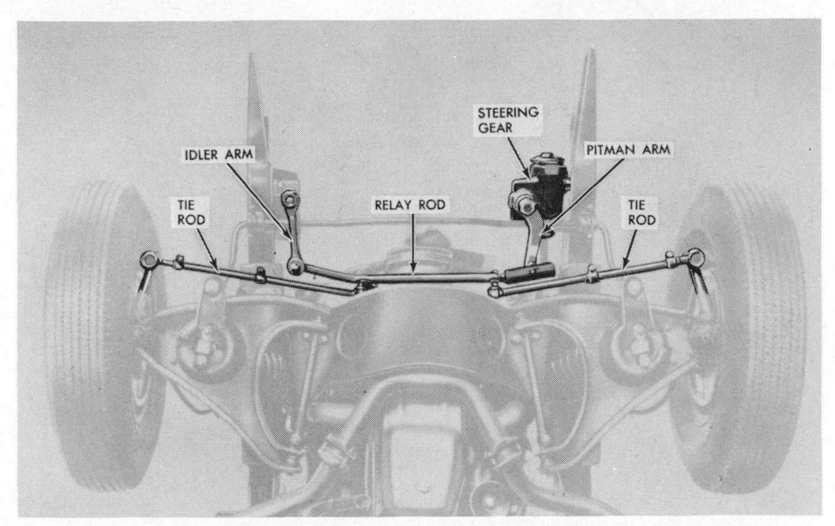

Fig. 20. Conventional steering linkage showing the various hookups between the steering gear through the Pitman arm to the steering linkage and to the front wheels.
(*Chevrolet Div.–General Motors Corp.*)

arms to hold the front wheels parallel as well as to control front wheel swivel. The steering knuckle arms, which are connected together by adjustable tie rods, are connected to the steering gear Pitman arm by means of rods and links. Different arrangements of these intervening links are used in different types and designs of suspensions. With independent front suspension, a separate tie rod is used for each steering knuckle. Separate tie rods are used because the distance between the steering knuckle arms varies as the front wheels flex independently of each other. If a single, one-piece tie rod were used, the distance between the front wheels would remain constant, causing the wheels to swivel or turn, at least to a small degree, at every road irregularity. This is not a problem when a solid beam front axle is used. Figure 20 illustrates a typical linkage assembly used with an independent front suspension.

In most cases, the steering linkage rods which join the various links and levers of the steering system are connected to one another and to those various links and levers by some type of ball and socket joint arrangement. The most common type of ball and socket joint consists of a short tapered bolt ending in a spherical form, the sphere fitting into a socket mounted on the linkage rod. The ball end is assembled into a socket by a special press and cannot be disassembled or serviced. The socket may be part of the rod. or may have a threaded stud which screws into the rod. A spring between the end of the ball and the bottom of the socket maintains a tension between the ball and socket to counteract wear and prevent

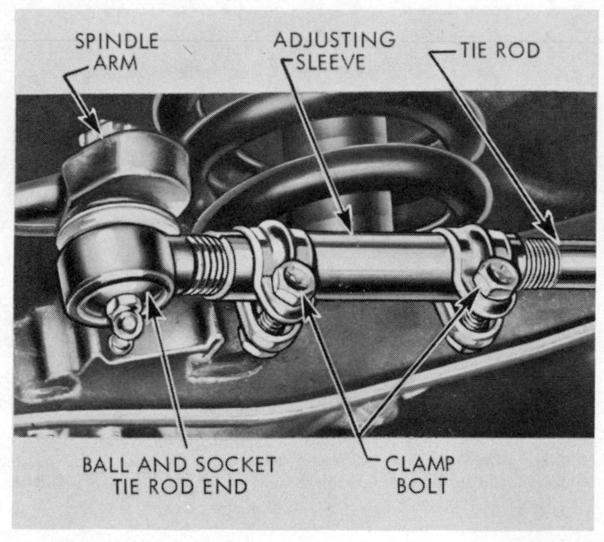

Fig. 21. Ball and socket joint used with a tie rod. This type of installation is known as a ball and socket tie rod end.
(Ford Div.—Ford Motor Co.)

free play. Figure 21 illustrates a ball and socket joint installed on a tie rod. A boot or seal is generally used to keep dirt and moisture out of the ball and socket installation.

In another type of ball and socket joint assembly, the socket is contained within the enlarged end of the tie rod or drag link and can be separated from the ball. Therefore, this type of assembly is adjustable. Figure 22 illustrates an adjustable ball and socket joint assembly attached to a Pitman arm. The ball may or may not be removable from the arm or linkage to which it is attached. Concave washers and one or more springs are located in the socket to maintain a slight tension on the ball. A threaded end plug in the socket enables the adjustment of spring tension on the ball, thereby compensating for wear and preventing free play.

The tie rod is a hollow rod or tube used to connect the steering knuckle arms together. Two tie rods are used on all independent front suspension systems. Either a relay rod or an intermediate

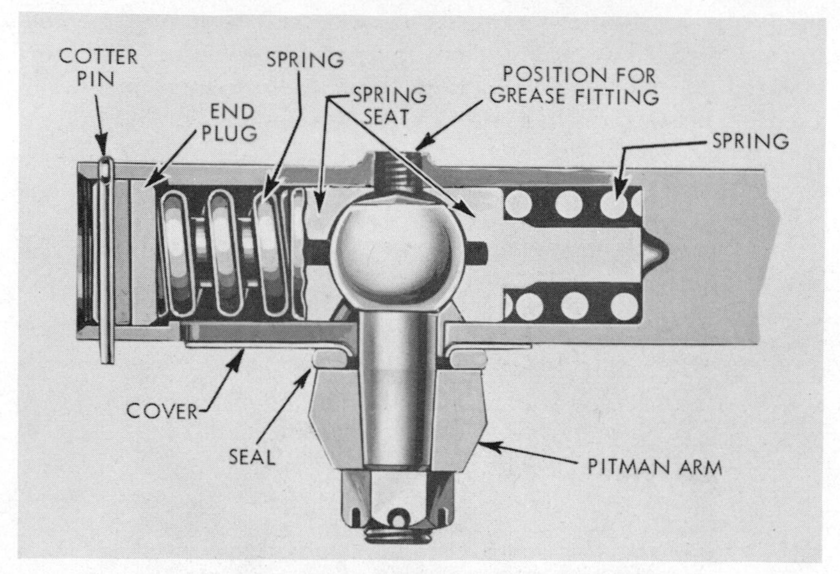

Fig. 22. Adjustable type ball and socket joint. The adjustment can be made by means of a threaded end plug. After removing the cotter pin, screw the end plug into the drag link to take up any excess clearance that may exist between the spring seat and the ball joint. (*Chevrolet Div.—General Motors Corp.*)

steering rod (arm) is generally located between the two tie rods as shown in Fig. 23. The difference between the two types of installations is that the relay rod is connected directly to the Pitman arm, whereas the intermediate steering arm, if used, is connected to the Pitman arm, by means of a rod known as the drag link.

The tie rod is attached to the steering knuckle arm by means of a ball and socket joint which is known as the tie rod end. The tie rod and tie rod end have matching threads enabling the tie rod to screw into the tie rod end. One tie rod end always has a right-hand thread, while the opposite tie rod end always has a left-hand thread. The threads are cut in this manner so that the tie rod assembly can be lengthened or shortened by turning the tie rod, either inward or outward on the two tie rod ends. The end of each tie rod is fitted with clamp bolts to prevent either or both tie rods from turning, once the desired length is obtained. Some installations employ a tie rod which is threaded only on one end. Therefore, a threaded sleeve is installed between the tie rod end and the tie rod as shown in Fig. 21. The sleeve has right-hand threads on one end and left-hand threads on the other. The sleeve is adjusted in the same manner as

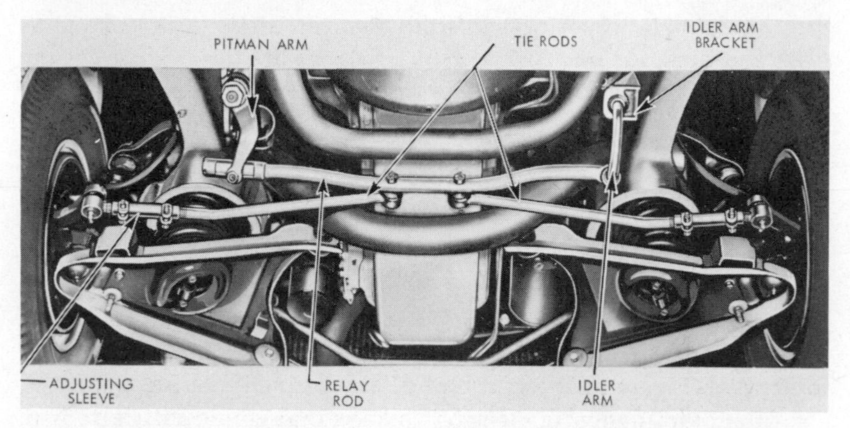

Fig. 23. Steering linkage using a relay rod. In this type of installation the tie rods are of equal length, one end of each tie rod being adjustable by means of an adjusting sleeve. (*Ford Div.—Ford Motor Co.*)

the tie rod; that is, the sleeve is turned either inward or outward to shorten or lengthen the tie rod.

Drag links and relay rods are similar in construction to tie rods. However, an adjustable type of ball and socket end joint is often used. The adjustable type of ball and socket is shown in Fig. 22. If the end socket is of the non-adjustable type and is a part of the tie rod, relay rod, or drag link, the entire rod must be replaced should excessive wear occur.

a. Types of Steering Linkages. Several features of the vehicle must be given consideration by the automotive engineers in the design and construction of steering linkages. The construction of the frame has an effect on the arrangement of the various components in the steering linkage. The rods and links must be so placed that the strength of the frame is not impaired by holes and notches in the frame structure. At the same time, clearances must be provided to allow unrestricted movement of the linkage throughout its range of travel. The location of the engine also has a bearing on the arrangement of the steering linkage. The policy of locating the engine as low in the frame and as far forward as possible makes it necessary to adapt the steering hookup to the available operating clearance. In addition to the effects of the frame and engine, the design and operating characteristics of the suspension itself are factors contributing to steering linkage construction.

Several types of linkages have been used to maintain the wheels in a straight-ahead position in spite of spring deflections. The most common design is one in which the tie rods are approximately the same length as the lower control arms and are situated parallel to them. In this manner the tie rods swing in the same arc as the control arm and, consequently, maintain the same distance from the center of the vehicle throughout spring oscillation. On turns, however, the tie rods do not remain parallel to the control arms because the arc of action on the Pitman arm causes the inner ends of the tie rods to rise and fall. In most designs of this type, the tie rods are connected through ball and socket joints to the Pitman arm on one end and an idler arm, equal in length to the Pitman arm, on the other end. Figure 23 shows a typical arrangement of this type.

In another design of steering linkage that employed tie rods of an equal length, the tie rods were attached to an intermediate steering arm at the center of the vehicle. Movement of the Pitman arm actuated the drag link which, in turn, moved the intermediate steering arm. The motion of the steering arm was carried through

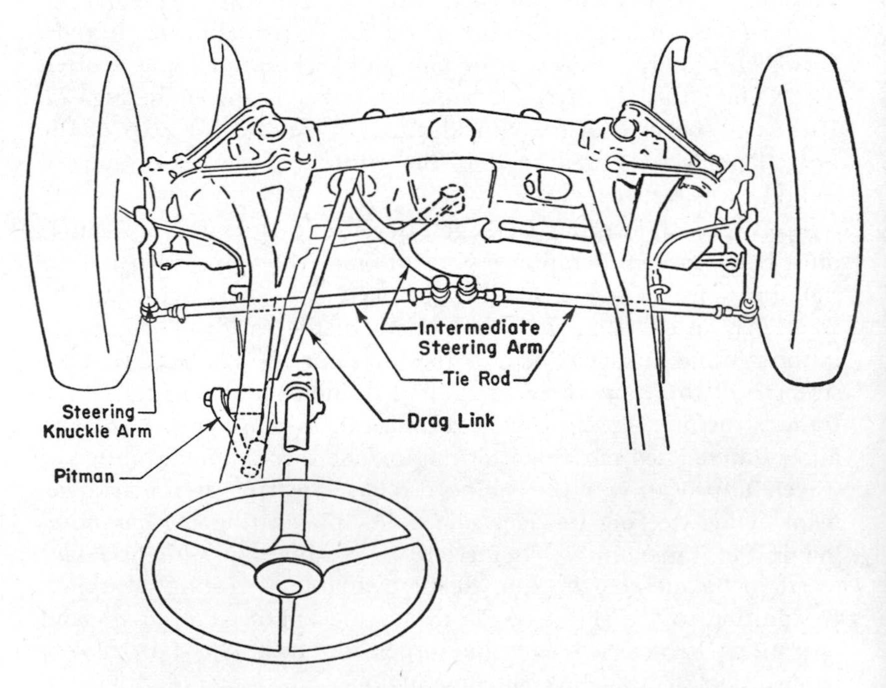

Fig. 24. Steering linkage using an intermediate steering arm which serves the same purpose as the relay rod.

the tie rods to the steering knuckle arm, thus turning the front wheels in the desired direction.

A typical design of a steering linkage with an intermediate steering arm is shown in Fig. 24.

A linkage having one long and one short tie rod has been used on some installations. In this type of installation, the steering gear is so constructed that the Pitman arm swings crosswise under the vehicle frame. The short tie rod connects the Pitman arm directly to one steering knuckle arm, while the long tie rod extends from the Pitman arm directly to the other steering knuckle arm. In order to compensate for the difference in the lengths of the tie rods, they are attached at different points along the Pitman arm. A design of this type is shown in Fig. 25. When the Pitman arm swings as the vehicle makes a turn, the short tie rod rises in a sharper arc than the long tie rod and, consequently, the short rod does not move as far in a crosswise direction as the long tie rod. This differ-

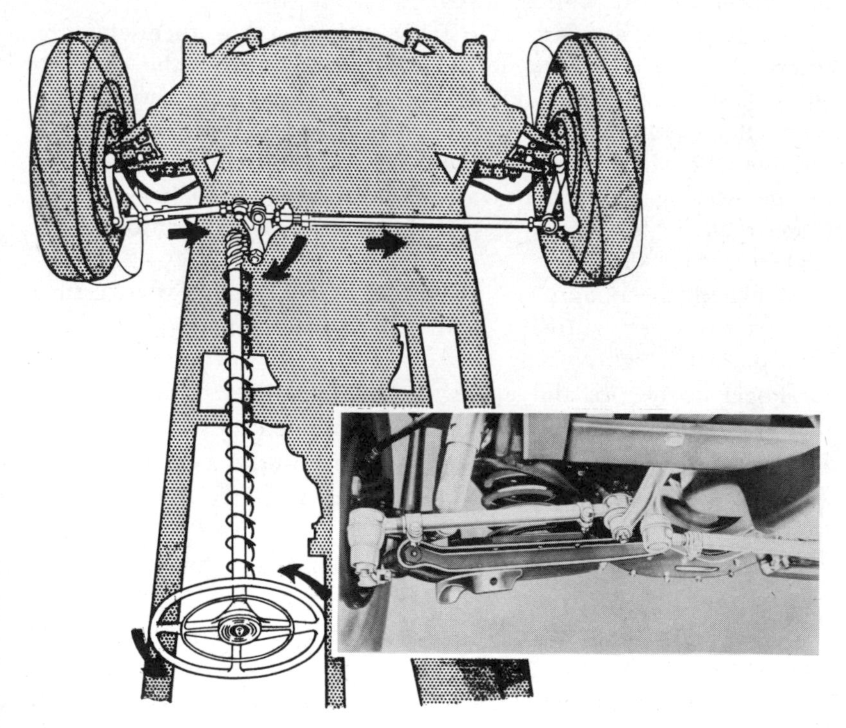

Fig. 25. Steering linkage with a center Pitman arm arrangement. Note that in this type of installation the tie rods are of different lengths, one short and one long.

ence in travel between tie rods at the Pitman arm causes the two front wheels to swivel to a corresponding degree.

Numerous other designs of steering linkages have been used but the operating principles, basic components, and servicing procedures are the same for all types of linkages.

Any free play that may develop in the steering linkage which cannot be removed by adjustment, therefore, necessitates the replacement of parts, generally: the tie rod, the relay rod, or the drag link and joints. Proper front wheel toe-in must be maintained by correct adjustment of the tie rods. Adjustment of the tie rods also affects the mid-position of the steering wheel.

IV. SERVICING THE STEERING GEAR AND LINKAGE

The safe operation of a vehicle depends a great deal upon the mechanical condition of the steering gear and its connection through the various types of linkage to the front wheels.

All steering gears are adjustable either within themselves or externally. Therefore, when the front wheels are in the straight-ahead position, there should be no lost motion or lash between the gears. If excessive lash does exist within the steering system, the innumerable slight bumps in the road that normally are absorbed by the steering connections will be transformed into hammer-like blows that are felt in the steering wheel. Such a condition is described as road shock.

To check the amount of lost motion in the steering system, turn the steering wheel until the front wheels are in the straight-ahead position. Then lightly grasp the steering wheel between thumb and forefinger at the rim and move the steering wheel back and forth to determine the amount of play. Manufacturer's specifications vary with respect to steering gear no lash adjustment. However, if any steering wheel play is found at the rim, the steering gear requires adjustment.

Binding of the various steering components is known as hard steering and is usually the result of improper (too tight) no lash adjustment, tight or worn bearings, or distortion of the steering column. Such conditions will affect the control and stability of the vehicle, resulting in wander and hard steering when the vehicle is in motion as well as when stationary.

After considerable use, a steering gear may become worn to the extent where adjustment is no longer able to restore satisfactory operating limits. Then, it becomes necessary to replace some of the working parts. Damage from undue stress or collision may also make repairs necessary.

a. Adjustment of Manual Steering Gears. There are three basic adjustments that must be made on a manual steering gear. These are: 1) worm bearing pre-load adjustment, 2) Pitman or cross shaft end play adjustment, and 3) high point or through center adjustment (gear lash). Since these adjustments made on the steering gear are for taking up normal wear, they consist of tightening only and should, therefore, result in a definite drag or pre-load but should *not* cause binding. It is advisable to disconnect the linkage from the lower end of the Pitman arm when checking or making steering gear adjustments.

(1) *WORM BEARING PRE-LOAD ADJUSTMENT.* In general, the worm bearing adjustment (amount of bearing pre-load) is determined by the amount of effort it takes to turn the worm as mounted between the worm bearings. The effort required to turn the worm is measured on the rim of the steering wheel by a spring scale somewhat similar in design and operation to that of a fish scale. If a spring scale is not available, a torque wrench may be used instead. Attach the torque wrench to the nut that mounts the steering wheel to the steering shaft.

An average worm bearing pre-load reading using the spring scale should be approximately one-half pound or eight ounces depending on the type of scale used. An average torque wrench reading would be six inch ounces.

Two basic methods are used to adjust the worm bearings. One method is the use of shims between the housing and a plate that is bolted to the lower or upper end of the housing. To increase the worm bearing pre-load, remove one or more shims from between the housing and the plate until the correct worm bearing load is achieved. If too much pre-load is obtained, for example the spring scale reads one pound at the rim of the steering wheel, a very thin shim would be replaced between the housing and the plate and the bolts re-tightened.

Another method employs a large round adjuster nut that screws into the steering gear housing. (See Fig. 26.) This nut may be located at either the upper or lower end of the housing. A steering gear that employs this type of adjustment is regulated by first un-

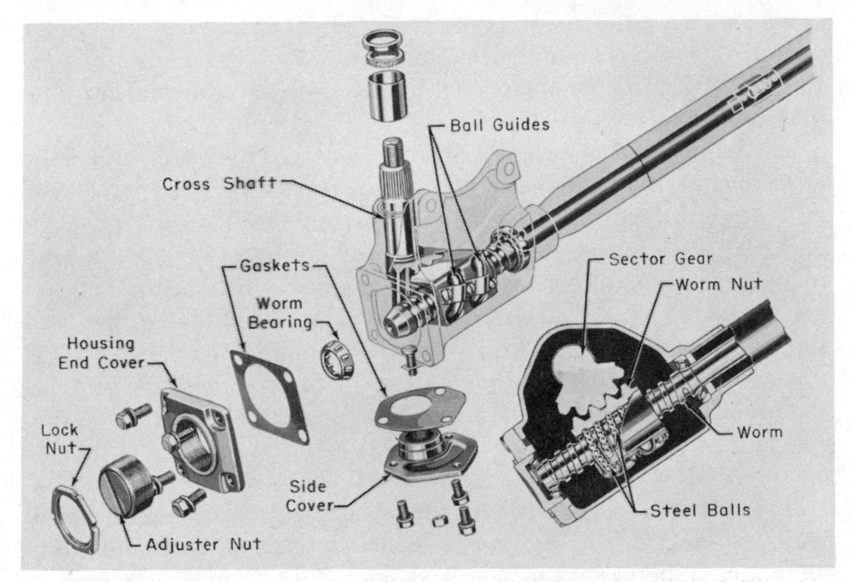

Fig. 26. Recirculating ball type of steering gear showing the arrangement of the various components in relation to the steering wheel shaft. The sector gear, which is mounted on the end of the cross shaft, meshes with the sector teeth cut on the worm nut.
(Buick Div.—General Motors Corp.)

screwing the jam nut that locks the adjusting nut in position, and then turning the adjusting nut into the housing to increase the bearing load or out of the housing to decrease bearing load. When the spring scale shows a one-half pound pull on the rim of the steering wheel, the adjusting nut should be locked in position by the jam nut.

(2) *PITMAN SHAFT END PLAY ADJUSTMENT.* Pitman shaft (cross shaft) end play adjustment is an internal adjustment, and the adjusting device is usually located within the steering gear housing. On some of the older steering gears, the adjustment was made by turning a screw located in the steering gear cover. This end play screw is often confused with a high point or over center adjustment screw incorporated on later model steering gears. To adjust the end play with the external screw, turn the screw into the housing until no end play (in and out movement) of the Pitman shaft or the sector gear shaft is felt.

On later model steering gears, the end play adjustment is an

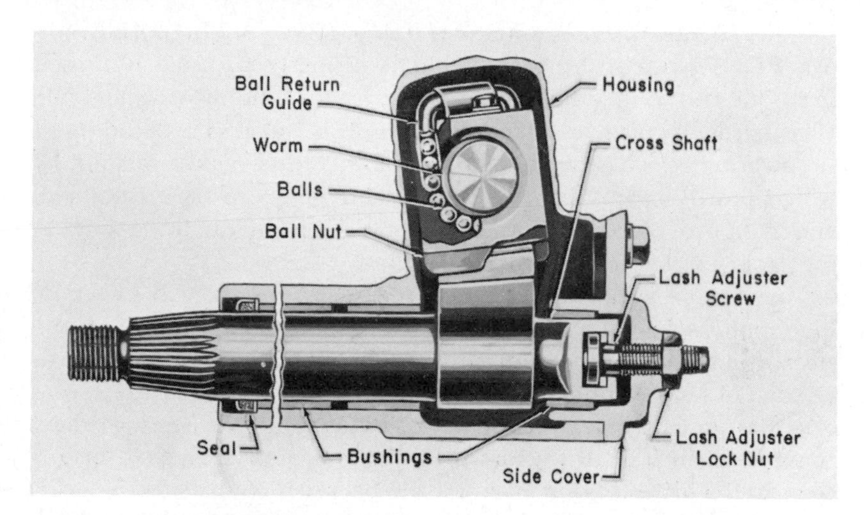

Fig. 27. Cross shaft construction in relation to the steering gear. Cross shaft lash is taken up by means of an adjusting screw located in a T slot within the cross shaft. The adjusting screw extends through the cross shaft housing cover and is held in position by means of a lock nut.

internal adjustment maintained by selective washers between the head of the high point adjusing screw and a T-slot milled in the end of the sector shaft. Figure 27 illustrates this type of adjustment. The clearance between the head of the high point screw and the bottom of the T-slot should not exceed .002 inch. If the gear is disassembled for service, this adjustment should be checked by installing a feeler gage between the bottom of the T-slot and the head of the bolt. If the clearance is greater than .002 inch, the end play of the sector shaft will be excessive.

To correct this excessive end play, place selective shim washers beneath the head of the screw. These selective shim washers are available in four thicknesses, the thickness of each being stamped on the shim surface. A number 3 stamped on the shim means the shim is .063 of an inch in thickness, a 5 means .065 of an inch in thickness, a 7 means .067 of an inch in thickness, and a 9 means .069.

If a number 9 washer is used with the bolt and the clearance between the head of the bolt and the bottom of the T-slot is over .002 of an inch, the bolt will have to be replaced. Some steering gears use a washer which is not selective. Therefore, to maintain the proper Pitman shaft end play, the bolt and shim must be replaced.

(3) *HIGH POINT OR THROUGH CENTER ADJUSTMENT.* When a steering gear that is properly adjusted is turned from one end of its travel to the other, it will bind or become somewhat harder to turn at the center point of its travel. This binding of the steering gear has two basic functions: 1) to provide a method by which positive adjustment of the steering gear can be maintained, and 2) to provide an aid to the driver to keep the car from wandering from the straight-ahead position.

In a properly aligned vehicle, the steering gear will be at its high point when the vehicle is traveling straight ahead and the steering wheel is at the midpoint. As the steering gear is turned to the end of its travel (lock position), it will be noted that the steering gear has an excessive amount of play, allowing the steering wheel to move an inch or two before the Pitman arm or cross shaft begins to rotate. This condition is called the backlash of the steering gear, and all steering gears having a worm and sector arrangement have this condition. To adjust the over center, high point, or no lash range of the steering gear, two methods are presently being used.

The high point adjustment of a worm and roller sector type of steering gear is made by either of the following methods: 1) moving the sector roller into closer mesh with the worm by a lash adjusting screw or 2) moving the worm closer to a fixed sector shaft roller by a lash adjusting lever.

1) To adjust the high point on a steering gear that moves the sector shaft closer to the worm, first attach a spring scale to the rim of the steering wheel. Next, apply just enough pressure on the scale to pull the steering wheel through the center of the steering gear travel. The spring scale should read one pound of pull more than the worm bearing pre-load. Therefore, if the worm bearing pre-load has been determined as a one-half pound pull, the high point load through center should be 1½ pounds. If the reading is less than one pound, the load may be increased by turning the lash or high point adjustment screw deeper into the housing until the maximum reading is 1½ pounds at the rim of the steering wheel. Make sure that the linkage is completely disconnected from the steering gear while this adjustment is being made. Attempting to make this adjustment with the linkage attached will give erroneous readings because the vehicle may have other steering parts which are binding.

2) The other method of adjustment in which the worm is moved closer to a fixed sector shaft roller is made in much the same manner

Fig. 28. Eccentric sleeve steering gear lash adjusting lever. In this type of installation the worm is mounted in an eccentric sleeve and steering gear lash is taken up by means of an adjusting lever.

(*Oldsmobile Div.—General Motors Corp.*)

as the first adjustment. A lever which rotates an eccentric sleeve inside of the steering gear is used to provide adjustment by moving the worm closer to the roller of the sector shaft. This type of adjustment is shown in Fig. 28. Care must be taken not to exceed 1½ pounds maximum high point adjustment or the steering gear may become damaged.

Many present-day vehicles use a re-circulating ball type of steering gear, and provisions for making the worm bearing pre-load and high point adjustments are similar to those found on steering gears of earlier design. On such steering gears, a one-half pound of pull at the rim of the steering wheel is an average worm bearing pre-load adjustment. This adjustment is made by a large nut located at either the top or the bottom of the steering gear housing. Screw the nut either into or out of the housing to increase or decrease bearing pre-load.

The end play of the sector gear shaft is an internal adjustment which can be accomplished only when the steering gear is removed from the vehicle or the steering gear is being serviced. The end play adjustment is maintained by the use of selective shim washers as discussed earlier in this chapter under the section Pitman Shaft End Play Adjustment.

The high point adjustment is an external adjustment for which, as noted earlier, the steering linkage must be disconnected from the steering gear. Turn the lash adjusting screw into the housing until the reading of the spring scale attached to the steering wheel is one pound more than that of the worm bearing pre-load.

The re-circulating ball steering gear must have the correct lubricant in order to give adequate service. Hence, a special steering gear grease is available for this type of installation. A steering gear that cannot be adjusted properly should be disassembled and the worn or otherwise defective parts replaced.

b. Power Steering Adjustments. The types of adjustment made on a power steering installation depends upon whether it is a linkage system or an integral system.

(1) *LINKAGE TYPE POWER STEERING ADJUSTMENTS.* The linkage type of power steering system consists of hydraulically controlled linkage used in conjunction with a conventional manual steering gear. Such steering gears are adjusted in the same manner as any other manually operated steering gear. The hydraulic part of the steering system has one adjustment. To make this adjustment, just remove the small cover at the end of the control valve which screws into the end of the relay rod. Under this cover is either a small self-locking nut or cotter keyed nut as shown in

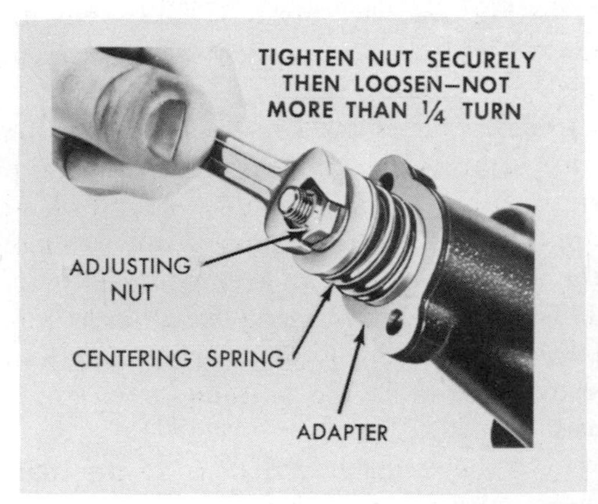

Fig. 29. Adjusting the control valve on the linkage type of power steering system.
(Ford Div.—Ford Motor Co.)

Fig. 29. This nut must be tightened firmly and then backed off a quarter of a turn or, if using a torque wrench, until the torque reading is 25 foot pounds. Later model vehicles using this type power steering employ a different method of adjusting the nut. Support the car on a hoist and disconnect the hydraulic ram from the frame of the vehicle. Start the engine, then turn the control valve nut in one direction until the cylinder or piston rod moves. Then turn the nut in the opposite direction until the cylinder or piston rod again moves. Notice the total turns made by the nut and turn the nut halfway between position where cylinder or push rod moved. If this adjustment is not made properly, the vehicle will pull or steer itself to one side of the road. Should the control valve leak hydraulic fluid, the valve may be removed and the hydraulic seals replaced. The seal in the hydraulic cylinder is also replaceable and should the cylinder leak fluid around the piston rod the seal should be replaced. The piston and piston rings within the cylinder cannot be serviced and, therefore, if either fail, the unit must be replaced.

(2) *INTEGRAL TYPE POWER STEERING ADJUSTMENTS.*

There are two basic adjustments to the integral type power steering system. These are: 1) thrust bearing pre-load adjustment and 2) high point adjustment.

1) Thrust bearing pre-load adjustment. Thrust bearing pre-load may be checked by turning the steering wheel to its lock position and in the lash range of the steering gear. The spring scale pull as measured at the rim of the steering wheel should be approximately one-half pound. If the spring scale registers less than one-half pound of pull, the steering gear must be adjusted. Usually, the steering gear will have to be removed from the vehicle. However, a later model rotary valve steering gear made by Saginaw Steering Division of General Motors may be adjusted while the unit is mounted on the vehicle.

2) High point adjustment. The high point adjustment for power steering is the same type of adjustment as described earlier in the section on Manual Steering Gear Adjustment. First remove the linkage from the steering gear. Then, using a spring scale, pull the steering wheel through its high point noting the amount of pull that this requires. A pull of one pound more than that of the thrust bearing load is considered adequate. The engine does not have to be running to adjust integral power steering gear except on the Chrysler power steering system.

With the constant control type power steering, the thrust bearing load is determined as outlined in section 1, but to make the high point or over-center adjustment the engine must be running so as to provide hydraulic pressure for the steering gear. The high point

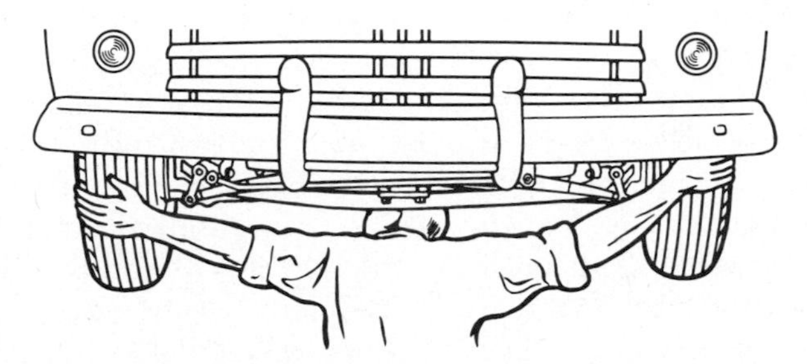

Fig. 30. Checking tie rod and drag link ends for excessive free play. Grasp the front of the front wheels and just push them away from each other and then bring them toward each other, observing the tie rods and drag link ends for looseness.
(Ford Div.—Ford Motor Co.)

adjustment screw located in the steering gear housing is turned into the housing until a very slight movement of the steering wheel will cause the front wheels to move. When all excess steering wheel play has been removed, turn the high point adjusting screw inward an additional one-half turn. This additional one-half turn will adjust a bind or high point into the steering gear. If all excess play is not removed from the steering gear after a few turns of the adjusting screw, the thrust bearings or the worm and ball nut are excessively worn, therefore necessitating the removal of the steering gear for overhaul.

A pressure gage and valve attachment should be used when checking all power steering gear systems. The pressure gage and valve are mounted between the hydraulic pump and the high pressure hose leading to the steering gear. If the power steering unit fails to give hydraulic assistance, the trouble may be due to either a faulty pump or a faulty steering gear. By using the gage, the faulty unit may be detected and repaired, thereby eliminating the possibility of testing both units. Turn the front wheels to their maximum position either left or right. The hydraulic fluid pressure within the system should be approximately 1,000 pounds. If the gage reads 500 pounds, the system is failing. By closing the valve mounted between the gage and the steering gear, the pump must produce maximum pressure. If it does not, the low reading, 500 psi pressure, is due to a faulty power steering pump.

c. Steering Linkage Service. The steering linkage, which connects the steering gear to the front wheels, must be maintained with a minimum of looseness at the connections for ease of steering and safe steering control. The various joints in the linkage must be properly lubricated since tightness or binding at the connections prevents self-correction by the other factors of alignment. To check the tie-rod and drag link ends for wear, grasp the front of the front wheels as shown in Fig. 30, first pushing them away from each other and then pulling them toward each other. At the same time, observe the tie rod and drag link ends for looseness. Either adjust or replace loose tie rod and drag link ends, and straighten or replace bent tie rods or drag linkage.

(1) *ADJUSTABLE BALL AND SOCKET JOINT.* Figure 31 illustrates an adjustable type ball end joint. Adjustment plugs are provided at the ends of the relay or tie rod to compensate for wear between the tie rod ball stud and the Pitman arm ball stud, idler arm ball stud, and respective sockets or seats.

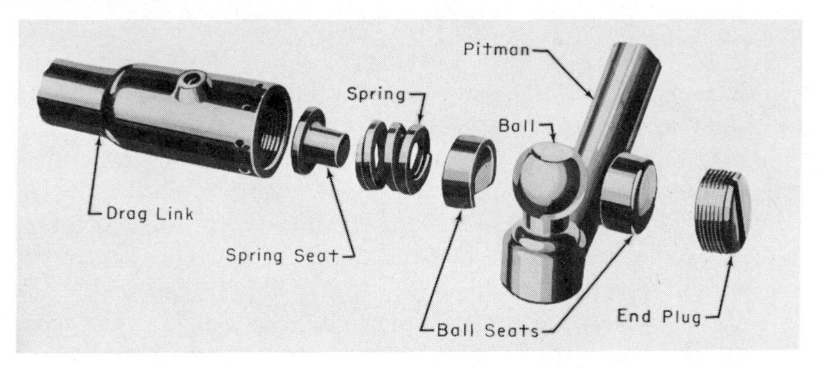

Fig. 31. Construction of a typical adjustable tie rod ball end joint and drag link. The drag link is similar in construction to the tie rod and is the link which connects the steering gear Pitman to one of the steering knuckles. Adjustment is made by means of a threaded end plug. (*Chevrolet Div.—General Motors Corp.*)

To adjust these various components, screw the adjustment plug into the end of the relay rod until it can go no further. Then back the plug approximately one-half to one turn and lock with a new cotter key. Be careful not to over-tighten as this will cause the vehicle to wander.

(2) *REPLACING TIE ROD END JOINTS.* To replace the tie rod end joints, it is necessary to press or drive the tapered shank of the ball out of the hole in which it is mounted. The tool shown in

Fig. 32. Ball shank press. This tool is used to remove the tapered shank of the ball end joint out of the hole in which it is mounted.
(K. R. Wilson Co.)

Fig. 32 is typical of the many excellent drivers and pullers that are available for this purpose.

After the tie rod end ball stud has been removed, take out the end joint by first loosening the clamp and then unscrewing the end joint from the sleeve or rod. Count the number of turns necessary to unscrew the end joint. When installing the new end joint, screw it in exactly the same number of turns so that the assembly will have approximately the original length. Be sure to tighten the clamp and, as a final operation, lubricate the new ball end joint.

To install the tie rod on the vehicle, insert the ball stud into the steering knuckle arm and draw up tight by means of the nut. Always recheck the toe-in and adjust as required after installing new tie rod ends.

(3) *REBUSH IDLER ARM*. The idler arm bushing which connects the idler arm to the idler arm bracket often becomes worn, allowing the relay rod to become loose. A quarter of an inch up and down movement is permissible, although more than a quarter of an inch of travel will cause the right front wheel to shimmy. When the bushing becomes worn, a new idler arm bushing must be installed.

TRADE COMPETENCY TEST

1. What are the functions of a steering gear assembly? (p. 89)
2. What is the Pitman arm attached to and what is its function? (p. 90)
3. Name the common types of manual steering gears in use. (pp. 91-94)
4. What is the cross shaft mounted on within the housing? (p. 91)
5. What are the major differences between the recirculating ball type steering gear and the other types of manual steering gears? (pp. 93, 94)
6. What type of adjustment is used on all manual steering gear assemblies to remove excessive cross shaft end play? (p. 91)
7. What are some of the factors which have brought about the need for power steering? (p. 94)
8. What are the characteristics that are common to all types of power steering? (p. 96)
9. What are the types of power steering now in use? (pp. 96-101)
10. What kind of fluid is used in a power steering system? (p. 96)
11. What type of control valve is used in a power steering system and how does it operate? (pp. 99, 100)
12. Why are two tie rods used to connect the steering knuckle arms together on an independent front suspension system? (p. 112)
13. What types of steering linkage are used on today's automotive vehicles? (pp. 115-118)
14. What is the most common reason for adjusting the steering gear and linkage? (p. 119)
15. Why is it important that the tie rods be adjusted to a certain length? (p. 128)

CHAPTER 6

WHEELS AND TIRES

PAGE

I. Operation of Wheel and Tire Assembly 131
II. Static and Dynamic Balance 133
III. Corrections and Adjustments 136
IV. Construction of Wheel and Tire Assembly 140
V. Servicing the Wheel Assembly 145

The rotation of the wheel and tire as an assembly can be affected by several factors, some of which are created by the alignment of the front end, while others are created by the assembly itself. A wheel assembly that is out of balance or alignment may affect the riding qualities of the vehicle, cause hard steering, or be responsible for rapid tire wear. Several symptoms which appear to be caused by wheel and tire troubles are also common to suspension and steering troubles. Therefore, an understanding of the construction and maintenance of the wheel and tire assembly will assist in determining where malfunctions of the steering system are located.

The wheel and tire assembly includes the wheel, a hub, a brake drum, a grease cup, a wheel cover, and the tire. The front hub is attached to the brake drum, the wheel in turn being bolted to the brake drum. The bearing cone and roller or ball assemblies are mounted on the steering knuckle spindle and rotate within the bearing cups. The bearing cups are pressed into the hub. A grease retainer is installed at the inner end of the hub to prevent lubricant from leaking into the brake drum. Figure 1 illustrates a typical front wheel assembly. The correct bearing pre-load may be established by means of an adjusting nut which is mounted on the wheel spindle. To take up the bearing pre-load, tighten the adjusting nut and to back off, loosen the nut.

When a vehicle is in motion, the entire wheel and tire assembly becomes a rapidly rolling mass. A passenger vehicle that uses a 7.50 x 14 tire when driven at a speed of 60 miles per hour, the wheel will roll approximately 750 revolutions per minute (the exact number of revolutions are difficult to calculate as the weight of the vehicle compresses the tire). The wheel and tire assembly represent a considerable weight, and when rolling on the road surface at this speed, sets up considerable centrifugal force. Any condition that disturbs

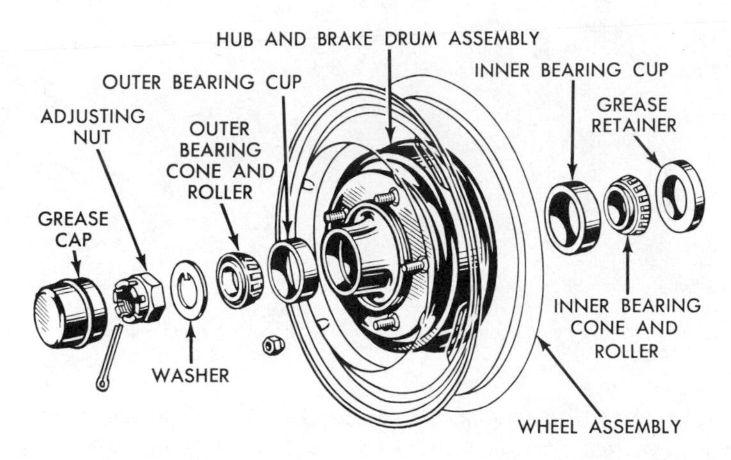

Fig. 1. Front wheel assembly showing the arrangement of all component parts. This type of construction is typical of most present day automotive wheels. Although the design and construction has changed to meet technological advances, the concept of the wheel is still the same as was used to carry man's load a thousand years ago.
(Ford Div.—Ford Motor Co.)

this rolling mass creates vibrations which are not only dangerous but destructive to structural parts of the vehicle.

I. OPERATION OF WHEEL AND TIRE ASSEMBLY

To understand what happens when a tire rolls over the road surface, take a small cardboard cylinder and roll it over a piece of paper. With a pencil, place O and X marks 180 degrees apart on the cardboard cylinder as shown in Fig. 2. Roll the cylinder along a straight line that has been drawn on the paper, this line representing the road surface. As the cylinder rolls along the surface of the paper, the spot marked X will at first move slowly at a right angle away from the point where it contacted the road surface. The X mark will then gradually gain speed and change its direction. By the time the X mark is at the top of the cylinder (one-half revolution) the direction of its movement will be parallel to the road surface, and its speed will now become twice that of the cylinder's axis.

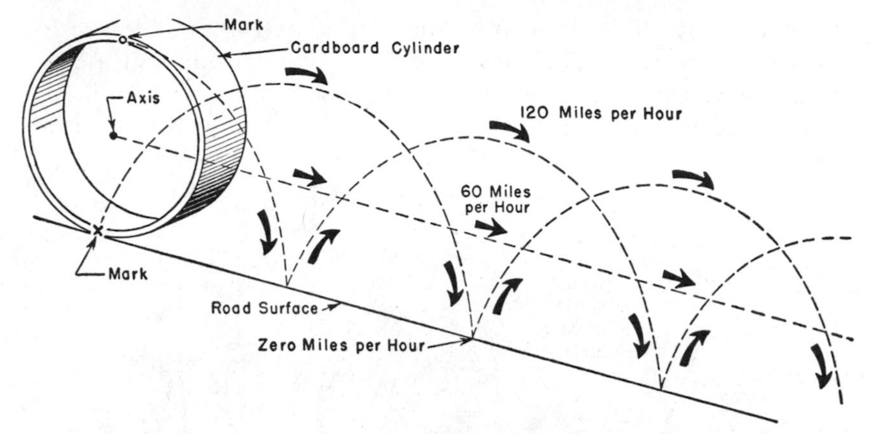

Fig. 2. Rolling a cardboard cylinder along a straight line. Mark the cylinder with an X on one end and O on the other. When rolling the cylinder, you will notice that the portion of the cylinder contacting the piece of paper will momentarily stand still before resuming its upward and forward travel.

In the meantime, the spot marked O in Fig. 2, at the beginning traveled at twice the speed of the axis, now rapidly decelerated until it approaches the road surface (on an arc) at almost zero speed. During the time the O mark is in contact with the road, it is perfectly motionless. Additional rolling of the cylinder will cause the O mark to leave the road, reversing its previous direction of movement.

Comparing this example to what happens to the wheel and tire assembly of a vehicle in motion, several facts become known. These are:

1) The bottom of the tire (the portion of the tire contacting the road) momentarily stands still, regardless of how fast the vehicle is traveling.

2) The top of the tire travels at twice the speed of the vehicle and in the same direction.

3) The back of the tire travels up and forward and accelerates at a rate that will bring it from zero speed to twice the speed of the vehicle in one-half revolution.

4) The front of the tire travels down and forward and decelerates at a rate that will reduce its speed from twice the speed of the vehicle to zero speed in one-half revolution of the wheel.

When the vehicle is traveling at 60 miles per hour, the portion of the tire contacting the road is standing still. As this portion of the tire moves one-half revolution, it rapidly gains speed until it is moving at 120 miles per hour.

An understanding of this principle is helpful when considering the effect of centrifugal forces which are produced when a wheel and tire assembly is in motion. A slight amount of weight added to one side of the wheel or tire and not counterbalanced by an equal amount of weight on the other side will result in a tendency for the heavy spot to travel in a straight line, rather than in an arc. This is due to the ever increasing speed of the heavy spot as it moves toward the top of the wheel and tire assembly. The result is a tendency for the wheel and tire assembly to move up and down or back and forth, causing a bouncing or jerking, commonly referred to as *wheel tramp,* as well as causing uneven tire wear.

II. STATIC AND DYNAMIC BALANCE

Whenever an unbalanced condition exists in the wheel and tire assembly, steps should be taken to correct the condition. Two types of wheel balancing, referred to as *static balance* and *dynamic balance* must be taken into consideration when attempting to check and correct an unbalanced condition.

a. Static Balance. When the weight of a wheel and tire assembly is equally distributed around a spindle, the assembly will not rotate by itself (if the wheel is off the ground and free to rotate), regardless of the position in which it is placed. Such a wheel assembly is said to be in static balance (not moving). A wheel and tire assembly that is out of balance will rotate by itself until the heavy side is at the bottom. As an example, a tire rolls over a muddy spot on the road and in doing so the tire picks up a small portion of the mud. The piece of mud that the tire has picked up will cause one end of the tire to become heavier than the other end, throwing that end out of balance with the other end of the wheel. If the wheel is free to rotate by itself, the end of the tire with the mud will cause the wheel to rotate until the heavy end is at the bottom.

Balancing a wheel statically is accomplished by adding an equal amount of weight on the opposite end of the wheel from the axis as the point to be balanced.

When tires are manufactured, great care is taken to keep the weight equally distributed around the tire to prevent an out-of-balance condition. Manufacturers of other parts such as the wheel, hub, and brake drum, also exercise care to retain balance in these parts. However, when component parts of the wheel and tire assemblies are removed and re-installed, or when tire repairs are made, a shifting of weight can occur, causing the assembly to become out of balance. For this reason the complete assembly may require balancing to offset an out-of-balance condition.

When a wheel is out-of-balance, the amount of unbalance is stated i*n inch ounces.* A simple explanation of the term inch ounce is as follows:

If a one-ounce weight, placed one inch from the axis of the wheel, would turn the wheel until the one-ounce weight is at the bottom, regardless of where on this one-inch circle the weight would be placed, the wheel would then be balanced to one-inch ounce or less.

If a 10 ounce weight were placed one inch from the center of the wheel, or if a one-ounce weight were placed 10 inches from the center of the wheel, the balance test would be stated as *10-inch–ounces.*

Formula: Weight in ounces multiplied by the radius in inches equals inch-ounces.

b. Dynamic Balance. So far we have considered weights that may be added to the outer flange of a wheel so as to balance it statically. It is possible for a wheel to be perfectly balanced statically (not in motion) and at the same time be unbalanced dynamically (in motion).

A rotating wheel will run true without any tendency to wobble or shake, if it is in dynamic balance. Static balance takes into consideration the amount of weight needed on one-half of the wheel to offset an equally heavy part on the other half of the wheel. Dynamic balance takes into consideration the distribution of the weight to be added to the wheel.

When the amount of weight required to maintain dynamic balance in a wheel and tire assembly is known, it is usually necessary to attach one half the amount of weight needed to the outside of the wheel rim flange and the other half of the weight to the inside of the wheel rim flange. This principle is illustrated in Fig. 3. By dividing the weight as required, an out-of-balance condition in the wheel assembly while it is rotating can be corrected and the wheel assembly will be in both static and dynamic balance.

A wheel balancer is needed to correctly balance the wheel and tire assembly. Various types of wheel balancing equipment are on the market, some of which check the balance of the wheel and tire only, while others check the balance of the wheel, tire, brake drum,

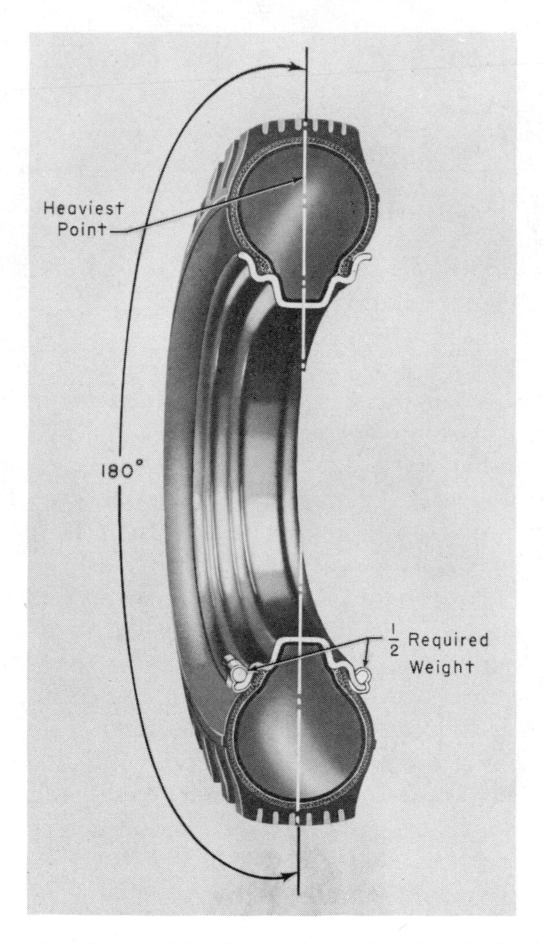

Fig. 3. Cutaway view of tire and rim showing the portion of weight for dynamic balance. Dynamic balance is the use of weights to keep the wheel and tire assembly in balance while the assembly is in motion.

(Plymouth Div.—Chrysler Corp.)

and hub as an assembly. Some equipment balances the wheel and tire assembly while on the vehicle spindle, while other equipment necessitates the removal of the assembly from the spindle.

Two other factors react in the same manner as unbalance in

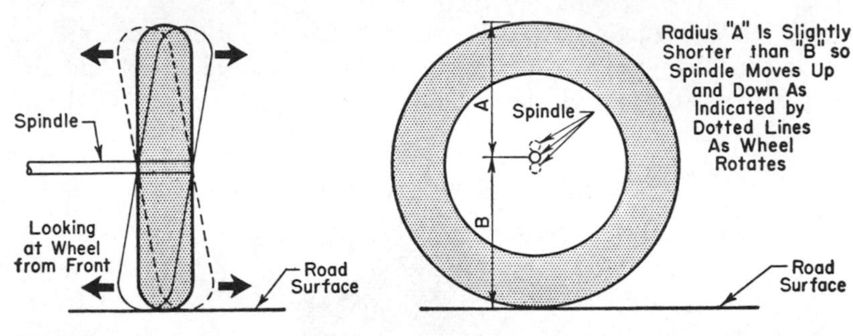

Fig. 4. Lateral run-out of wheel.

Fig. 5. Radial run-out of wheel.

relation to satisfactory steering control. These are: lateral run-out (wheel wobble) and radial run-out.

The condition in which the top and bottom of a wheel alternately moves in toward and out from the center of the vehicle as the wheel rotates on the spindle is known as *lateral run-out.* A wheel and tire assembly having lateral run-out could be perfectly balanced statically but be out of dynamic balance. This condition is illustrated in Fig. 4. Lateral run-out may be caused by a bent wheel or an improperly mounted tire. Generally the maximum allowable run-out is from 1/16 to 1/8 of an inch.

Excessive radial run-out of the wheel, generally in the form of a bounce, has a very pronounced effect on the steering of the vehicle. Radial run-out, in addition to destroying the balance of the wheel (both static and dynamic), causes the spindle to rise and fall in the amount of the run-out on each revolution of the wheel. This condition is shown in Fig. 5. Radial run-out occurs when the radius of the tire, when it contacts the road, is not equal around the entire tire circumference.

III. CORRECTIONS AND ADJUSTMENTS

a. Tire Movement on the Road. Tire wear, aside from cutting as occurs on crushed stone, shell, or cinder roads, is always the result of one of the following conditions:

1) Anything that has a tendency to restrain the wheel from rolling or any tendency of the wheel to spin.

2) Any condition that causes the tire to leave the road at a different point than where contact was first established.

3) Any condition that in effect causes the tire or a portion of

the tire to have a smaller rolling diameter than its actual diameter.

The rolling radius of the wheel and the area of tire contact with the road are controlled by the amount of air in the tire and the load that the vehicle imposes upon it. Most automobile and tire manufacturers publish specifications for correct tire pressures for the various sizes of tires in use. Tire pressures should be maintained as recommended.

If the tire pressure is lower than recommended or required by the particular tire or load, the increased contact area between the tire and road will change the self correcting influences of the other factors of steering control. In addition, abnormal tire wear will result.

Too high a tire pressure will cause the tire to wear in the center of the tread; however, the total wear may be less than would be true with the recommended pressure. Overinflation increases the tire rolling radius as well as creating a hard ride.

The grooves incorporated in all tread designs provide space for the excess rubber that piles up as the wheel revolves. This condition is brought about because the rolling radius of the tire is

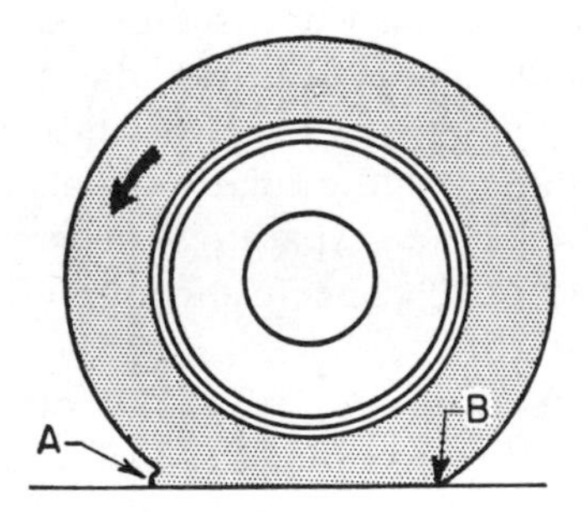

Fig. 6. Excess rubber will pile up ahead of the contact area (A) if the grooves of the tire are no longer effective in providing space for the excess rubber which results from tire rotation. Since the rolling radius of the wheel is smaller than the actual radius of the tire, space in the tire groove must take up the excess rubber as the tire rotates.

smaller than the actual tire radius. If a tire is worn smooth, underinflated or overloaded, the grooves in the tread are no longer effective and the excess rubber piles up ahead of the point of contact, as shown at A in Fig. 6. When the limit of distortion is reached, the excess rubber is compressed and finally passes under the wheel in a lump. Slippage occurs at B (in Fig. 6) as the distorted rubber is released from the restraint of the road and the tread resumes its original position. This results in *cupping* of the tire, which wastes tread rubber. However, more serious than the wasted rubber is the fact that once the cupping has developed, the tread obtains a series of depressions on its surface. These depressions transmit a jerking effect through the steering mechanism, causing wear of the steering gear, and the steering linkage and jerking of the steering wheel.

b. Improper Tire Wear. Normal tire tread wear varies in relation to the type and condition of road surface, the amount of traffic, temperature, and the driving habits of the driver. Abnormal tire wear will occur under certain circumstances. Therefore, the type of tire wear found is often an indication of a particular condition in the suspension or steering system, or of improper operation or abuse. Abnormal wear in varying degrees can be accounted for by such conditions as incorrect tire pressure, faulty wheel alignment, improper brake operation, and vehicle overloading.

Tire wear can be divided into two general classifications which are: fore-and-aft wear, and cross wear.

The tire wear illustrated in Fig. 7 is an example of lengthwise or fore-and-aft wear due to underinflation. The excessive rubber forced to pile up ahead of the wheel scraped the road surface as it returned to its original shape, causing uneven wear around the tread, already mentioned twice. Excessive flexing of the tire side wall will take place due to underinflation, causing the side wall to crack or break, and the plies to separate. The tire is also more prone to bruising if underinflated when it encounters road irregularities, thereby shortening tire life.

Wear around the tread is also due to the following: 1) Fore-and-aft wear is accelerated by anything that increases the tendency to either spin or resist rotation, as, for example, dragging brakes, excessive use of brakes, tight wheel bearings or spinning of the wheels during rapid acceleration. 2) Due to excessive camber the tire will have several diameters.

When the wheels have the correct amount of toe-in, little or no cross wear occurs on the tires. Therefore, if you look for indications of cross wear, it will become an easy matter to identify vehicles which need attention (provided, of course, that they are operated mostly on pavement).

Pass the palm of your hand across the tread of the tire, first in one direction and then in the other. The presence of crown wear will be indicated by one or the other edge of the tread being either

Fig. 7. Cupping of tread on the shoulder of the tire. In the above illustration the fore-and-aft wear of the tread was caused by underinflation.
(Ford Div.—Ford Motor Co.)

sharp or featheredged, as shown in Fig. 8. The sharp edge can be felt as the palm is passed over the tread. If the sharp edge is felt as the hand is moved toward the center of the vehicle, the tire does not have enough toe-in. If the sharp edge is felt as the hand is moved away from the center of the vehicle, the tire has too much toe-in.

c. Switching Tires. Front tires have a tendency to wear unevenly (due to going around curves and being driven on crowned roads), even if kept in perfect alignment. When misalignment factors are present, uneven tire wear will not only occur sooner but be more pronounced. Weight distribution and driving force will cause the rear tires to wear more rapidly than the front tires, although the wear on the rear tires will be even. Cupped or unevenly worn tires have a tendency to wear in evenly when placed on the rear wheels.

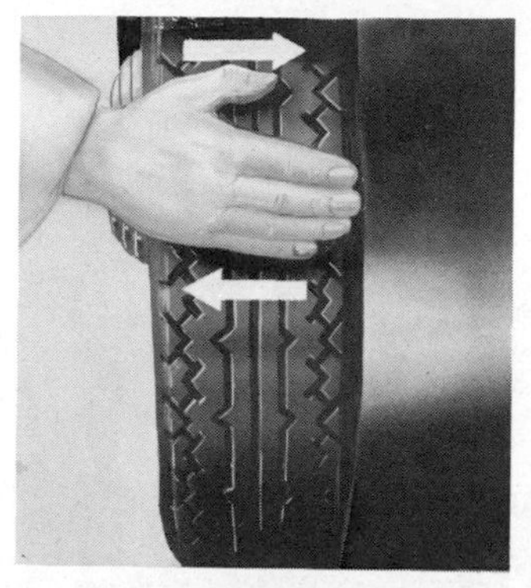

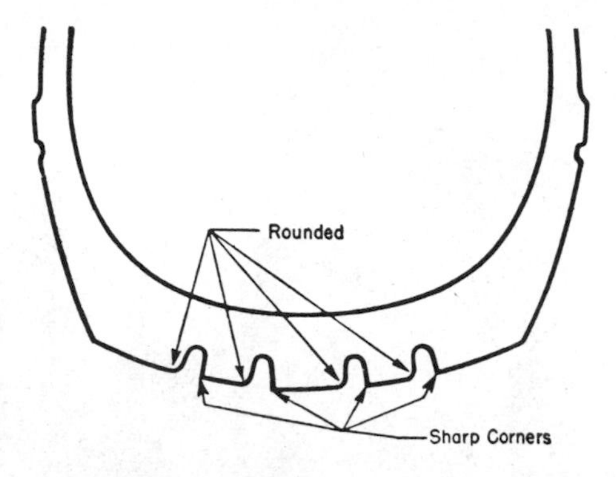

Fig. 8. A method of detecting tire cross wear (left) by pressing the palm of the hand first toward and then away from the vehicle center. The presence of cross wear will be indicated by one or the other edge having sharp corners as compared to the rounded corners of the tire tread (right).

(Ford Div.—Ford Motor Co.)

Most car manufacturers recommend switching the tires every 5000 miles to equalize tire wear and by utilizing the spare tire, it is possible to increase tire life. Figure 9 illustrates one method of switching tires, with or without using the spare. Several other patterns for switching tires are in common use, all of which are good. Nevertheless, to derive the full benefits of switching tires, the pattern should always remain the same for each vehicle.

IV. CONSTRUCTION OF WHEEL AND TIRE ASSEMBLY

a. Wheel Construction. Wheels used on today's automobiles are of the drop-center, demountable, steel disk type. The center of the rim is lower than the tire bead seat, to permit the forcing of part of the tire bead into the drop center section, thereby allowing the removal of the tire. Rim flanges keep the side walls from expanding in an outward direction when the tire is inflated. A typical wheel and tire assembly is shown in Fig. 10. Note the position of the rim flanges.

Some rims have a raised section between the rim flange and the rim drop center, as shown in Fig. 11. This raised section is often referred to as the *bead lock.* Inflation forces the bead over this raised section (bead lock) and holds the bead of the tire against the flange even during rapid deflation as would occur with a puncture or blow-out.

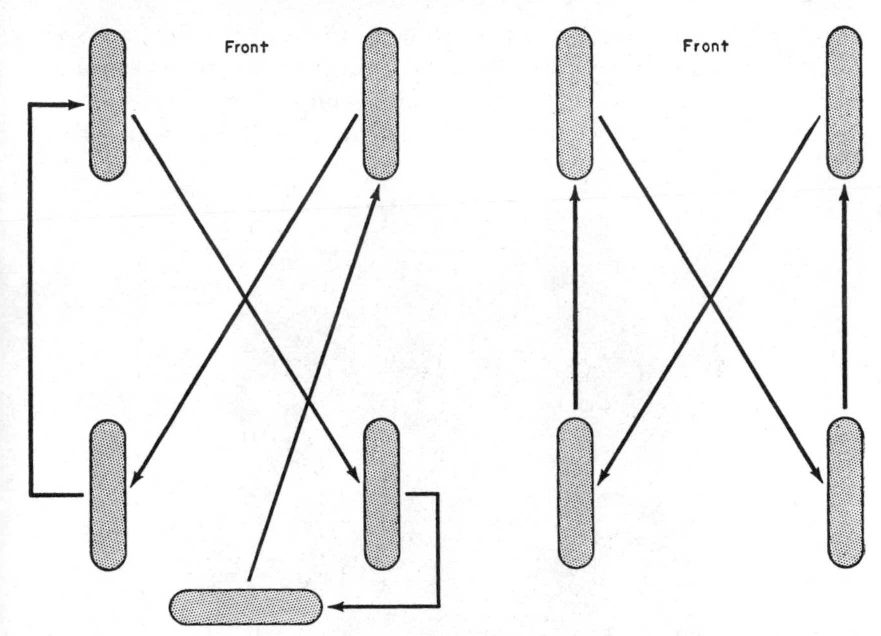

Fig. 9. Methods of switching tires with a spare (left) and without a spare (right) to equalize tire wear.

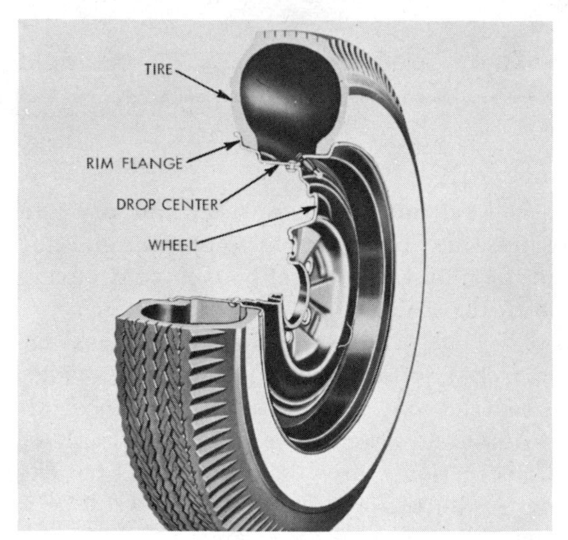

Fig. 10 Cutaway view of a typical wheel and tire assembly showing the rim flange to which weights are added in wheel balancing procedures.
(Lincoln Div.—Ford Motor Co.)

The wheel is attached to a machined surface of the hub or axle shaft with bolts or stud nuts. The matching face of the wheel and hub or axle must be kept clean. Stones, lumps of mud, or grease wedged between the wheel and the matching surface to which the

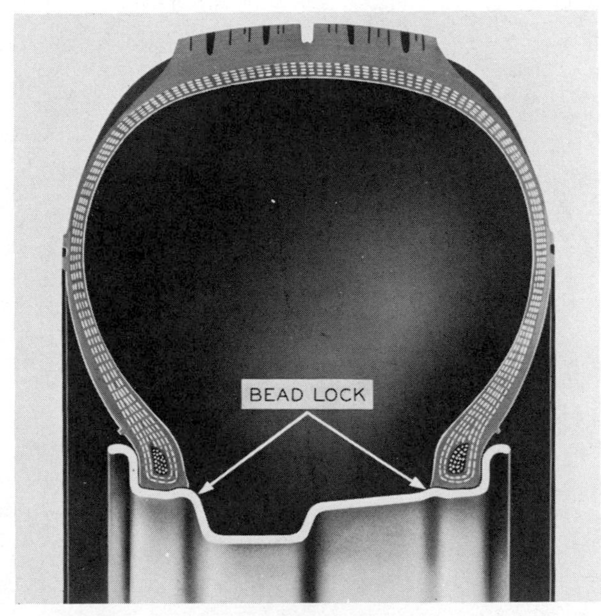

Fig. 11. Safety wheel rim showing the tire bead lock which keeps the bead from slipping out of position.
(Plymouth Div.—Chrysler Corp.)

wheel is attached can unbalance a wheel and tire assembly. The bolts or stud nuts must be kept tight to prevent movement between the wheel and the hub. Loose wheel bolts or stud nuts can result in an elongation of the stud holes.

The rim of a wheel used with tubeless tires must be kept clean and free from nicks and roughness in order to provide an airtight seal between the rim and the tire bead. If a wheel or wheel rim which is bent cannot be straightened, it must be replaced.

b. Tire Construction. Tires used on today's passenger vehicles are of the low pressure, air cushion type. Over a period of years wheel diameters have been reduced and wheel rims made wider. This has permitted tire manufacturers to develop a tire with a wide cross sectional diameter. This type of tire requires a large volume of air which will carry the vehicle weight at a low air pressure, thereby providing greater cushioning effects.

Tires perform several functions. The tire forms a cushion between the wheel and the road surface. When the vehicle passes over

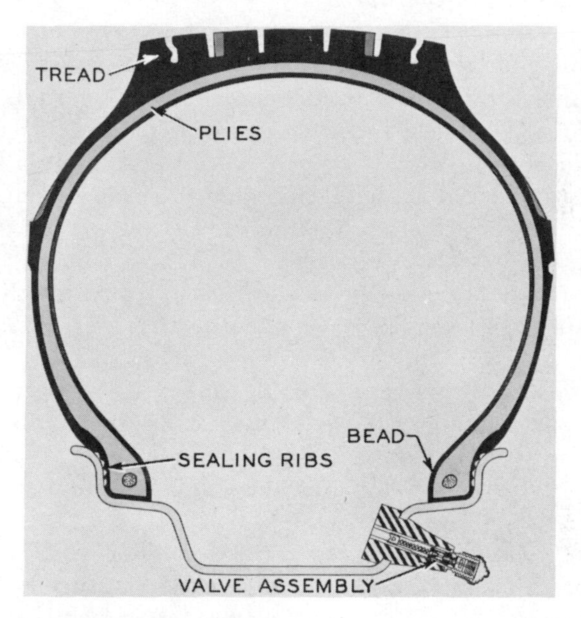

Fig. 12. Cross sectional view of a typical tubeless tire showing the various component parts as well as showing the location of the valve assembly.
(Pontiac Div.—General Motors Corp.)

bumps in the surface of the road the tire flexes, thereby reducing the shock transmitted to the passengers. Tires provide a frictional contact between the wheel and the road surface. A high friction contact surface creates good traction for transmitting power on acceleration and braking as well as reducing the tendency of the vehicle to skid on turns.

Two types of tires in general use are: 1) the type employing an inner tube which is known as the tube type and 2) the type that does not use an inner tube which is known as the tubeless tire. On tires using an inner tube, both the tire and tube are mounted on the rim of the wheel. The inner tube is inflated with air which causes the tire to resist any tendency to change shape. Generally speaking, standard equipment tires on today's vehicles are of the tubeless type. The construction of the tubeless tire is the same as the tube type tire except that the tubeless tire has a number of small rubber ribs around the bead of the tire to form an airtight seal between the tire bead and wheel rim. The valve assembly is installed in the rim of the wheel.

A tire casing for either the tube or tubeless type of tire is built up of rubber impregnated layers of cotton, nylon, or rayon cord incorporating a reinforced bead on each side. Figure 12 shows a cross sectional view of a tubeless tire. Most passenger vehicle tires have four layers of cord called *plies.* Rubber side walls and thick rubber tread material is placed over the cord and the entire assembly is vulcanized into one unit. *Vulcanizing* is a process of heating rubber under pressure. Vulcanizing, as well as bonding the cord and rubber together, also forms the tread pattern which provides traction and space for the excess rubber to compress as the tire flexes.

The tire size is moulded into the side wall of the tire. A tire marked, as an example, 8.00×14 means that the rim diameter of the tire is 14 inches and the tire radius is 8.00 larger than the rim. The inflated diameter of a tire of this size, not mounted, would be $(8 + 8 + 14) = 30$ inches.

Puncture sealing tubeless tires are available. A coating of a rubber like plastic material covers the inner surface of such a tire. When the tire is punctured, internal air pressure forces the plastic material into the hole made by the foreign object and the plastic material then hardens to seal the puncture.

A puncture sealing inner tube which acts on the same principle is also available for tube type tires. Another type of safety tube is also on the market. The safety tube consists basically of two tubes, one smaller than the other, both tubes jointed at the rim base. Both tubes are filled with air. When a blowout or puncture occurs the air is lost between the two tubes. However, the inside tube retains its air pressure and is strong enough to support the weight of the car until the vehicle is brought to a stop.

Tire service includes regular inflation checks to make sure the tire is properly inflated and periodic inspections so that any small damage or defects may be repaired before major damage occurs. The tire should be kept inflated to manufacturers recommendations. Do not adjust the tire pressure when the tire is hot or immediately after a drive of considerable length, since when the tire cools, the pressure will drop. Tire pressures recommended by the tire or vehicle manufacturers are for cold tires.

V. SERVICING THE WHEEL ASSEMBLY

The wheel assembly includes the hub, the brake drum, the wheel, the tire, the tube, the hub cap, and any decorative rings that are mounted on the assembly. Since the wheel assembly includes everything that revolves on the spindle any factor that has an influence on the revolving wheel also influences steering control and tire wear.

a. Tire Inflation. Check the air pressure in the tires with a tire gage and inflate to the recommended pressure. If the front tires are cupped or show signs of uneven wear, they should be changed to a different location in accordance with tire switching recommendation.

b. Front Wheel Bearing Adjustment. Raise the front wheels off the ground. It would be a good idea to check the front wheel bearings for packing since the wheel is off the ground and if the bearing grease is dirty to the point of wearing out the bearing, then repack the bearing with clean grease. Rotate one front wheel slowly and note any tendency of that wheel to bind. Grasp the front wheel at the front and back, alternately push it in toward and away from the center of the vehicle. Repeat this procedure for the opposite wheel. If any free play (or binding) is noticed, adjust the wheel bearings.

To adjust the front wheel bearings, remove the grease cap and the cotter pin and run the adjusting nut up as tight as it will go. A cut-away view showing the relation of the front wheel bearings is shown in Fig. 13. Rotate the wheel to insure that the bearings are not cocked or misaligned. Then back off the nut one castellation slot, and turn back to the nearest cotter pin hole. Install a new cotter pin. Replace the grease cup and lower the wheel to the ground.

c. Check Wheel Wobble. Raise the front wheels off the ground. Spin one wheel by hand and observe the amount of wheel wobble. If the wheel wobble is more than $1/8$ of an inch the wheel should be straightened or replaced.

d. Check Wheel Run-out. Spin the front wheel by hand and observe the radial run-out at the top of the wheel. If the run-out is in excess of 1/16 of an inch make sure that the tire is seated properly on the wheel rim. If the tire is installed properly but still has ex-

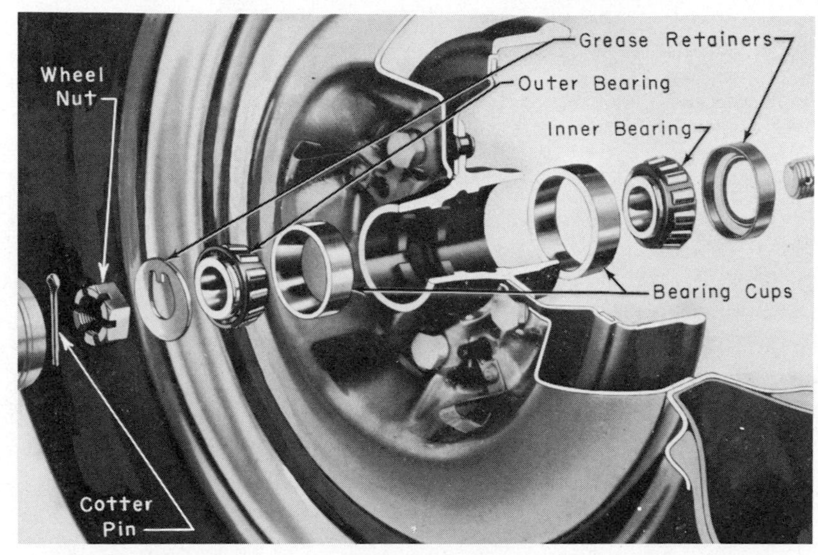

Fig. 13. Exploded view of the various wheel spindle mounting parts showing both tapered front wheel bearings which are known as the inner and the outer bearings. *(Dodge Div.—Chrysler Corp.)*

cessive run-out, it may be advisable to install the wheel on the rear axle.

e. Wheel Balancing. A wheel that is statically unbalanced will rotate upon a near frictionless axle until it comes to rest at the same place from which rotation started. A simple method by which the front wheels of a vehicle may be balanced statically is to loosen the wheel bearing adjusting nut and back off the brake shoes from the brake drum. This lets the wheel's heavy spot settle to the bottom. A weight made of lead which can be attached to the wheel rim by means of a steel clip, is then attached to the rim to balance or equalize the heavy spot of the tire.

Wheel weights normally range in size from one quarter ounce to four ounces, in quarter ounce increments. From four to six ounces, these weights are usually available in ½ ounce increments. When a tire and wheel assembly requires two or more ounces to balance it statically, the amount of weight needed is divided into two equal parts. For example, a wheel needing two and one-half ounces to balance it satically would have a 1¼ ounce weight on both sides of the wheel. These weights would be placed directly opposite the

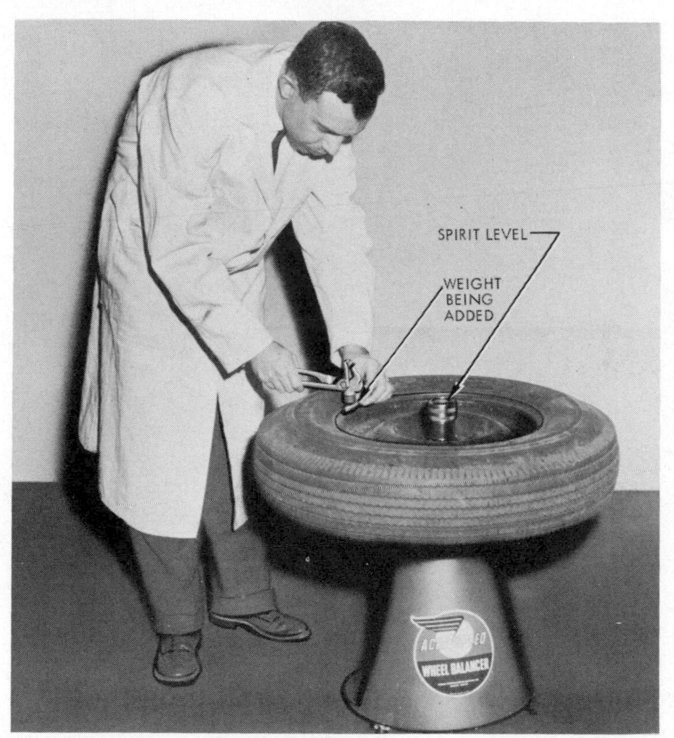

Fig. 14. Acra-Speed type of wheel balancer. This machine balances the wheel and tire assembly statically. The bubble of the level will be in the center of the level when the wheel and tire have been balanced; that is, when the correct weights are added to the assembly in the correct spot, opposite the heavy spot of the wheel and tire. Usually this type of balance procedure requires that the correct weight be halved, one portion of the weight added to either side of the wheel.

(*John Bean Corp.*)

heavy spot of the tire and directly opposite each other on both sides of the wheel. By correcting the static unbalanced condition in this manner, the wheel will not be thrown out of dynamic balance.

A number of balancing machines of the teeter totter design or bubble balancer, as shown in Fig. 14, are used instead of the above method since too much time must be taken to loosen the wheel bearing and back off the brake shoes.

Another type of static balancer, as shown in Fig. 15, is one which may be used without removing the wheel from the vehicle. This type of balancer uses a wheel spinner to rotate the wheel at the approximate speed where static unbalance is felt when the car is

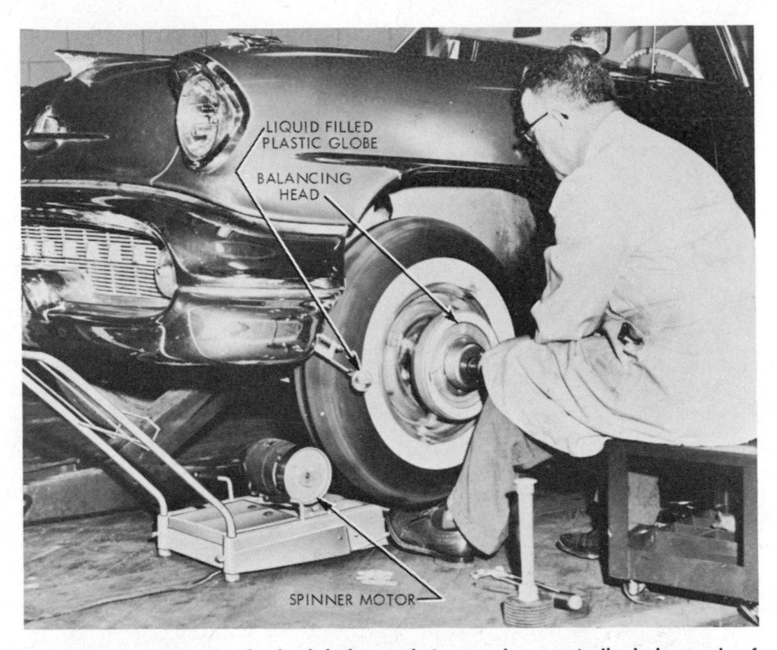

Fig. 15. On-the-car type of wheel balancer being used to statically balance the front wheel of a vehicle. Notice that the vehicle is supported by a floor jack placed at the center of the front suspension cross member. The small, round object attached to the bumper (above the spinner motor) is a liquid filled plastic globe. When the wheel is revolving smoothly, the liquid in the globe will not ripple. A balancer of this type may be used on wheels, the diameters of which may range from 12 to 16 inches without special adaptors. (*John Bean Corp.*)

driven. The balancing head which attaches to the wheel of the vehicle determines the amount of weight needed to smooth out the vibrations of the wheel as it is rotated. One advantage of this type of balancer over the balancer shown in Fig. 14 is that the balancer statically balances not only the tire and wheel, but also the hub and the brake drum. Many of our modern day passenger vehicles which are supported on coil springs have problems of wheel balance which did not exist some years ago. The hub and drum in some cases must be balanced or a vibration will be felt when the vehicle is driven.

The *on the car balancer* may also be used to statically balance the rear wheels. When balancing the rear wheels with this type of balancer, the rear end of the vehicle must be supported by a floor jack. Place the jack against the body or frame and in front of the

Fig. 16. Stewart-Warner wheel balancer. This type of balancer tells you how much weight is needed and at what point to install the correct weight to achieve balance of the wheel, tire, hub, and brake drum assembly.
(*Stewart Warner Corp.*)

wheel to be balanced. One wheel rests on the ground and the other wheel is free to rotate. After the balancer is attached to the rear wheel, then start the engine and place the vehicle in drive position. Caution: one person should remain in the vehicle at all times when the engine is running and keep one foot on the brake pedal, to keep the vehicle from slipping off the jack. As a statically unbalanced rear wheel is revolved, the rear axle will vibrate. The balancer is then operated to smooth out the rear wheel vibration. Be careful not to exceed 35 miles per hour on the speedometer as this is the speed of 70 miles per hour at the rear wheel due to gearing in the differential.

When balancing the rear wheels of a vehicle which is equipped with a limited slip or positraction rear axle, support the frame or body of the vehicle so both rear wheels are off the floor and remove the tire and wheel from the rear axle of the wheel that is not being balanced.

A strobe light (an instrument which uses a light for measuring motion) type of on-the-car balancer uses a pickup (jack) which rests against the suspension of the vehicle, as shown in Fig. 16. When the pick up is placed under the suspension, the machine balances

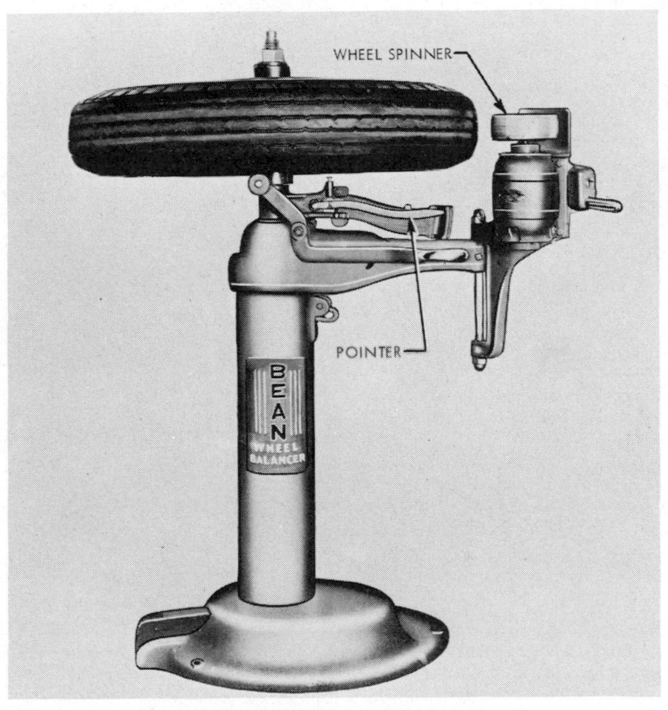

Fig. 17. Mechanical type of static and dynamic wheel balancer. The wheel is mounted in a vertical position on a frictionless bearing and the heavy spot of the tire will, therefore, settle in a downward position. Weights are then added to the wheel rim at the top of the tire until the wheel no longer rotates by itself. After the wheel is statically balanced in this manner, it is then tilted to a horizontal position. The wheel spinner is now brought against the tire and the wheel is rotated at highway speeds. A pointer will determine the correct weight to be added to the wheel.

(John Bean Corp.)

the wheel assembly statically. When the pickup is placed against the brake backing plate in a horizontal position, the machine will dynamically balance the wheel, hub, and brake drum assembly.

Stationary or off the car wheel balancing equipment are capable of balancing a wheel both statically and dynamically. Two types of these machines which will either balance the tire and wheel assembly or balance the hub, brake drum, and wheel assembly as a unit are

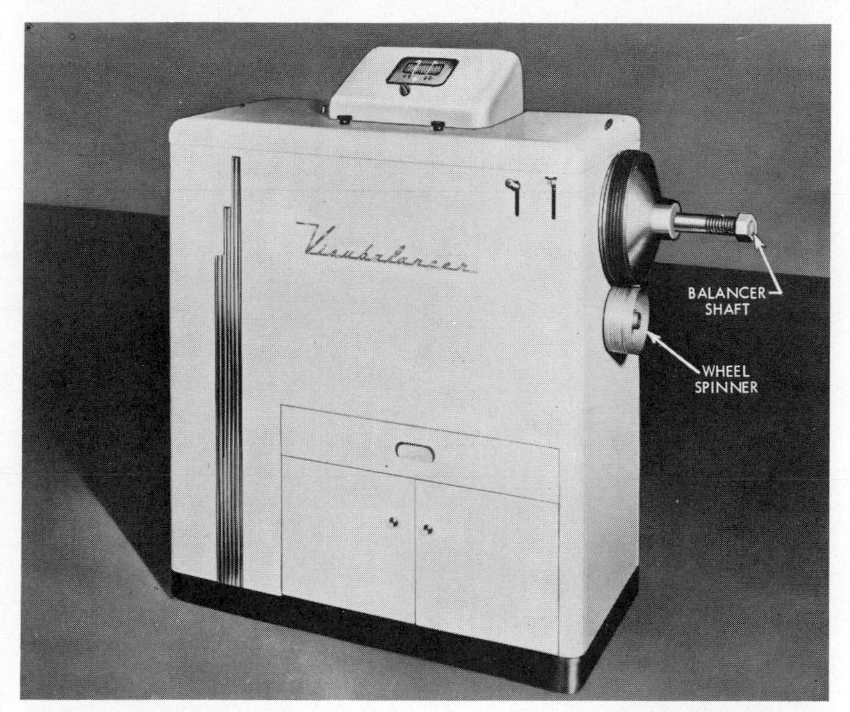

Fig. 18. The Visubalancer type of static and dynamic wheel balancer. The hub and drum of the wheel assembly are mounted on the balancer shaft and the heavy spot of the tire will settle to the bottom. Weights are then added to balance the wheel statically. The wheel is now rotated and the light beam inside of the machine will show how much weight must be added to what spot to the rim to balance the wheel dynamically.
(John Bean Corp.)

shown in Figs. 17 and 18. From the point of view of safety, balancing the wheel, the hub, and the brake drum assembly not only takes the vibration out of the front suspension, but also enables the wheel balancing operator to inspect the wheel bearings and condition of the brake system of each wheel.

TRADE COMPETENCY TEST

1. What are several factors which affect the rotation of the wheel and tire assembly? (p. 130)
2. Describe the action of a wheel and tire assembly as it rotates. (pp. 130-133)
3. What is static balance and how is it corrected if an unbalanced condition exists? (p. 133)

4. What is dynamic balance and what is the effect of operating a tire that is dynamically unbalanced? (pp. 134, 135)
5. What could cause wheel wobble? (p. 136)
6. Why are all new tires made with grooves in the tread? (p. 137)
7. What are the causes of improper tire wear? (pp. 136, 137)
8. How do you check for abnormal tire wear? (pp. 138, 139)
9. What are the advantages of switching tires around on a vehicle? (pp. 139, 140)
10. What is the difference in construction between a puncture sealing tire and an ordinary tire? (p. 144)
11. How do you adjust front wheel bearings? (p. 145)
12. What is the advantage of balancing the wheel assembly while it is on the vehicle? (p. 148)
13. If a vehicle is traveling at 40 miles per hour, how fast will the top of the tires be traveling? (p. 132)
14. What precaution should be taken where an on-the-car type of balancer is used to balance the rear wheels?
15. How often do most car manufacturers recommend switching tires? (p. 140)

CHAPTER 7

WHEEL ALIGNMENT FACTORS

PAGE

I. Caster 155

II. Steering Knuckle Inclination (Angle) 162

III. Camber Angle 165

IV. Point of Intersection 168

V. Toe-In 170

VI. Toe-Out on Turns 172

The satisfactory operation of a vehicle is possible only when it can be so controlled that it will maintain a true course on the highway. Any looseness in the steering wheel, shake, wobble, or tendency of the vehicle to pull, either constantly or intermittently to either side, is intolerable and quickly tires the driver. The driver must have absolute steering control at all times. Any sense of insecurity takes away the pleasure of driving and driving then becomes work.

A vehicle propelled over the highway represents a heavy mass traveling at high speed creating tremendous forces that tend to resist any change in the direction of vehicle travel. Even at high speed, the driver must be able to change the direction of the vehicle at will. When the direction of the vehicle has been changed, it must be possible for the driver to resume a straight ahead course with ease.

The need for almost effortless control of the vehicle has resulted in the development of stable suspension systems and easily controlled steering gears. As speeds and loads increased, the early concepts of what was required had to be changed repeatedly. Often as new problems of control arose and were mastered, either the problem or the cure imposed added problems of tire wear. Thus the first successful attempts to improve stability and ease of steering control also resulted in rapid tire wear, and many designs had to be either discarded or changed. As a result, stability, control of the vehicle, and tire life are now considered as one common problem, usually thought of and referred to as *wheel alignment. Stability: The word* stability *as used in connection with wheel alignment means the ability of a vehicle to maintain a true course on the highway without the need for continual steering effort on the part of the driver.*

Any condition which affects the movement or the rolling of the wheel and tire assembly is a factor contributing to unstable steering.

The ball joints (kingpins on older models) which allow the front wheels of a vehicle to turn and the spindles, which carry the front wheels on bearings, are positioned at various angles to attain ease of steering, stability, and maximum tire life.

The mechanism used to connect the steering gear and linkage to the front wheels must provide a minimum of friction and looseness to allow the driver to hold the front wheels in any desired position while operating the vehicle. The steering connections must be able to flex with the movement of the front suspension and front wheels without restraining the stabilizing influences of the other factors of wheel alignment. Any condition which affects the adjustment or operation of the steering gear and its connections is a factor of wheel alignment.

Any condition that alters the positioning or operation of the springs, shock absorbers, frame, and other parts which are used to support the weight of the vehicle are factors that affect wheel alignment.

Springs, shock absorbers, the vehicle frame, and other parts that support the weight of the vehicle control the positioning of the wheels in relation to the vehicle as a complete assembly. Misalignment of the wheels may be the result of misalignment of structural parts which support the wheels.

In all types of suspensions, automotive manufacturers strive to accomplish two major objectives in suspension design. These objectives are 1) stability with ease of steering control and 2) maximum tire life.

While some factors of wheel alignment create stronger influences than others, no single factor (or angle) in itself imparts stability to the vehicle. A single misalignment factor, however, can destroy stability. In other cases, rapid tire wear or the lack of stability can be the result of a combination of things.

Likewise, two misalignment factors, each of which alone would create instability, may cancel out each other, with the result that the vehicle has stability when in motion. In such a case, the correction of only one factor might remove the counteracting force with the result that the vehicle would lose its stability.

Therefore, while each factor of wheel alignment may be considered as an individual subject, the combined result of all factors produce the desired objectives—proper contact between the tire and the road for stability, ease of steering control and maximum tire life.

The influences and factors that combine to create stability, ease of steering control and maximum tire life are brought about by the angular relationship between the front wheels, the front wheel linkage, and the vehicle frame members. The angle of the steering knuckle (away from the vertical), the toe-in or toe-out of the front wheels, and the tilt of the front wheels from the vertical are all involved in front-end geometry. Each angle imparts an influence upon the front wheels causing the wheels to either toe-in or toe-out. By offsetting one influence with an opposing influence, it is possible to create steering stability as the vehicle travels in a straight ahead direction. The various factors that enter into front-end geometry and influence steering are classified as 1) caster, 2) steering knuckle inclination or angle, 3) camber, 4) point of intersection, 5) toe-in, and 6) toe-out on turns. When all of these factors and influences are in the correct relationship to one another the portion of the tire which contacts the road surface will be momentarily stationary upon contact. Therefore, the wheels will tend to remain in a straight ahead position when in that direction, and minimum effort will be required to steer the vehicle. Also the front wheels will straighten themselves out after the vehicle has made a turn.

In all factors of wheel alignment, a true appreciation of the influences created by each individual factor or angle is possible only if its contribution is considered alone so as not to confuse its influences with those of other factors. For this reason the tendencies created by each of the various angles are treated as though they are the only factors to be considered.

I. CASTER

Directional stability is obtained in varying degrees on the different makes of passenger vehicles by using the caster principle for attaching the steering knuckle. An understanding of the caster principle can be obtained by examining an ordinary furniture caster, as shown in Fig. 1.

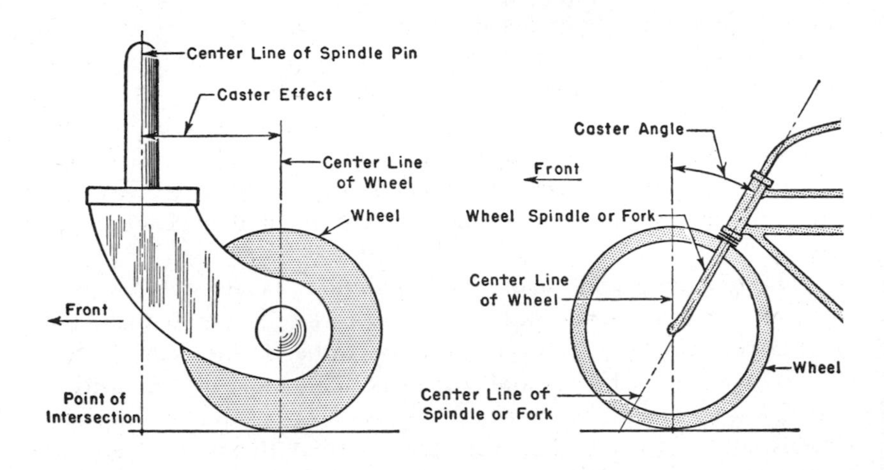

Fig. 1. (Left) Caster effect of a furniture caster. When the piece of furniture is moved, the caster wheel will line itself up with the direction of travel because it is pulled in that direction by its spindle pin; that is, the wheel will trail behind the spindle pin, causing the furniture to move in a straight line. The same principle applies to the automotive wheel, giving the vehicle directional stability. Fig. 2. (Right) Caster effect in a bicycle. The fork of the bicycle serves as a spindle which causes the wheel to move in a straight line.

When a piece of furniture mounted on casters is pushed, the caster wheel lines itself up with the direction of travel because it is being pulled by its spindle pin. The caster wheel trails behind its spindle pin. This action of the furniture caster causes the piece of furniture to roll easily and in a straight line. It should be noted that a vertical line projected through the center of the wheel contacts the floor behind the center line of the spindle pin. The distance between these two center lines is known as *caster effect.*

Another example of the same effect is employed in bicycles. The front wheel of a bicycle is mounted in a fork in such a manner that the projected center line of the wheel is also behind the projected center line of the fork, as shown in Fig. 2. This causes the wheel to trail behind the center line of the fork in the same manner as a furniture caster. When the speed of the bicycle is increased, it has more directional stability. The front wheel has a tendency to stay in the straight ahead position as long as the rider keeps the bicycle vertical and does not turn the handle bars. In an automobile, caster is the term applied to a similar trailing effect imparted to the front wheels. This effect is established by the projected center line through the ball joints (kingpin on older models) intersecting the

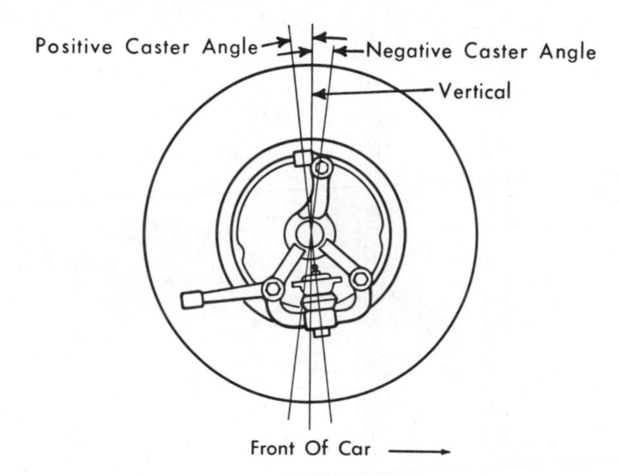

Fig. 3. Caster effect on automobile front wheels. A backward tilt of the steering knuckle produces a positive caster effect while forward tilt of the steering knuckle produces a negative caster effect.

(*Cadillac Div.—General Motors Corp.*)

road surface at a point ahead of a vertical line projected through the center of the wheel. It should be noted that the positioning of the steering knuckle on late model passenger cars is controlled by ball joints. On older model vehicles the tilt of the steering knuckle is controlled by kingpins. The same principles apply in both cases. As shown in Fig. 3, this effect is obtained by tipping the top of the steering knuckle rearward from the straight up-and-down position.

On most vehicles the steering knuckle is tipped backward to obtain a caster effect while on other vehicles the steering knuckle is placed ahead of the center line of the wheel. When the steering knuckle is placed ahead of the center line of the wheel the steering knuckle may be exactly vertical; however, the caster effect is the same as that obtained with the furniture caster. With this design, the top of the steering knuckle might actually be tipped forward slightly without losing the caster effect. This is also illustrated in Fig. 3.

Regardless of design, caster effect is always obtained if the center line through the steering knuckle intersects the road at a point ahead of a vertical line through the center of the wheel.

Tipping the top of the steering knuckle forward results in negative caster, whereas tipping the top of the steering knuckle

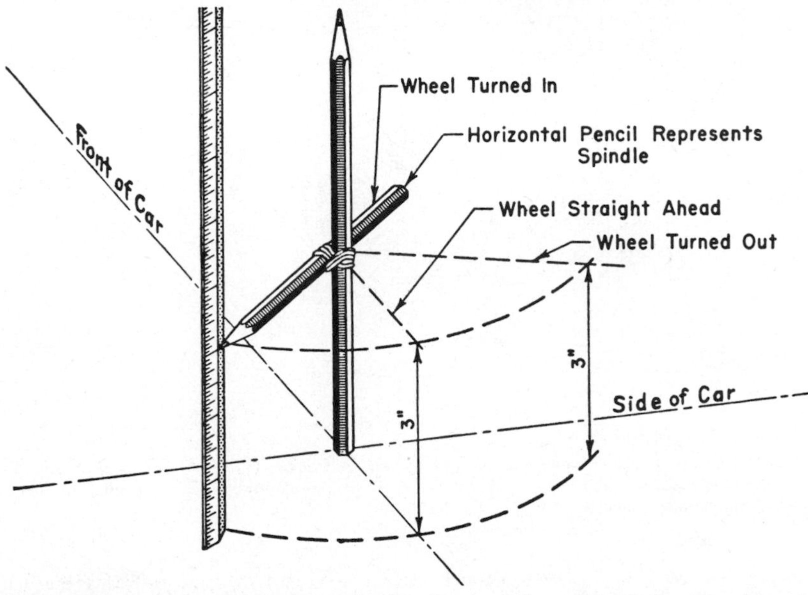

Fig. 4. Example of a vertical steering knuckle. The vertical pencil is tilted neither forward nor backward and, therefore, can be compared to a steering knuckle having no caster.

rearward results in positive caster. Some vehicles are designed with positive caster, while others are designed with negative caster.

When the steering knuckle is tipped rearward to create a positive caster effect, the vehicle lowers slightly when the front wheel is turned toward the center of the car (straight ahead position). This is easily demonstrated by means of two pencils as shown in Figures 4 and 5. In both illustrations, imagine that the vertical pencil and the ruler are both standing on the same flat surface which we will refer to as a table. In Fig. 4, the vertical pencil can be compared to a steering knuckle having no caster. As the vertical pencil is turned, the horizontal pencil (representing the wheel spindle) maintains the same distance from the table. In a vehicle, if the steering knuckle were exactly vertical, the front of the vehicle would neither raise nor fall when the front wheels were turned.

In Fig. 5, the vertical pencil representing the steering knuckle has been tipped to simulate the caster angle of the steering knuckle in a vehicle. As the horizontal pencil (representing the spindle) is turned forward (representing front wheel turned in) the distance from the pencil to the table increases. When the horizontal pencil

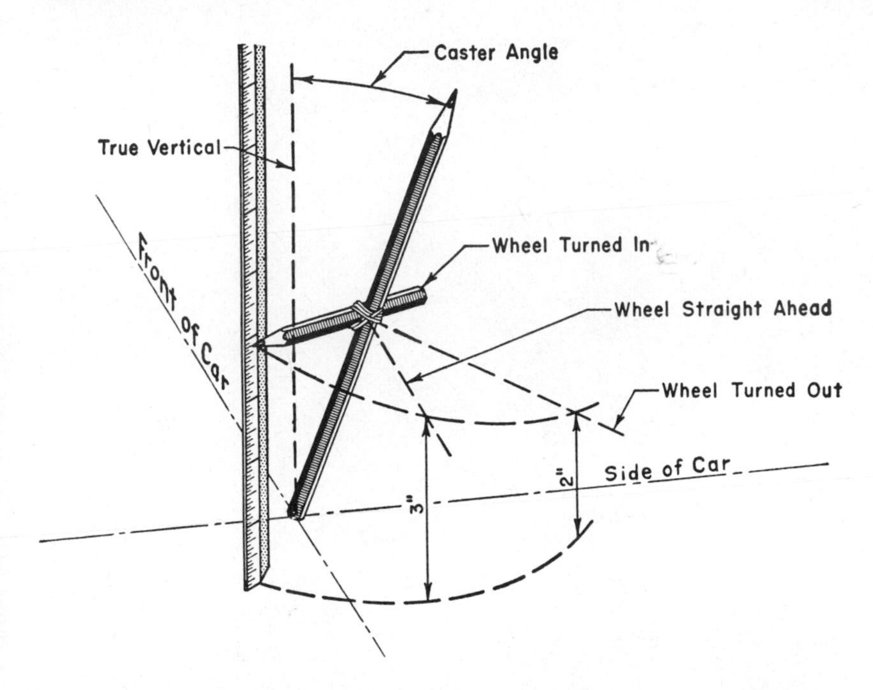

Fig. 5. Example of a steering knuckle having positive caster. Since the vertical pencil is tilted backward, it can be compared to a steering knuckle having positive caster. The caster angle being the difference between the top of the tilted pencil and a true vertical as seen from the front of the vehicle.

is turned rearward (representing front wheel turned out), the distance from the pencil to the table decreases.

In a vehicle, the same results are obtained except that the distance from the end of the spindle to the road remains the same, since this is established by the size of the wheel. Therefore, instead of the spindle rising and falling, the steering knuckle and the front end of the vehicle itself raises as the front wheel is turned inward and falls as the front wheel is turned outward.

With positive caster, the front of the vehicle is nearer to the surface of the road when the wheel is turned inward (straight ahead position). Therefore the weight of the vehicle working through the caster angle of the steering knuckle creates a tendency for the front wheel to toe-in. This, then is the influence of positive caster. With negative caster (top of the steering knuckle tipped forward) the opposite tendency is created. Negative caster creates a tendency for the wheel to toe-out.

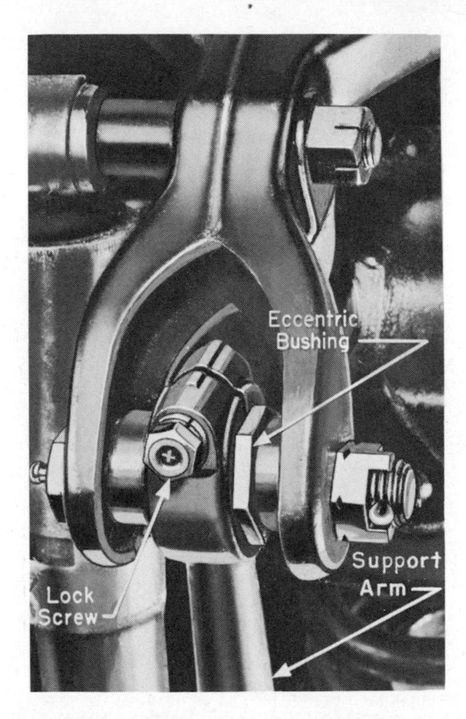

Fig. 6. Eccentric bushing type of caster adjustment. An eccentric bushing is a bushing in which the bore has been machined offcenter. Turning the bushing so that it will travel along the pivot pin changes caster.

If the positive caster angle is the same on both sides, a tendency is created for the front of both wheels to turn in toward each other. However, the distance between the wheels is rigidly maintained by the suspension system and the tie rod. Therefore the tendency of one wheel to turn inward is balanced or offset by the same tendency of the other wheel.

If caster on left and right wheels were uneven, however, the tendency of the side having the most caster would be stronger than the tendency at the other wheel, with the result that the wheel having the most caster would turn inward, causing the wheel having less caster to turn outward. With such a condition, a tendency would be created for the vehicle to pull constantly to one side (away from the side having the most caster).

Caster angle can change in a vehicle due to bent, distorted, or worn parts involved in the establishment of the caster angle. Any

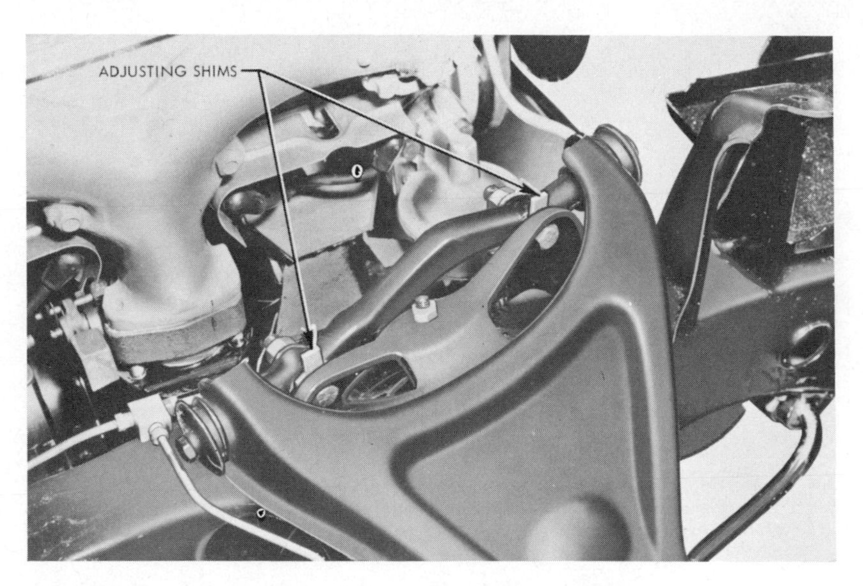

Fig. 7. Caster adjusting shims. Shims, mounted between the frame and the pivot pin on mounting bolts, provide a means of reducing or increasing caster. To make an adjustment, either remove or add shims as needed.

(*Chevrolet Div.–General Motors Corp.*)

change in caster due to damage resulting from an accident may affect the camber angle, toe-in or toe-out of front wheels, or the kingpin sidewise inclination.

A caster adjustment is incorporated into the front suspension system to permit making caster corrections. Before making adjustments all worn or damaged parts should be repaired or replaced.

Two of the most common methods of caster adjustments are the eccentric bushing type employed on older model vehicles, and the type using adjusting shims on the late model vehicles. Figure 6 illustrates the eccentric bushing type of caster adjustment. The inside of the bushing is threaded and the outside of the bushing has a groove on its radius which holds the support arm in position. Turn the bushing to move the support arm either backward or forward to tip the steering knuckle and thereby change the caster setting. Figure 7 illustrates the shim arrangement used for adjusting caster. Adding shims at the front bolt or removing shims at the rear bolt will decrease positive caster. Removing shims at the front bolt or adding shims at the rear bolt will increase positive caster. The removal or addition of shims at one bolt or the other

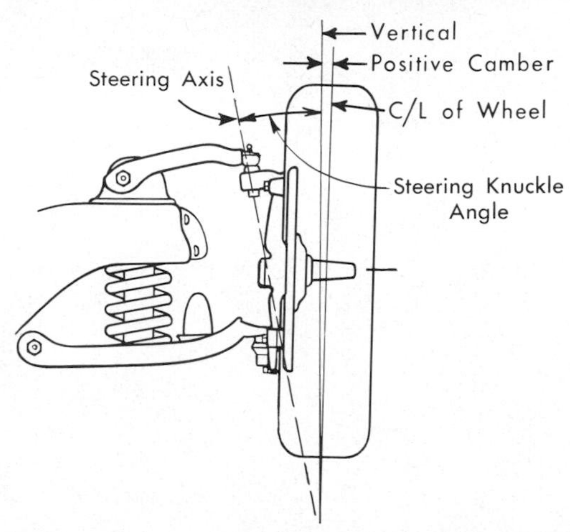

Fig. 8. Steering knuckle angle. Steering knuckle angle is the difference between the vertical center line of the ball joints and the vertical center line of the wheel, as viewed from the front of the vehicle.

(*Cadillac Div.—General Motors Corp.*)

tilts the steering knuckle either backward or forward, thereby changing the caster angle.

In the past most vehicles were designed with relatively high caster for the directional stability obtained through the trailing action that caster imparted. This tendency, however, can be created by several other means, chief of which are sidewise inclination of the steering knuckle and increased width of the contact area of the tires.

II. STEERING KNUCKLE INCLINATION (ANGLE)

On older model vehicles a kingpin was used to attach the steering knuckle to the support arm. When this type of installation was used the angle created by tipping the kingpin outward was referred to as *kingpin sidewise inclination.* The kingpin has been replaced in effect by ball joints on late model vehicles; however, the same angular principles have been retained. This tilt to the steering knuckle is referred to as the *steering knuckle sidewise inclination.* The same influences which apply to the tilt of the steering knuckle will also apply to the kingpin inclination.

Sidewise inclination of the steering knuckle establishes the point of intersection of a center line projected through the center of the ball joints and a center line projected through the center

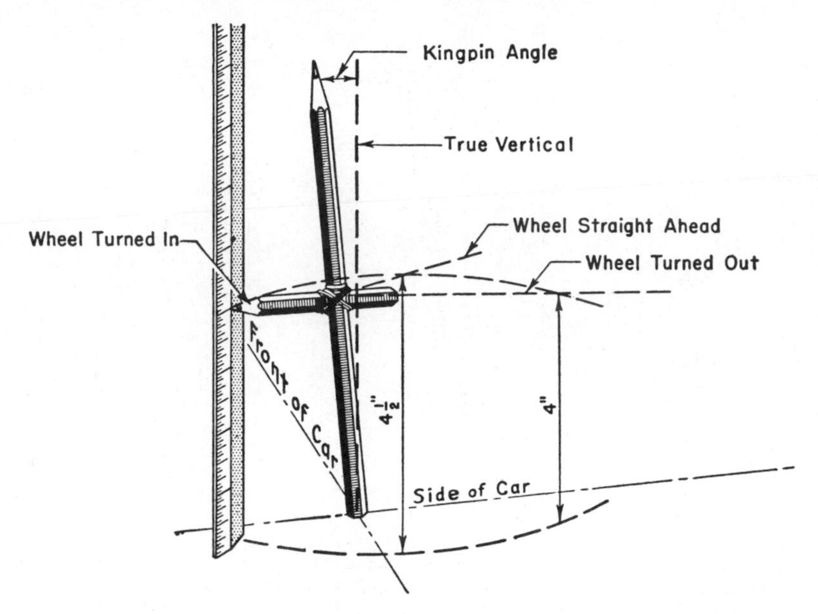

Fig. 9. Example of steering knuckle angle sometimes referred to as the sidewise inclination of the kingpin. Note that the horizontal pencil representing the wheel spindle is farther away from the table when the pencil is at right angles to the true vertical. In the automotive vehicle, the wheel spindle is farther away from the road surface when the vehicle is in a straight ahead position.

of the tire. These two center lines intersect at approximately the center of the area of the tire in contact with the road, as shown in Fig. 8. This provides a pivot point on which the wheel can be turned easily, especially when the vehicle is not in motion, as is the case when parking. Sidewise inclination of the steering knuckle also aids directional stability.

Steering knuckle angle is created between the center line of the steering knuckle and a true vertical line as viewed from the front of the vehicle. The upper end of the steering knuckle is attached to the upper control arm so that it is closer to the center of the vehicle than the bottom of the steering knuckle; thus it tilts the steering knuckle inward.

If the steering knuckle was not tilted in this manner, the wheels would roll in an arc around the point where the center line projected through the ball joints contacts the road surface. By tipping the steering knuckle sidewise, as shown in Fig. 9, the projected center line is made to contact the road approximately in the center

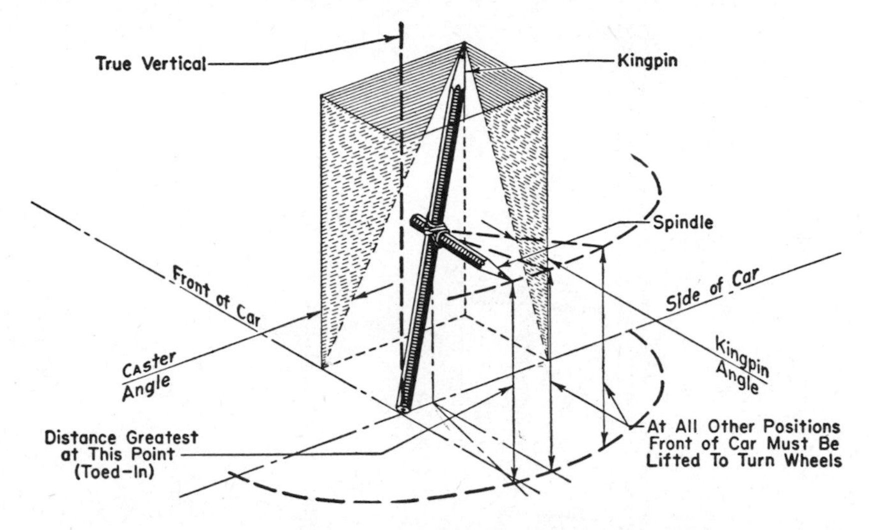

Fig. 10. Example of combined caster and steering knuckle angle or in vehicles using kingpins, the combined angle would be the caster and the kingpin inclination angle. The two pencils illustrate the result of both caster and steering knuckle angle.

of the contact area of the tire. This results in the wheel pivoting around the point of intersection without actually rolling.

Disregarding that the steering knuckle may be tipped backward to create a caster effect, the two pencils shown in Fig. 9 demonstrate that steering knuckle sidewise inclination causes the end of the horizontal pencil to be farther away from the table when it is at right angles to the direction of travel, that is, when the wheels are in a straight ahead position. This demonstrates what happens to the steering knuckle due to sidewise inclination.

In actual practice, the diameter of the wheel establishes the distance from the end of the spindle to the road, and instead of the end of the spindle rising and falling as the wheel is turned, the steering knuckle and the front end of the vehicle rises and falls. This means that the vehicle is closer to the road when the wheels are in a straight ahead position, due to the sidewise inclination of the steering knuckle. As a result, the weight of the vehicle actually must be lifted in order to turn the wheels to any other than the straight ahead position.

Steering knuckle sidewise inclination, therefore, has a stabilizing influence which tends to keep the front wheels in a straight ahead position. In many vehicles, the tendency of the wheels to maintain

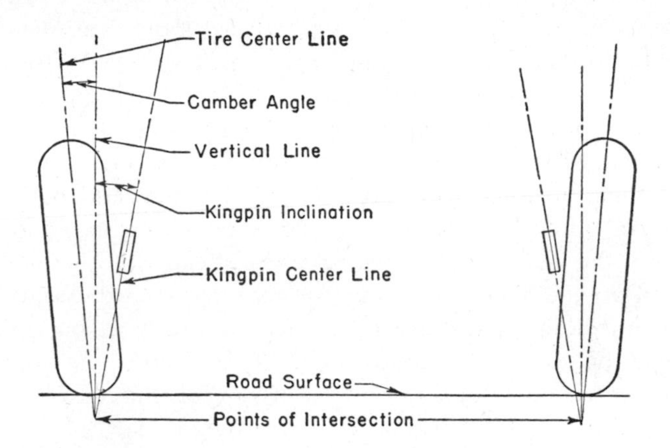

Fig. 11. Camber angle and steering knuckle inclination. The top of the front wheels of an automobile are tipped either inward toward the vehicle center or outward away from the vehicle center providing a condition which is known as camber. The difference between the tire center line and a true vertical is known as the camber angle. Where the tire center line, the vertical center line, and the steering knuckle or kingpin center line meet, is known as the point of intersection.

a straight ahead course created by the steering knuckle sidewise inclination and the width of the tire contact permits a reduction in caster angle. In fact, in some vehicles the tendencies are so pronounced that the front end is designed with no caster, or with negative caster, so as to reduce or counteract these tendencies and reduce steering effort while still retaining the desired amount of directional stability.

Figure 10 illustrates the net result of a combination of both caster and steering knuckle angle.

There is no adjustment provided for steering knuckle inclination. If other alignment angles are correct and the steering knuckle angle is incorrect, the knuckle or attaching parts are bent and must be straightened or replaced.

III. CAMBER ANGLE

Camber is the tilting of the wheel from the vertical. The front wheels of most passenger vehicles are tipped outward at the top, a condition known as positive camber. The camber angle is shown in Fig. 11. If the wheels are tipped inward at the top, the condition would be known as negative camber. Some cars are designed with positive camber while others are designed with negative camber.

Camber is established by tipping the outer end of the spindle downward. The combination of camber angle and steering knuckle sidewise inclination is sometimes referred to as the combined angle.

Camber in effect makes a cone of the front wheels. With positive camber, unless restrained, the wheel will roll outward in a circle around the apex (point) of the cone. If the degree of this tendency to roll outward is the same at both front wheels (since the tie rods prevent their turning in opposite directions), the tendency of each will cancel out or counteract the same tendency in an opposite wheel and the vehicle will travel straight ahead.

When a cone effect is present the wheel and tire assembly will have several diameters. Since the actual diameter at both sides of the tire is the same and since all of the tread makes the same number of revolutions, the outermost portion of the tread (smallest rolling radius) must move faster than the actual vehicle speed. Therefore, the excess tread must slip over the road, resulting in tire wear.

The tendency toward the use of tires with larger cross sections and larger areas of contact has caused manufacturers to design vehicles with less camber and with greater steering knuckle sidewise inclination to maintain steering stability. Since camber causes tire wear, it is desirable to have less camber so as to reduce tire wear.

Usually, maximum tire life and mileage are obtained when the average *running* camber angle is zero, since all portions of the tread have the same rolling radius. This does not necessarily mean that the camber angle should be zero when the vehicle is unloaded. It does mean, however, that with an average load and average operating conditions the tire wear will be less if the camber is approximately zero.

Referring back to the two pencils in Fig. 5, it will be noted that in addition to the fact that the end of the horizontal pencil (representing the spindle) rises and falls due to the caster angle, the angle of this pencil in relation to the horizontal also changes.

Due to the caster angle, this is likewise true of the spindle on which the front wheels turn. As a result, when the wheel is turned toward the center of the vehicle, the camber angle is reduced. As the wheel is turned away from the center of the vehicle, the camber angle is increased. Both of these changes are accounted for by the caster angle of the steering knuckle, and the degree of camber change is in proportion to the caster angle. The more the caster, the more the camber change. This provides a means of measuring the caster angle through the change in camber during a turn of an

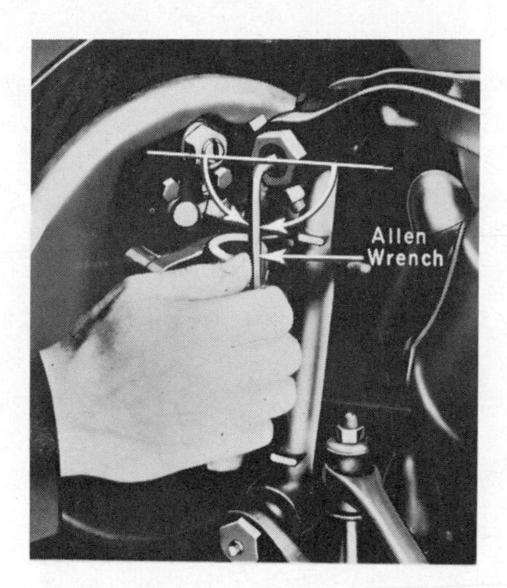

Fig. 12. Eccentric bushing type of camber adjustment. An Allen wrench is used to turn the eccentric bushing to restore the camber to its correct adjustment. However, camber adjustment by this means is limited to ½ turn in either direction.
(Pontiac Div.—General Motors Corp.)

exact number of degrees.

A camber adjustment is provided to permit compensation for changes which may take place due to wear or distortion. Two most common methods of camber adjustment are: 1) the eccentric bushing type on older model vehicles and 2) the type using adjusting shims on the late model vehicles. In either case the camber adjustment is usually combined with the caster adjustment. Figure 12 illustrates an eccentric bushing type of camber adjustment. An eccentric located between the steering knuckle support arm and upper control arm can be turned to move the support arm closer to or farther away from the center of the vehicle, thereby changing the camber setting. Figure 13 shows the shim arrangement used for making camber adjustments. Adding an equal number of shims at both bolts increases the camber angle while removing an equal number of shims at both bolts decreases the camber angle (positive camber). Removing an equal number of shims at both bolts tips the top of the steering knuckle toward the center of the vehicle whereas adding an equal number of shims at both bolts tilts the top of the tire away from the center of the vehicle.

The combined angles of caster, steering knuckle sidewise inclination, and camber are interrelated. A change in either caster angle or steering knuckle angle or both will also cause a change in

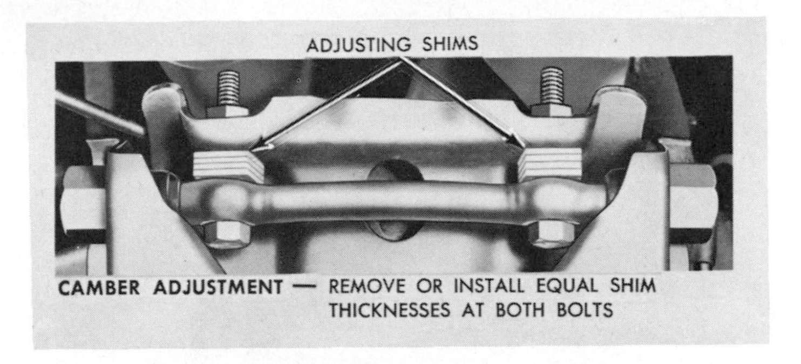

Fig. 13. Camber adjusting shims. Shims are mounted on the bolts which mount the pivot pin to the vehicle's frame.
(Ford Div.—Ford Motor Co.)

the camber angle as well. It is necessary, therefore, to recheck the camber angle if either of these factors are changed.

IV. POINT OF INTERSECTION

The point of intersection refers to the point where the center line of the wheel and tire assembly is intersected by the center line through the ball joints of the steering knuckle.

The point of intersection, as shown in Fig. 11, is controlled by camber, sidewise inclination of the steering knuckle, the rolling radius of the wheel, and the distance from the wheel to the pivot points of the steering knuckle. These conditions impart a tendency to the wheel to either toe-in or toe-out, depending on whether the point of intersection is above or below the surface of the road.

If the point of intersection for each front wheel is above the road surface, the front wheels will have a tendency to toe-in. If the point of intersection for each front wheel is below the surface of the road, the wheels will have a tendency to toe-out. This tendency can be demonstrated by pushing a sheet of paper over the surface of a table with a pencil, as shown in Fig. 14. If the pencil is centered on the paper, you can move the paper forward without its turning. If, on the other hand, the pencil is not centered on the paper, you cannot move the paper forward without its turning toward the side of the paper that has the largest contact with the table.

If the point of intersection is below the surface of the road, the largest portion of tire contact area is outside of the center line of the steering knuckle. Therefore, a tendency for the wheel to turn out (toe-out) is created. If the point of intersection is above the sur-

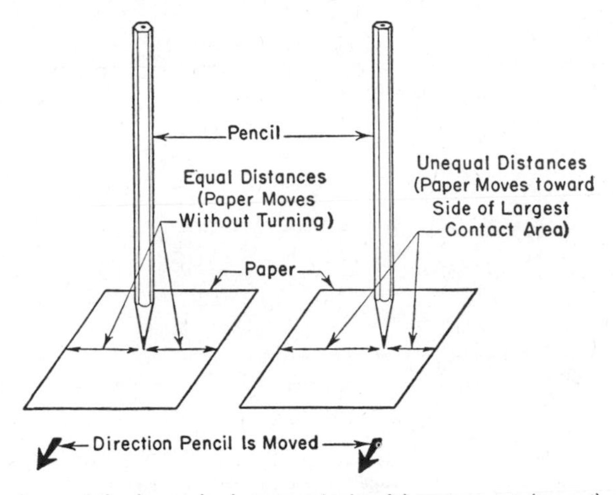

Fig. 14. Tendency of the front wheels to turn in (toe-in) or turn out (toe-out) changes with the point of intersection, as shown by the two pencils in the above illustration. With the pencil placed on the center of the paper, the paper can be moved forward without the paper turning. However, if the pencil is placed away from the center of the paper, the paper, when moved forward, will turn in the direction of largest contact area.

face of the road, the largest portion of tire contact area is inside the projected center line through the ball joints of the steering knuckle. Therefore, a tendency for the wheel to turn in (toe-in) is created.

If the point of intersection is neither above nor below the road surface under normal loading, each slight change of rolling radius would change the location of the point of intersection. At one moment the point of intersection might be slightly below the road surface, and a tendency for the front wheels to turn out would be created. At the next moment the point of intersection might be above the road surface, and a tendency for the front wheels to turn in would be created. Under such conditions a tendency for hunting, wandering or darting could result.

In all factors of wheel alignment, it is usually more desirable to create positive tendencies which can be counter-balanced by other positive tendencies in the opposite directions than to have indefinite tendencies. For this reason, most vehicles are designed with the point of intersection below the surface of the road, thus creating a positive tendency for the wheels to turn out.

If the point of intersection is higher on one front wheel than the other, the tendency of the wheels to either toe-in or toe-out will not be equal on both wheels, and the vehicle will pull toward the

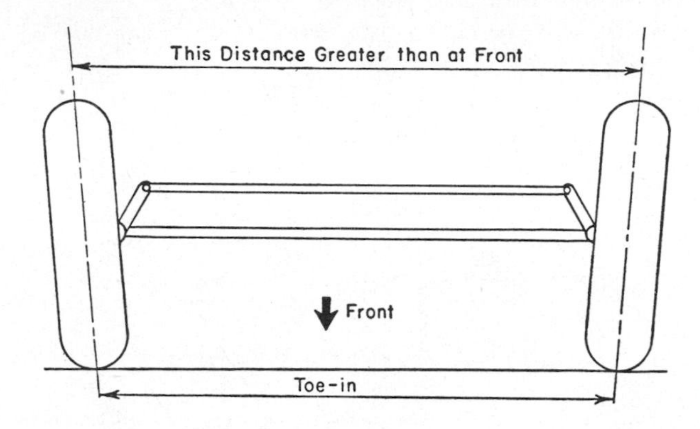

Fig. 15. Toe-in of the front wheels. Toe-in is a condition that exists when the front of the wheels are nearer together than the rear of the wheels.

side having the lower point of intersection (lower combined camber plus steering knuckle sidewise inclination angle).

Changes in the point of intersection are usually the result of a bent steering knuckle, worn ball joints, worn kingpins and bushings (if used), or loose wheel bearings. However, if front wheels or tires are used which are larger than originally intended, the point of intersection will then become raised. Wheels having a greater "dish" will also raise the point of intersection, if installed. If wheels of less "dish" are used, the point of intersection will be lowered. Note: *The dish of the wheel is a term used to indicate the distance from the center line of the tire to the mounting surface of the wheel.*

Considered separately, the point of intersection is not a factor in tire wear. However, camber, which is one of the factors that establish the point of intersection, *is* a factor of tire wear.

V. TOE-IN

The various rods and levers that make up the steering linkage and steering connections either restrain the influences of the other factors of alignment or transmit them. They likewise transmit to the front wheels the turning force from the steering gear. The prevailing tendencies of the front wheels to turn out are restrained by the tie rods. The tie rods hold the front wheels parallel in the straight ahead position and maintain the correct relationship between the front wheels on turns. To keep the front wheels parallel in a straight ahead position while the vehicle is moving, it is generally necessary to adjust the tie rods so that the front wheels have toe-in when the vehicle is stationary.

The term toe-in refers to a condition that exists when the front of the wheels are closer together than the rear of the wheels, as shown in Fig. 15. If the front wheels are exactly parallel, the condition is referred to as zero toe-in. If the front of the front wheels are farther apart than the back of the front wheels, the condition is referred to as toe-out. Toe-in of the front wheels is maintained by means of adjustable tie rods which are connected to the steering knuckle arms.

Toe-in (even the correct amount) is an evil that always results in tire wear. The ideal condition is for the back portion of the tire to begin its forward and upward movement at the exact point where it contacts the road. Since there are more factors which create a tendency for the front wheels to toe-out (camber and point of intersection below the road) than there are factors which create a tendency for the front wheels to toe-in (caster), the resultant tendency is for the wheels to turn outward. The tie rods, which are used to establish toe-in, restrain this influence. However, some lash always exists in the steering connections which permits the wheels to turn out slightly in spite of the tie rods. To compensate for this slight movement, the tie rods are adjusted so that when the vehicle is stationary and the influence to toe-out is not in effect, a slight toe-in is established. When the vehicle is in motion, the strong tendency for the wheels to turn out will take up this lash, and hence the wheels will have no toe-in.

A change in one or all of the various factors of alignment will result in a change in the toe-in of the front wheels. Thus, toe-in and/or the resultant tire wear become the best means of spotting trouble.

In addition to tire wear, when the adjustment of toe-in is not correct, a condition sometimes results in which first one wheel aligns itself, throwing all the error to the opposite wheel, then the opposite wheel aligns itself, throwing the first wheel out of alignment. This cycle may be repeated several times for each revolution of the wheel, resulting in a shimmy of the wheel and, of course, excessive tire wear.

The front wheels can be adjusted to correct a condition of excessive toe-in or toe-out. Toe-in is adjusted by changing the length

Fig. 16. Tie rod adjusting sleeves make it possible to change the length of the tie rod. After the tie rod has been adjusted to the correct length, tighten the clamp bolts on the sleeve to prevent the tie rod from loosening.

(*Chevrolet Div.—General Motors Corp.*)

of the tie rods. The tie rods are usually built with threaded fittings at both ends or with an adjusting sleeve between the fitting and the tie rod, as shown in Fig. 16. One end of the fitting has a right-hand thread, while the other end of the fitting has a left-hand thread. This arrangement makes it possible to change the length of the tie rod by turning the sleeve or the tie rod on the end fittings (tie rod ends).

VI. TOE-OUT ON TURNS

Toe-out on turns refers to the difference in angles between the two front wheels during turns.

When a vehicle is traveling straight ahead, both front wheels must be parallel in a straight ahead position if the vehicle is to maintain steering stability. During a turn, however, this is not true. Figure 17 illustrates the positions assumed by the front wheels during a turn. The inner wheel is rotating on a smaller radius than the outer wheel when the vehicle is rounding a curve, therefore the spindle of the inside wheel must be turned at a sharper angle to reduce side slippage. As shown in Fig. 17 the outside wheel is turned at a 20° angle from straight ahead position while the inside wheel is turned at a 23° angle from the straight ahead position. When this situation exists the wheels are no longer parallel or toed-in, but are actually toed-out, resulting in a greater distance between the front of the front wheels than the rear of the front wheels. This is known as toe-out on turns and is always referred to by its full name to avoid confusion with toe-out as referred to when the wheels are in the straight ahead position.

Toe-out on turns is accomplished by having the center line which extends through the ends of the steering knuckle arms closer together than the center line which extends down through the steering knuckle ball joints. The design of the steering knuckle arms controls the toe-out on turns. If the steering knuckle arms are bent, there is little to be gained by attempting corrections other than by straightening or replacing the bent steering knuckle arm.

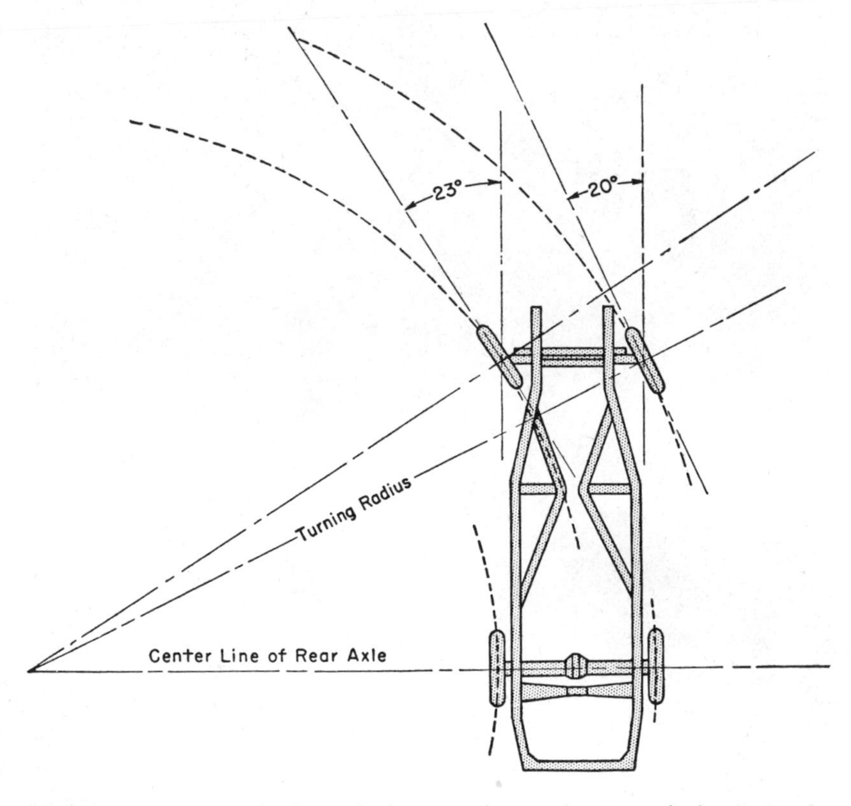

Fig. 17. During a turn the front wheels are toed-out, and as a result the distance between the front of the front wheels is greater than the distance between the back of the front wheels.

Toe-out on turns has very little effect on steering control. Incorrect toe-out on turns, however, results in some tire wear and may cause a slight loss of stability on turns.

The degree of toe-out on turns is slightly affected by both toe-in and caster. Correction of either of these factors will change the toe-out on turns at least slightly.

Wheel alignment factors may be arranged in two groups: The first group consisting of camber, toe-in, toe-out, and toe-out on turns are related in that each deals with the wheel's position in ref-

Fig. 18. Mechanical wheel alignment using a protractor. The camber of the wheel will be shown on the stationary graduated scale.

erence to the road. The second group consisting of caster and steering axis inclination are related in that they both deal with the steering axis.

Direct measuring methods are used to check camber and toe-in or toe-out. Direct measuring means that the measurement is taken directly from some part of the wheel assembly. Indirect measuring methods are those that measure the angles through the change of some other angles or parts.

Fig. 19. Portable wheel alignment gage mounted to the rim of the wheel. The gage is adjusted until the bubble is centered in the spirit level. Camber reading will be shown on the 60-degree scale of the gage. A reading which is outside of zero would indicate negative camber. Readings toward the wheel from zero would be positive camber readings.

(John Bean Corp.)

There are a number of different gages and machines manufactured to determine the wheel alignment angles. Some of the basic gages and machines will be briefly discussed here. A complete operating manual is available for a specific type of machine from its manufacturer.

a. Camber Angle. Camber is the tilting of the wheel from the vertical. All instruments measure camber by the actual tilt of the wheel from the vertical line.

Camber reading gages may be mounted against the tire, on the rim of the wheel, on the hub, or on the spindle.

Before these gages that mount to the wheel or the tire are used (Figs. 18 and 19), a provision must be made to compensate for the lateral run-out of the wheel. Lateral run-out is a sidewise movement of the wheel as it rotates. This can easily be determined by holding a piece of chalk against the tire or wheel, depending on where the gage will come in contact with the wheel. A chalk mark

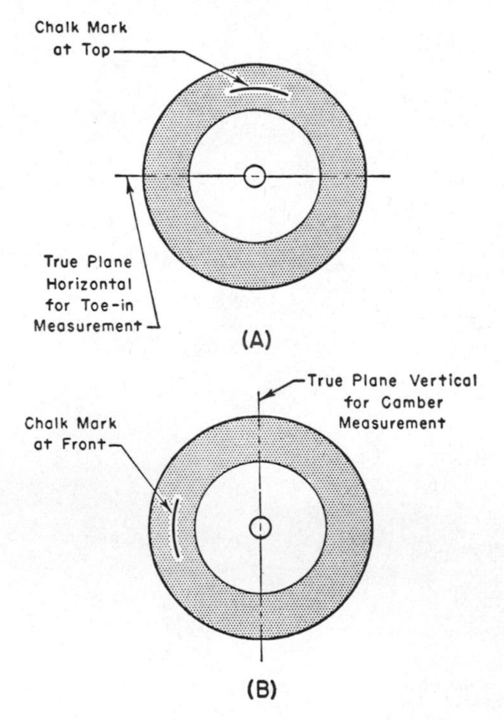

Fig. 20. Chalk marks for measuring (A) toe-in and (B) camber.

on the wheel or tire will indicate where the wheel and tire assembly is bent. Before attaching the above type of gages (Figs. 18, 19) to measure camber, rotate the wheel until the chalk mark is facing the front of the car. Fig. 20B shows position of wheel for measuring camber. Fig. 20A shows position for measuring toe-in.

Another portable gage used to measure camber is held to the wheel hub by strong magnets. Run-out of the wheels need not be measured since the outer end of the hub is machined concentric with the spindle.

The Visualiner, as shown in Fig. 21, uses a mirror assembly which is mounted to the rim of the wheel. Run-out must be compensated for in order to obtain an accurate reading of camber.

Fig. 21. Visualiner with a short rack installed in a pit. Tools can be added to this type of rack to enable a wheel alignment operator to correct damage to a vehicle as a result of a collision as well as all normal wheel alignment of vehicles regardless of their tread width. *(John Bean Corp.)*

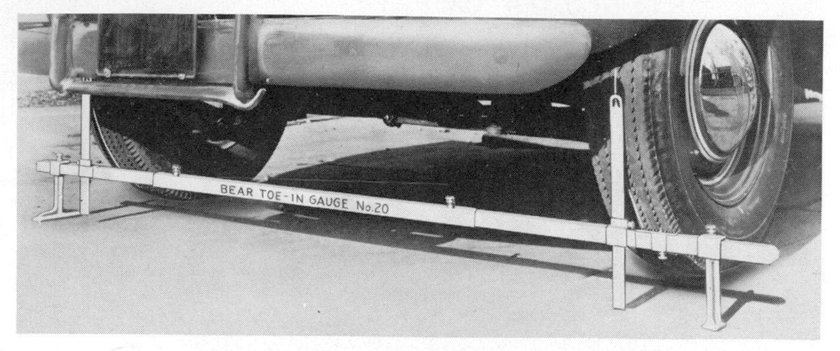

Fig. 22. Trammel used to check toe-in from scribed line.
(Bear Manufacturing Company)

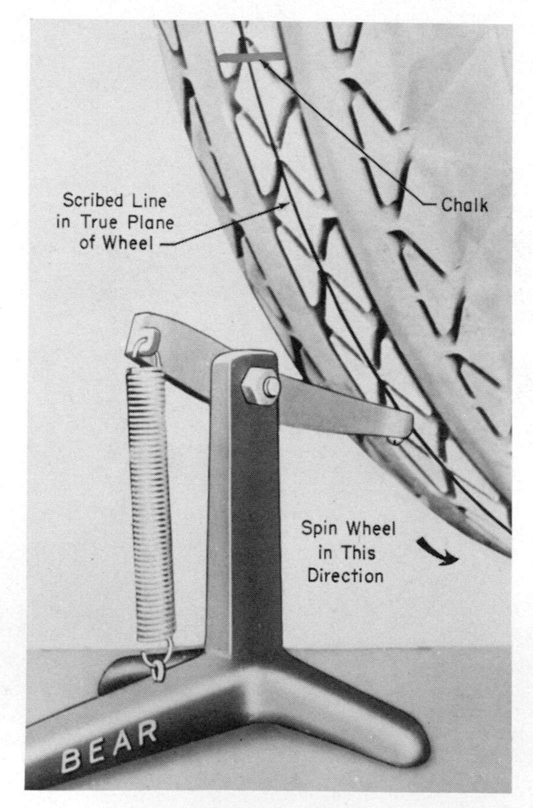

Fig. 23. Tire scriber in position to mark the tire. The wheel is rotated against a sharp point of the scriber leaving a mark completely around the tire.
(Bear Manufacturing Company)

b. Toe-in or Toe-out. Toe-in or toe-out is measured by determining the distance between the two front wheels at the front of each wheel as compared to the distance between the front wheels at the rear of each wheel. If the distance at the front of the front wheels is greater than the distance at the rear of the front wheels, the wheels are toed out. If the distance at the front of the front wheels is less than the distance at the rear of the front wheels, the wheels are toed in. The simplest way to check toe-in is to use a tape measure and measure the distance between the front of the front wheels and compare it to the distance between the rear of the front wheels. However, this method could give an incorrect reading since a bent wheel would give an erroneous width dimension.

Figure 22 illustrates a trammel which determines the amount of toe-in or toe-out by using a line previously scribed around the tire. The two lines (one on each tire) are accurate measuring points not affected by wheel run-out. Figure 23 illustrates a scribing tool for making the line. This method may also be used to measure toe-in of the rear wheels which in most cases should be 0.

Figure 24 shows an inexpensive tool which can be used to measure toe-in of the front or rear wheels. The gage reading is not affected by a bent wheel because the wheels and gage total together as the vehicle is moved.

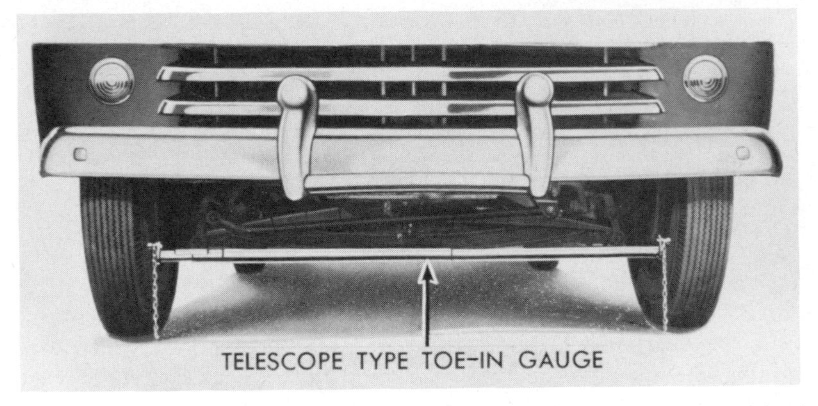

Fig. 24. Telescope type toe-in gage. This gage is mounted between the wheels at a height where the chains just touch the floor at the front of the wheel. The gage is set at zero. The car is then pulled forward until the chains just touch the floor at the rear of the wheel. The amount of toe-in or toe-out will now show on the gage.

(Ford Motor Company)

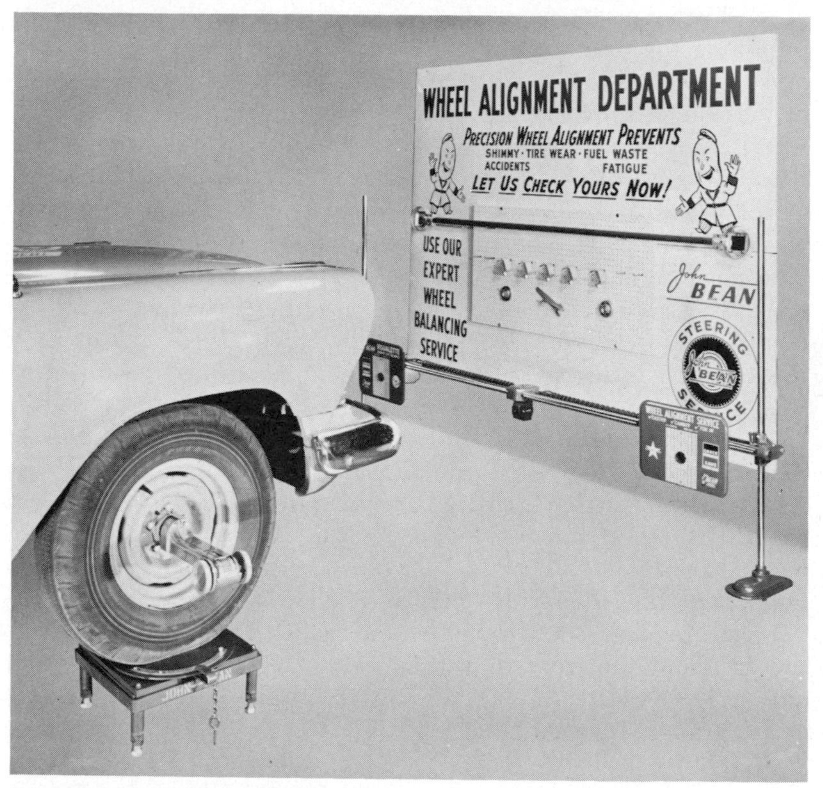

Fig. 25. A portable magnetic gage uses a beam of light to determine toe of the wheels. The light source coming from the center of the chart shines on a mirror mounted on the wheel. A reflected cross falls on the toe chart and tells the toe of the wheel. By placing one wheel on zero toe, the other chart will show the toe-in or toe-out of the two front wheels.

(John Bean Corp.)

Figure 25 shows one method of measuring toe-in which allows easy adjustment. The operator can watch the toe change as he adjusts the tie rod sleeves.

c. Toe-out on Turns. To measure toe-out on turns, a degree plate or a graduated turntable is used. Figure 26 shows a turntable.

To measure toe-out on turns, turn the wheels to the right until the left wheel is at 20 degrees in a right hand turn. The right wheel will now show the amount of toe-out. Next, turn the wheels to the left until the right wheel is at 20 degrees in a left hand turn. The left wheel will now show the amount of toe-out. The two readings should agree with or be within 1 degree of each other. If the two

Fig. 26. A pointer attached to the graduated turntable shows the amount of table turns in degrees. Straight-ahead position is zero. Turning the wheels either left or right is calibrated on the scale 30 degrees each way.

readings are not within 1 degree of each other, one or both steering arms are bent. Vehicle manufacturer's manuals usually will give the recommended toe-out on turns for their vehicles.

d. Caster. Caster is the rearward tilt of the top of the steering axis or in a kingpin suspension, the rearward tilt of top of the kingpin. Since positive caster is the rearward tilt of the top of the steering axis, the upper ball joint on a ball joint type suspension would be slightly behind the lower ball joint. When reference is made to caster, it usually means that condition by which the front wheels are controlled by the rearward tilt of the steering axis.

Negative caster occurs when the top of the kingpin is tilted forward, or in the ball joint type suspension, the upper ball joint is in front of the lower ball joint. Sometimes negative caster is called reverse caster.

If a vehicle has positive caster, the right wheel is turned to the right and the camber of the wheel is taken, then the wheel is turned inward or to the left, a change in camber of the wheel will be noticed. Caster gages are designed to measure the caster through the amount of camber change as the wheel is turned in an arc of 40 degrees. If the camber of a wheel changes 3 degrees as it is rotated from 20 degrees to 20 degrees, the caster will be approximately 2 degrees. This does not have to be computed each time the caster is taken since this is built into the caster scale of the machine.

Most gages operate in the above manner. A few, however, determine a caster reading by turning the wheel inward at the front 20 degrees and setting the gage on 0 on the caster scale, then turning in their wheel until the wheel is turned 20 degrees inward at the rear and the scale will now give the caster reading. Either method will give you the same numerical value of the caster angle, but if a gage is designed to read caster by turning the rear of the wheel in first and then it is done in a reverse manner, the caster will change signs. Or in other words, if the steering axis of the wheel has positive caster, and the gage is used in the reverse manner of which it is designed, the gage will read that the wheel has a negative caster. Figure 27

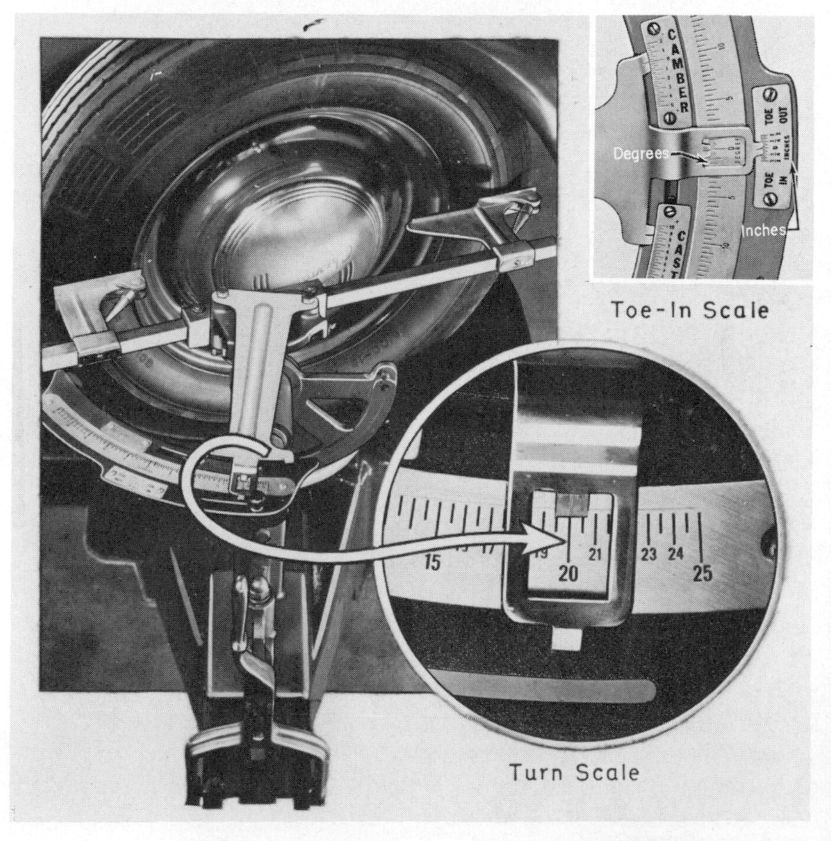

Fig. 27. Note that the wheel is turned 20 degrees inward at the rear. At this point the caster scale is adjusted to read zero. The wheel is then turned about its steering axis until the gage reads 20 degrees with the wheel turned in at the front. The caster scale will now indicate the caster reading.

(John Bean Corp.)

illustrates an alignment machine that measures caster by this method.

Figure 28 shows a portable type of wheel alignment gage that contacts the outer edge of the wheel. This type of gage must be used with a turntable such as the one shown in Figure 26. Chapter 8 gives a complete discussion on the operation of the Visualiner when measuring caster.

e. Steering Axis Inclination. When the steering axis is tilted inward toward the center of the vehicle from a vertical line, the included angle is called S.A.I. or *steering axis inclination.* This

Fig. 28. A mechanical wheel alignment machine measures caster when the wheel is turned in 20 degrees at the front, the gage is set at zero, and the wheel is then turned in 20 degrees at the rear. What is shown is the caster reading of the steering axis of the wheel.

angle is not adjustable. On kingpin type suspensions, steering axis inclination is called kingpin inclination or K.P.I. Steering axis inclination is a built-in feature of the steering knuckle. As the camber of the wheel is changed, so is the steering axis inclination changed. As camber is increased in the positive direction, the steering axis inclination is decreased. Therefore, the reverse is true in that as the camber is moved in the negative direction, the steering axis inclination is increased.

Steering axis inclination is measured in the same manner as caster is measured, that is, by turning the wheel about its steering axis until the rear of the wheel is in 20 degrees. The steering axis gage, which is usually built into most wheel alignment equipment, is set on 0 on the steering axis scale. The gage must be mounted to the spindle; however, it may be mounted to the hub or to the wheel if the brakes are applied. As the wheel is rotated about its steering axis, the steering axis inclination causes the spindle to turn or roll about its center. When the wheel reaches 20 degrees in at the front, the steering axis gage will give the steering axis inclination of that wheel.

If the steering axis inclination reading does not agree with the specifications given on the wheel alignment chart, the spindle or another part of the steering knuckle may be bent. Steering axis inclination, S.A.I., on a wheel alignment specifications chart is given as so many degrees at a certain camber angle. For example, a typical steering axis inclination angle may be stated as 4 degrees steering axis inclination or kingpin inclination at 1/2 degree positive camber. A steering axis inclination will be 4 degrees only when the camber angle is 1/2 of a degree positive. If the camber of the wheel is 0 degrees, the steering axis inclination angle should be 4 1/2 degrees. If the camber is 1 degree positive then the steering axis inclination should be 3 1/2 degrees.

If the steering axis inclination in the above example was taken and found to be 3 degrees when the camber was 0, then the steering knuckle is damaged. A steering knuckle cannot be repaired and therefore should be replaced.

TRADE COMPETENCY TEST

1. What are the objectives which automotive manufacturers strive to attain in suspension design? (pp. 153, 154)

2. What should be the results of a properly aligned front-end? (p. 155)
3. What should be the relationship of the bottom of the tire to the road surface on a moving vehicle?
4. What is the principle of caster and what is its effect on steering? (pp. 155-162)
5. Why can correct wheel alignment factors be obtained with negative caster? (pp. 158, 159)
6. What is the effect of uneven caster? (p. 160)
7. What are the methods of caster adjustment and how is caster changed? (p. 161)
8. What is the purpose of steering knuckle sidewise inclination? (pp. 161, 162)
9. What influence does camber have on a rolling wheel? (p. 166)
10. What will cause the camber angle to change? (pp. 160, 161)
11. Where should the point of intersection be located in relation to the road and why? (p. 168)
12. Why are front wheels toed-in and what controls toe-in? (pp. 170, 171)
13. Why is toe-out on turns necessary? (p. 172)
14. How is toe-out on turns accomplished? (p. 173)
15. What alignment factor do we check in order to measure the caster? (p. 181)

CHAPTER 8

CUSTOMIZED VEHICLE ALIGNMENT

PAGE

I. Pre-Alignment Visual Inspection 186
II. Pre-Alignment Road Test 191
III. Vehicle Repair 192
IV. Checking Wheel Alignment Equipment 192
V. Vehicle Alignment 193

Various steering control and tire wear problems arise due to misalignment, wear, unbalance, improper tire pressures, and defects in the suspension system and the related steering linkages. Misalignment cannot be corrected unless the cause can be found. Each abnormal steering condition or excessive tire-wear pattern should be checked since it should provide a valuable indication as to the cause of the trouble. Frequently more than one condition is at the root of the trouble. It is best, accordingly, to make a complete front-end check whenever steering difficulties and/or excessive tire wear become apparent.

This chapter outlines the procedure for checking the vehicle and provides the information you will need to carry out an alignment once you have analyzed the nature of the problem.

I. PRE-ALIGNMENT VISUAL INSPECTION

Alignment problems are more intimately concerned with the physical makeup, working habits, and personal psychology of the customer than are many other kinds of repair work. As this chapter unfolds, the truth of this observation will become clear. At the outset it is important to stress that the goal of an alignment shop should be to give the customer the best alignment job he can get for his money.

Before the actual adjusting of the vehicle alignment takes place, the vehicle must be visually inspected. Bear in mind that the way in which the customer has expressed his complaint may be a valuable aid in making the proper diagnosis and in repairing his vehicle. The visual inspection will enable the operator to understand the cus-

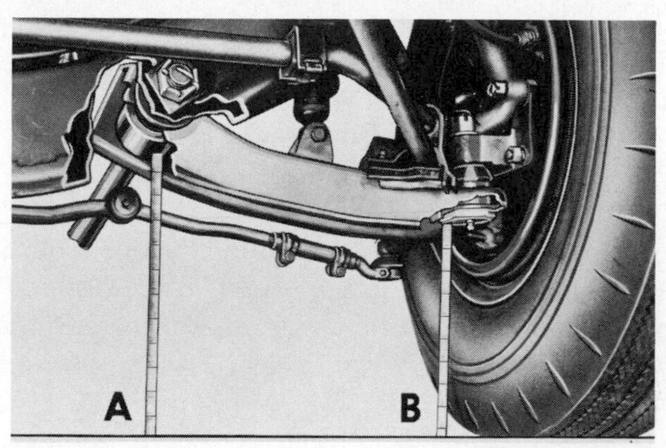

Fig. 1. The lower control arm of the front suspension system measures lower at the wheel (B) than at the center of the vehicle (A). This condition indicates that the curb height is satisfactory.

(John Bean Corp.)

tomer's complaint and to begin the process of alignment. Steps to follow are explained below.

a. Curb Height. First, inspect the vehicle to see how it sits in relation to the road surface. Curb height, which is usually specified by the manufacturer, is the distance between a stated point on the car (usually the lower edge of the bumpers) and the road surface when the vehicle is fully loaded with fuel, oil, and water—standing free and without driver, passengers, or load.

When looking at an independent suspension, if the lower control

Fig. 2. Camber wear on tires results in unevenness at the edges. Positive camber wear appears on the outside tread. Negative camber wear appears on the inside tread.

(John Bean Corp.)

arm is higher at the center of the vehicle than at the outer end, or if it is horizontal, the curb height is satisfactory. See Fig. 1.

b. Tire Condition. To insure the best alignment service a vehicle must be equipped with good front tires. A worn front tire, even though the vehicle is properly aligned, may cause erratic steering. Look at the tires for the following wear:

(1) *CAMBER WEAR.* This condition is caused by the design of the front suspension and by worn or bent suspension parts. Excessive negative camber causes wear on the inside tread of the tire. Improper positive camber causes wear on the outside tread. See Fig. 2.

(2) *UNDER-INFLATION WEAR.* Observe the tire inflation and note if tire wear is caused by improper inflation. See Fig. 3.

(3) *TOE WEAR.* Observe the toe wear of the tires which may be caused by maladjustment or by worn or bent steering linkage. Place your palm on the tire tread and move your hand, first, toward and then away from the center of the vehicle. Toe-out wear may be ascertained by feeling sharp edges on the tread design when pushing the hand inward toward the center of the vehicle. Toe-in wear is noted if the edges are sharp when the hand is pulled away from the center of the vehicle. See Fig. 4.

(4) *SCALLOPING WEAR.* This may be the result of several causes. The wheels may be out of balance; severe brake applica-

Fig. 3. Under-inflation wear appears on both edges of the tire, leaving the center treads to protrude when proper inflation is made. Over-inflation wear is the opposite of this condition. (*John Bean Corp.*)

Fig. 4. Toe-in and toe-out wear occur as a result of worn or bent steering linkage. Test for it by feeling for sharp edges when pulling the hand across the tire. If the inner edges are sharp, the condition is toe-in wear. If the outer edges are sharp, the condition is toe-out wear.
(John Bean Corp.)

tion may have worn an initial flat spot; either excessive positive or negative caster may have caused a shimmy which has become exaggerated; by worn steering system parts; or inoperative shock absorbers may have caused uneven and eccentric tire wear. See Fig. 5.

Fig. 5. Scalloping or heel-and-toe wear may be caused by a number of road conditions, certain driving habits, and faulty adjustments in the automotive suspension system. It is an uneven and eccentric condition.
(John Bean Corp.)

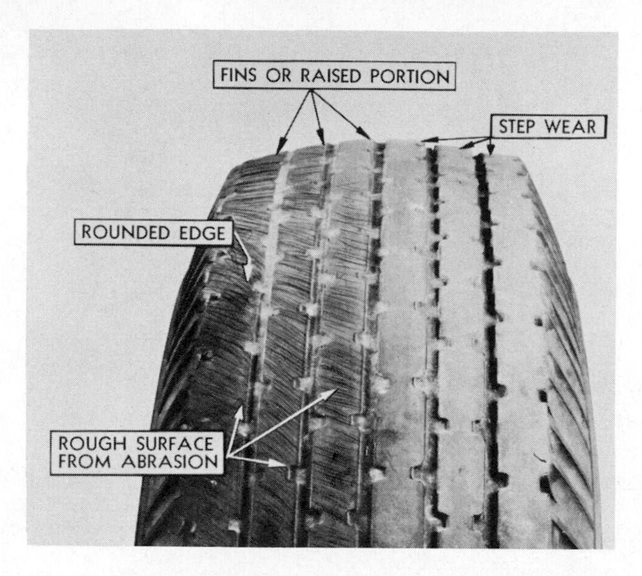

Fig. 6. A typical example of cornering wear brought about either by excessive turning at high speeds or by extreme negative caster.
(*John Bean Corp.*)

(5) *CORNERING WEAR.* This condition is caused by excessive speed in turning or by extreme negative caster. See Fig. 6.

c. Steering System Inspection. Check the steering system for excessive looseness by turning the wheels straight ahead and then moving the steering wheel back and forth. *No* (repeat *No*) play should exist between the steering wheel and the road wheels. A vehicle must have a tight steering system if any realignment correction is to be effective. For this reason adjustment of the steering gear and linkage must be part of the alignment job.

d. Vehicle Track. This term applies to the rear wheels following directly behind or in the tracks of the front wheels. A vehicle which is out of track may not handle properly on the road even though the front wheels are in correct alignment. There are two ways of visually detecting this condition. The first is to follow directly behind the car as another person drives it on a straight road, observing the offset condition of the rear wheels in relation to the front wheels. Do not be misled by a vehicle on which the rear tread width (distance between wheels) is more or less than the tread width of the front wheels. The other method is to observe the imprint of the tire tracks on a garage floor after the vehicle has been driven in a straight

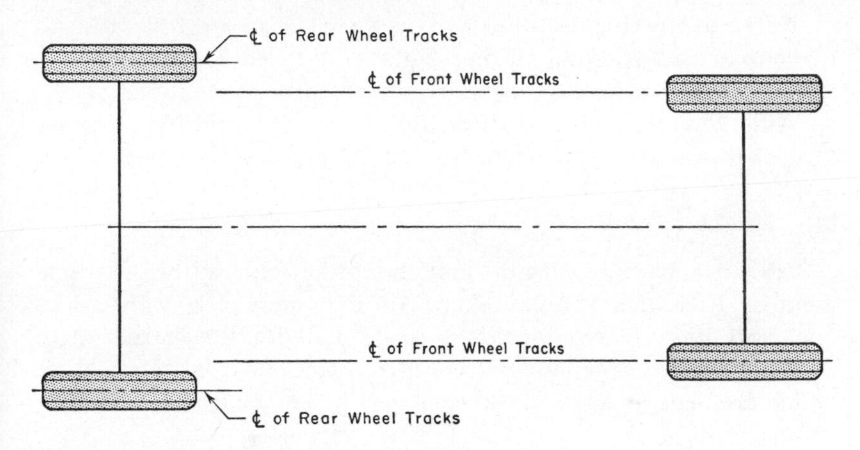

Fig. 7. Vehicle track may be observed by observing the marks made by the front and rear wheels after the automobile has been driven more than a dozen feet. Tracks should be parallel, but they need not overlap.
(*John Bean Corp.*)

line for a dozen feet. If the rear wheel imprints do not evenly overlap the front wheel imprints, the vehicle may be out of track. See Fig. 7.

e. General Vehicle Appearance. A final and important check pertains to the general appearance of the vehicle. An obviously new paint job or apparent repair work on the body may be indications that a collision could have damaged the suspension system. Unless you check it this damage will go undetected and unrepaired.

II. PRE-ALIGNMENT ROAD TEST

After these visual inspections have been made and the operator is still not satisfied as to the nature of the car's trouble, he should road test the car. A definite route *typical* of roads regularly used by the vehicle should be chosen for the test. During the road test the operator should watch for the following conditions:

a. Pulling. A vehicle will pull or drift to one side because of faulty brakes, a tire with low pressure, or improper alignment.

b. Excessive Noise and Vibration. Pitted or loosely adjusted wheel bearings will cause excessive noise and vibration. A *klunking* sound as the brakes are applied may be due to worn ball joints, worn upper or lower outer pivot pins, or worn bushings. Unbalanced wheels and loose steering parts will also cause a vibration.

c. Hard Steering. A vehicle may be hard to steer because of inadequate lubrication, an improperly adjusted steering system, excessive positive caster, or under-inflated tires.

After completing the road test the operator should have an idea of the cause of the vehicle's erratic handling.

III. VEHICLE REPAIR

All parts that are worn or bent should be replaced before alignment of the vehicle is undertaken. An alignment rack—which is an expensive piece of equipment—is to be used for the correction of a vehicle's alignment and *not for the replacement of parts.* Parts which are bent or worn can be replaced in any stall in the shop.

IV. CHECKING WHEEL ALIGNMENT EQUIPMENT

Before starting any alignment job, the equipment must be checked for calibration. This operation should be done every day to assure absolute accuracy. In general, all alignment machines must be level. They are usually calibrated to zero degree camber and zero inch toe. All manufacturers provide calibration instructions with their equipment, and it is advisable to check these instructions before beginning calibration. See Fig. 8.

The caster measuring feature of present equipment cannot be calibrated by the operator. If there is any reason to doubt its accuracy, the manufacturer must be informed so that he can adjust it.

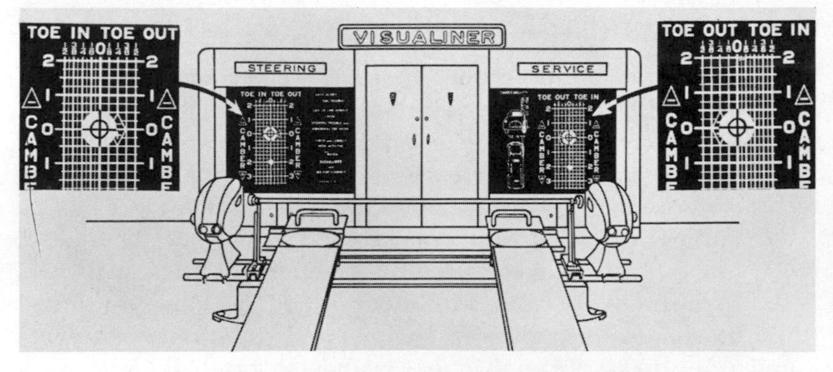

Fig. 8. All alignment equipment should be tested for accuracy each day. They must be absolutely level. Ordinarily they are set at zero degrees camber and toe.
(*John Bean Corp.*)

V. VEHICLE ALIGNMENT

The vehicle is ready to be aligned after the steps outlined above have been completed. The procedure described in this section applies to aligning a vehicle on a John Bean Visualiner.

a. Putting the Car on the Rack. First, adjust the alignment rack to the wheel tread width of the vehicle to be aligned. Next, drive the vehicle on the rack up to the turntables and block one rear wheel. Caution: Do not let the engine run while the vehicle is on the rack. Then, inflate all four tires to the manufacturer's specifications.

b. Adjusting Vehicle Curb Height. Adjust the vehicle to the manufacturer's specified curb height. (Refer to Fig. 1.) If the vehicle is lower in the rear than in the front, the condition may be due to broken or fatigued rear springs, lowering-blocks on the vehicle, or an excessive load in the trunk. If, however, the load of the vehicle is the one it normally carries (for example, a heavily loaded salesman's car), proceed with alignment with the load in the

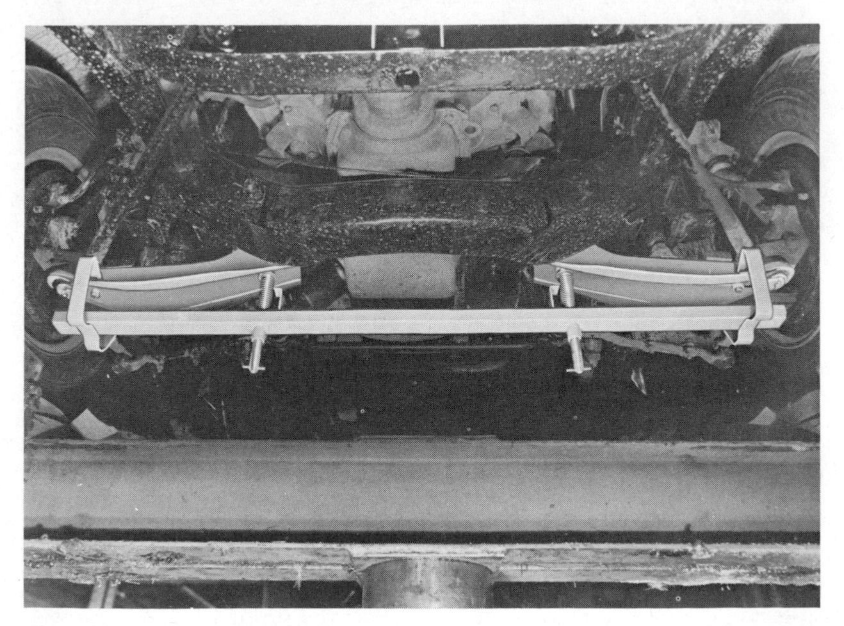

Fig. 9. Adjusting torsion bars by means of a torsion-air gage installed to aid in getting the correct curb height. Compare with Fig. 1.
(John Bean Corp.)

car. Each customer's requirements are different. Weak rear springs may be boosted by overload springs. Spacers may be used to strengthen coil springs.

If the vehicle leans to the left or to the right, the reason may be a sagged spring on the weak side. Usually the only occupant of a vehicle is the driver; accordingly, it is not abnormal for a vehicle to lean slightly to the left.

To correct fatigued front springs replace the sagged springs with new ones. Always replace front springs in pairs since failure to do so may cause the vehicle not to be level. Another method of correcting faulty curb height is to insert spacers or blocks between the coils of the spring. Still a third means is to use spacers underneath the spring—that is, between the bottom of the spring and the lower control arm. Torsion bar readjustment is accomplished by means of special adjustment screws, which are part of the bars themselves. Specifications for this operation are supplied by the manufacturer. See Fig. 9.

c. Adjusting and Checking Wheel Bearings for Loose Parts. Pull the vehicle on the turntables and reblock the rear wheels. Lift the left front wheel under the lower control arm until the wheel just clears the turntable. Check for loose parts by shaking the wheel in a direction horizontal to the ground. This test will reveal loose ball joints and steering system parts. By shaking the wheels vertically, you will be able to check loose kingpins, worn ball joints, and loose wheel bearings. A movement of more than one-quarter inch of the wheel either inward or outward—at the bottom of the wheel—must be considered excessive. Such a condition may necessitate replacement of the kingpins or ball joints. Write on the work order the designation of the parts which may need replacement.

To adjust the wheel bearings, first tighten the spindle nut firmly and then back off one-sixth of a turn. If a cotter pin hole is not lined up with a slot in the nut, move the nut slightly to align the hole with a slot. When the nut is correctly adjusted, you will not be able to move it with the fingers if the installation is of the ball-bearing type. Roller bearing installations require that the nut be movable by the fingers. Finally, install the cotter pin and be sure to bend it properly so that it will not interfere with the static collector in the grease cap. Note: From this point on it is essential that you understand the contents of Chapter 7 as background for the technical instructions which follow.

Fig. 10. Mounting mirror on the wheel.
(John Bean Corp.)

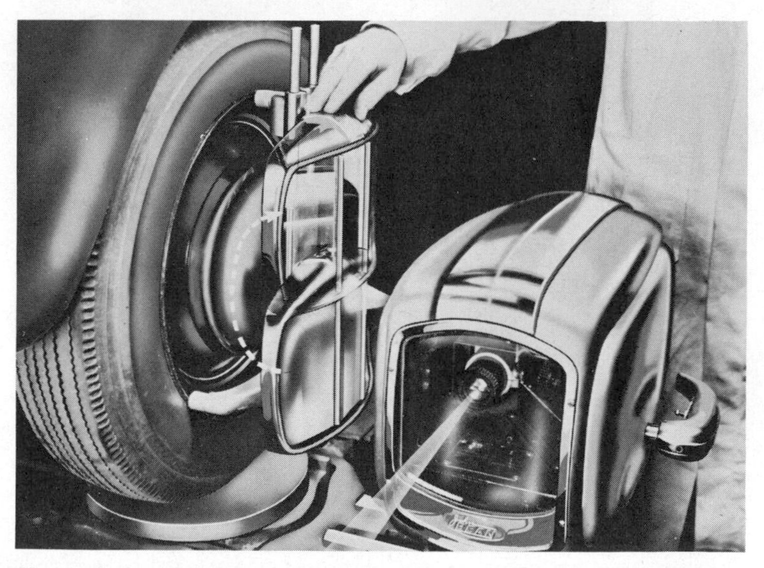

Fig. 11. In checking the mirror assembly located next to the projection head, rotate the mirror about its axis and note if the cross hair spot stays at the same place on the screen. If the spot moves, the mirror assembly should be sent to a factory service center for readjustment.
(John Bean Corp.)

d. Clamp Mirror to Wheel. Place two mounting feet (brackets to hold mirror to wheel) against the lip of the wheel rim. Slide the mirror on its bar assembly until the shaft of the mirror is in line with the center of the wheel's spindle. Place a third mounting foot against the wheel rim and rotate the clamp to lock the mirror assembly on the wheel. Rotate the mirror assembly to check for the accuracy of the wheel mirror assembly. The cross hairs should remain in the same spot on the screen. See Figs. 10 and 11.

e. Rotate Left Wheel to Compensate for Lateral Run-Out. Lift the vehicle with a jack and observe the pattern that the cross-hair spot makes on the screen. Observe the total vertical travel of

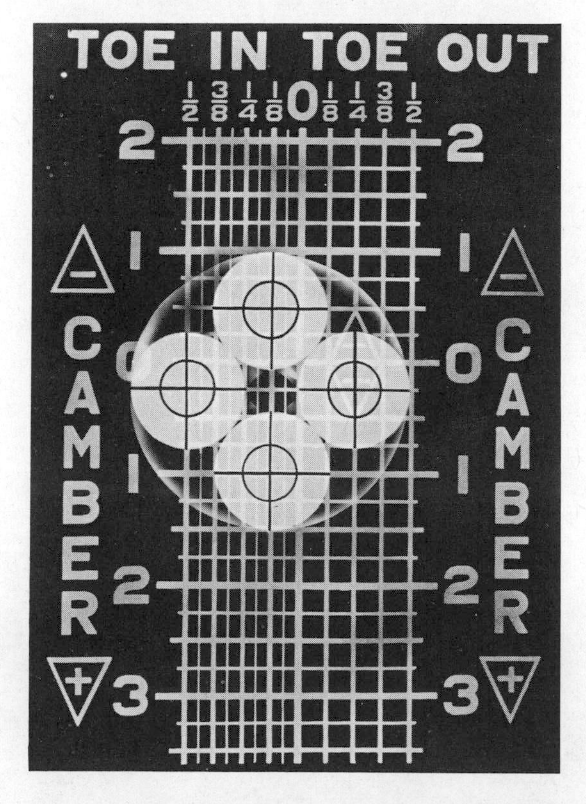

Fig. 12. Vertical travel is the distance from the negative one-half degree to the positive one degree. One-half of the total movement is three-quarters of one degree. A vehicle wheel that has a total run-out of three-quarters of one degree vertically or three-eighths of one inch horizontally would have to be straightened or replaced.

(*John Bean Corp.*)

Fig. 13. Camber reading of the left wheel shows the cross hair at one-half degree below the zero mark. This means the reading is one-half degree positive.
(John Bean Corp.)

the cross hair. Lower the wheel to the turntable when the cross-hair spot is in the lowest position on the screen. Divide the total amount of vertical travel by two and mark the spot corresponding to this calculation on the wall chart below the zero degree line. (A good way to mark the spot is to use a small bar magnet and assume its center is the line you want.) Now turn the knob on the rear of the projection head to bring the zero degree camber mark in line with the center of the magnet you have placed on the chart. The cross-hair spot will now show the camber of the left wheel. Record this reading on the work order. See Figs. 12 and 13.

f. Camber Reading of the Right Wheel. Lift the vehicle with a jack and repeat the procedure described above for the right wheel. Record the camber reading on the work order. See Fig. 14.

g. Check Toe of Both Wheels. Manipulate the left front wheel until it is recorded at zero degree toe. The cross-hair spot on the right wheel screen will now indicate the total front wheel toe-in.

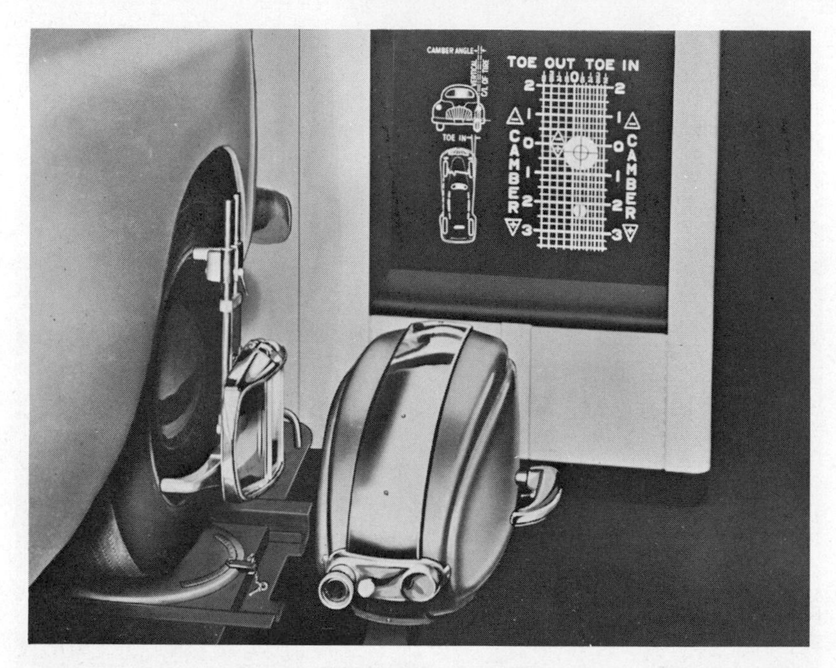

Fig. 14. Camber reading of the right wheel shows the cross hair at one-quarter degree below the zero mark. This means the reading is one-quarter degree positive.
(*John Bean Corp.*)

This reading has no relationship to the final toe reading since readjustment of camber or caster will change the toe of the front wheels. The real purpose of checking toe at this stage is to aid in making an accurate check of *steering geometry*. Steering geometry is the term applied to toe out during turns and is the difference in angles between the two front wheels and the car frame when a turn is made.. The inner wheel turns out more.

h. Check Caster of Right Wheel. Turn the knob on the rear of the projection head until the caster chart is shown on the screen. To determine the caster of the right wheel, move the rear of the wheel inward toward the body of the car (which means the car would be turning to the right) until the cross-hair spot on the caster chart on the screen shows the wheel is turned twenty degrees. Now turn the knob on the rear of the projection head until the zero degree line on the caster chart falls on the horizontal line of the cross-hair spot.

Now turn the wheel inward at the front an arc of twenty degrees (vehicle turning to the left). The location of the cross-hair spot on the caster chart now indicates the caster angle of the right wheel.

i. Check the Steering Geometry of the Left Wheel. Move to the left wheel and turn the knob on the projection head until the caster chart is on the screen. Since the right wheel has been left at a twenty-degree angle, the caster chart on the left side of the machine will indicate the steering geometry or number of degrees of toe-out on turns of the left wheel. If the toe reading when the wheels were straight ahead was toe-out, then the toe-out on turns will be too high.

j. Check Caster of Left Wheel. Follow the steps in Section "*h*" above and record your findings on the work order. Make sure the wheel is turned twenty degrees into a left turn. See Figs. 15 and 16.

k. Check the Steering Geometry of the Right Wheel. After recording the left wheel caster, note that the left wheel is in

Fig. 15. To set the caster chart turn the rear of the left wheel in 20 degrees and move the 0 degree mark on the caster chart over the cross hair spot.
(*John Bean Corp.*)

Fig. 16. When the wheel is turned in 20 degrees at the front, the cross hair spot shows the caster of the left wheel. Caster reading indicated in the photograph above is one and one-half degrees positive.

(*John Bean Corp.*)

twenty degrees into a left turn. This means that by looking at the right wheel caster chart the right wheel toe-out on turns may be recorded.

l. Check Kingpin Inclination. All readings have now been taken except kingpin (steering axis) inclination. Normally such inclination is not measured unless the steering knuckle is suspected of misalignment. Fig. 17 illustrates the kingpin inclination gage in use.

m. Caster and Camber Specifications. Read from the specification chart the camber and caster angles and toe-in adjustment for the year and model of the vehicle. A specification of one-half degree for either camber or caster means *plus* (positive) one-half degree. A tolerance of plus or minus one-half degree applies to all camber and caster specifications on the chart when a single angle is shown. For example, one-half degree is given as a caster angle; therefore one-half degree positive caster with the tolerance may

Fig. 17. The kingpin inclination gage is installed on the nut. The movement of the bubble as the wheel is steered through an arc of 40 degrees is the kingpin inclination. The space between each full line on the bubble represents one degree.

(John Bean Corp.)

be adjusted on the vehicle from one-half plus one-half or one, to one-half minus one-half, or zero. Record the camber, caster, and toe-in specifications on the work order.

The specifications as given on the chart are for both front wheels. If the vehicle were driven on a flat level road and with a uniform passenger load, the same caster and camber angles for each wheel would be satisfactory. Since, however, most roads are crowned to promote drainage, and most vehicles carry only a single person, setting the camber and caster of each wheel the same amount will not result in a satisfactory alignment job.

n. The Customized Alignment Job. There are some useful guides for doing a proper alignment job. A few of them are included in this section.

A vehicle will pull to the wheel having the most positive camber. Details are explained in Chapter 7. The left wheel, accordingly, should have the more positive camber setting to compensate for the road crown which tends to pull the vehicle to the right. For example, if the camber specification is zero degree or zero plus one-half or minus one-half or minus one-half to plus one-half, the left wheel could be set at plus one-half degree camber and the right wheel at zero degree camber. This is the maximum difference allowed between front wheels. An average crowned road would be compensated for by a one-quarter degree difference between the camber of the two front wheels. An example would be: left wheel plus one-half degree, right wheel plus one-quarter degree.

Practical camber specifications are from zero to plus one-half of a degree. Setting camber at less than zero may cause inside tire wear, while adjusting camber at more than plus one-half on the left wheel may cause outside tire wear.

A vehicle will pull toward the wheel having the least positive or the most negative caster. Therefore, the left wheel should be adjusted to have less positive or more negative caster than the right wheel. This arrangement will compensate for the crown in the road. If the caster specification is minus one-half degree, leeway—with the permissible variation of one-half degree—would be from zero to minus one degree. The left wheel could then be set at minus one-half degree and the right wheel at zero degree. To compensate for the crown of the road, one-half degree caster is the maximum permissible difference allowed between front wheels.

Either camber or caster may be used to compensate for the right pull of the vehicle on the crowned road. On severe crowns both camber and caster adjustments may be used.

If a heavy person rides in a small car by himself, adjust the camber equally on both front wheels. The driver's weight will cause the vehicle to lean to the left, making the left wheel camber become positive and the right wheel camber become negative, automatically compensating for the crown in the road.

Caster is usually varied in its range of specification to give better handling of the vehicle. The operator should adjust caster toward the negative extreme of the specifications (that is, zero plus or minus one-half degree would be adjusted to minus one-half degree) if the vehicle is to carry heavy loads or if the driver wants a vehicle that is easy to steer. On the other hand, he should adjust caster toward the positive side (plus one-half degree) if the vehicle is to travel mountain roads or if the driver wishes more stability on flat, level roads.

o. Determine Corrections. Determine the camber and caster angles from the specifications chart and alter them to suit the needs of the vehicle. Record these angles next to the angles you wrote down when you checked the vehicle. With the two readings side-by-side determine which way you must move the wheel or steering axis to readjust the camber and caster on the left front wheel. For example, if the actual camber reading had been minus one-quarter degree and the new specification calls for plus one-half degree, you should move the top of the wheel outward three-quarters of a degree. If the caster reading had been plus one-half degree and should be zero degree, the top of the kingpin or upper ball joint should be moved one-half degree toward the front of the car.

p. Camber Adjustments. Eccentric pins have been used on early independent front suspension in connection with kingpins. To operate the eccentric a screwed-in grease fitting must be removed from the upper pin bushing and a lock bolt holding the pin loosened. Insert an Allen wrench into the pin through the grease fitting hole. Turning the pin one-half turn changes camber approximately one degree. A full turn will not change camber because the pin is an eccentric. See Fig. 18.

Eccentric bushings are located on the upper control arm outer pin inside the steering knuckle support. They are kept from turning by a bolt which is fitted through the steering knuckle support. Camber change per turn of the bushing is approximately the same

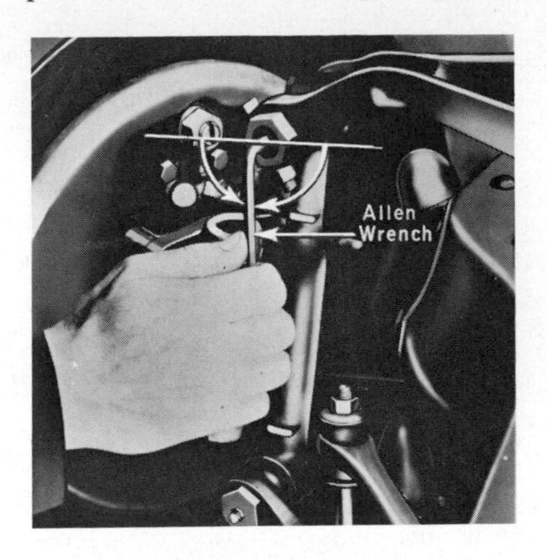

Fig. 18. Eccentric pin.

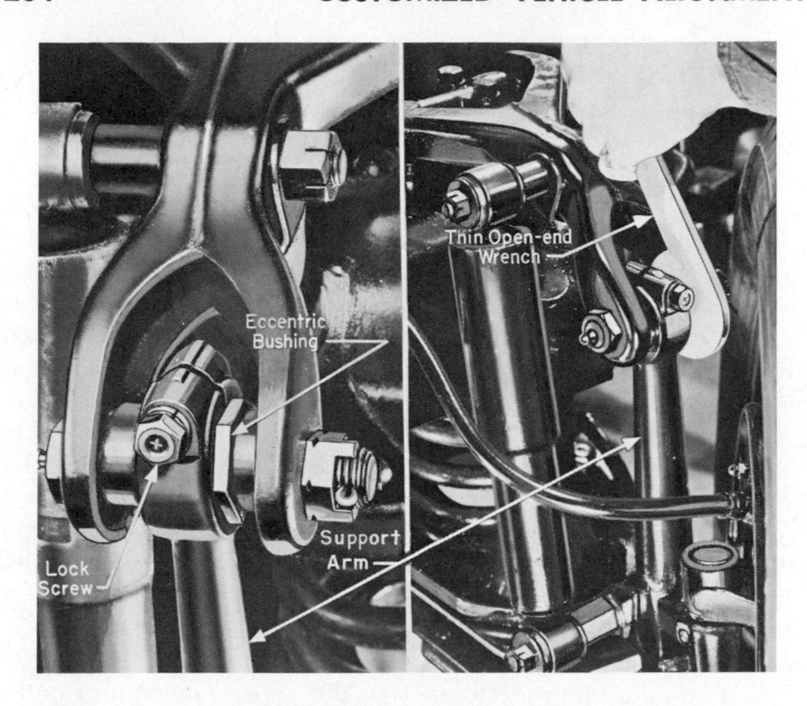

Fig. 19. Eccentric bushing.

as with the eccentric pin. One-half turn of the bushing will change the camber angle a maximum of one degree. See Fig. 19.

Eccentric washers are used to connect either the upper pivot shaft to the upper control arm or the lower pivot shaft to the lower control arm. In either instance both washers (one at each side of the control arm) must be rotated the same amount and in the same direction or the caster angle will be changed. See Fig. 20.

Shims are usually used between the upper pivot shaft and the vehicle frame to change camber. They can also be placed between the upper pivot shaft bracket and the frame side rail. Adding shims will result in positive camber in some installations; in others it will result in negative camber. See Fig. 21.

Camber correction tools are used when a vehicle has been involved in a minor collision or when it would not be economical to rebuild the front suspension to stop tire wear. The maximum possible change of camber is approximately three degrees with the kingpin type of suspension and one degree for the ball joint

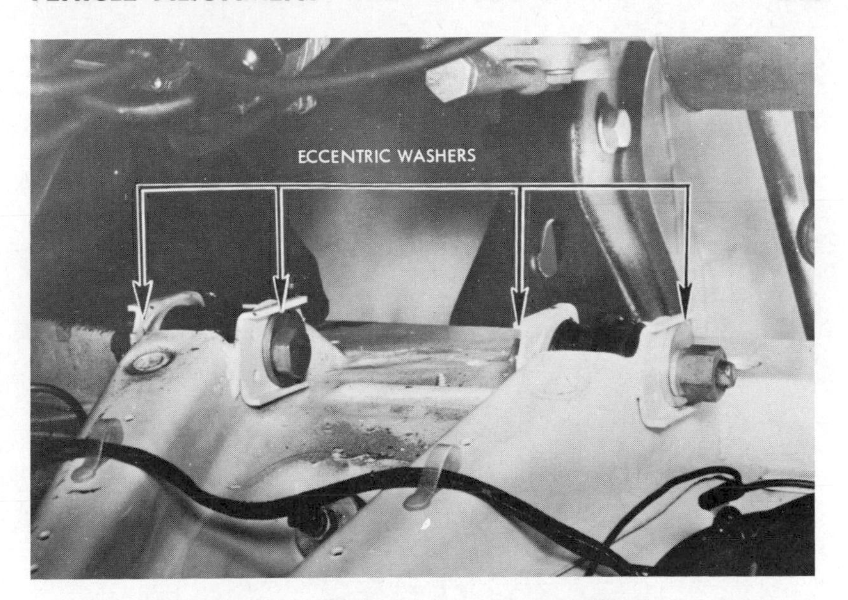

Fig. 20A. Eccentric washers on upper control arm.
(*American Motors Corp.*)

Fig. 20B. Eccentric washers on lower control arm.
(*American Motors Corp.*)

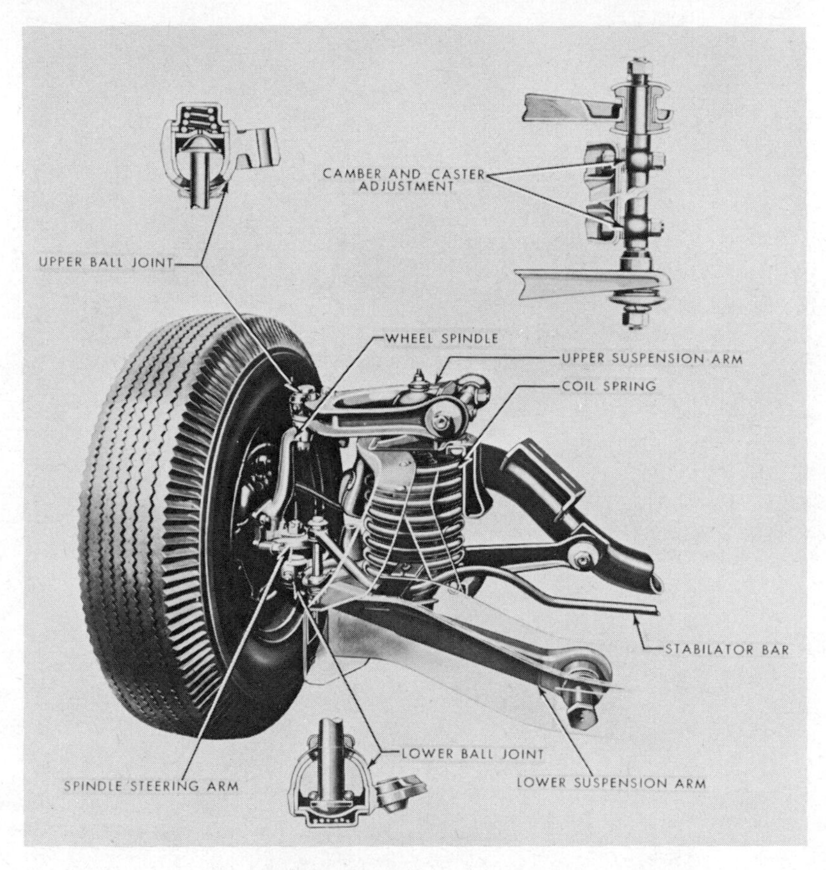

Fig. 21. Adding shims decreases camber.
(John Bean Corp.)

type. Three camber correction tools are shown in Figs. 22, 23 and 24.

q. Caster Adjustments. Caster is usually the first element checked because more adjustment is possible for caster than for camber. There are several ways to accomplish the necessary adjustment.

As explained above in section *p,* eccentric pins and bushings are used in installations with kingpins. Camber adjustment is accomplished by manipulation of these eccentrics. As the pin or bushing is turned to achieve a camber change, however, the steering knuckle support is moved either forward or backward. This movement causes a change in caster. A forward placement of the

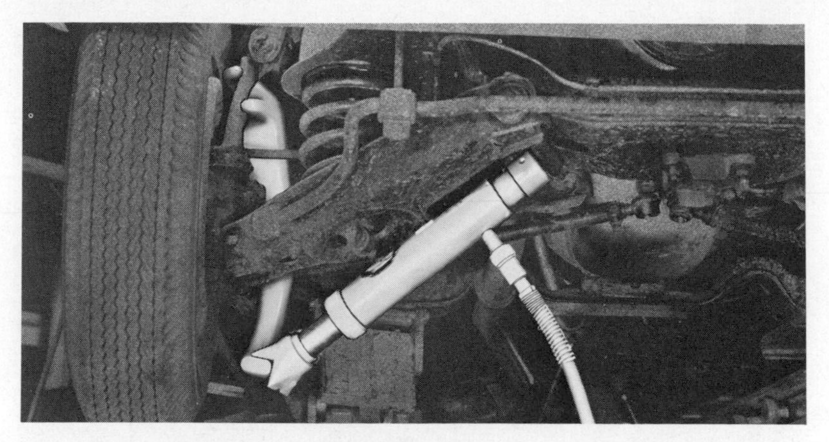

Fig. 22. Camber correction tool to straighten the steering knuckle support. (*John Bean Corp.*)

Fig. 23. Camber correction tool to flatten the upper control arm. (*John Bean Corp.*)

steering knuckle support results in a negative caster. A backward movement produces positive caster. Usually, two turns of the bushing will result in a total caster change of about two degrees.

Shims are used to change caster only if they are changed equally

Fig. 24. Camber correction tool used on ball joint suspensions.
(*John Bean Corp.*)

at both front and rear shaft mounting bolts. If only one shim is removed from the front mounting bolt, the camber goes in the positive direction and the caster goes in the positive direction. See Fig. 21.

Shims are used on kingpin type suspensions to change caster whenever the usual adjustments do not suffice. Adding a shim between the lower control arm shaft and the vehicle frame cross member at the front will cause the lower pin to move toward the rear of the vehicle, thus increasing negative caster. Adding shims only at the rear will result in a more positive caster. There is usually a camber change when caster is adjusted. This means that camber must be readjusted after a caster change.

No special tools are used for caster correction work. Sometimes, however, a hydraulic ram may often be placed between the rear outer end of the lower control arm and a chain looped tightly around the frame. By expanding the ram, the lower control arm and other suspension parts may be corrected back into place. Hitting a curb too hard while angle parking will cause excessive negative caster at the right wheel. Using a hydraulic ram will help to re-establish the correct relationships. Do not use this method, however, if you can actually see bent or misshapen parts. Suspension parts which are visibly bent must be replaced.

r. Centering the Steering. After caster and camber have been adjusted, the steering gear and linkage should be adjusted. For the proper background you should review the material covered in Chapter 5 (Steering Gears and Linkages).

Make sure that the steering wheel is centered before the toe-in is adjusted. When the vehicle is traveling in a straight-ahead direction, certain factors are true with regard to the relation between the vehicle and the road. These factors are:

1) The rear wheels have approximately zero inches toe unless the rear axle housing is bent.

2) The steering wheel is in its position of high point; that is, in the correct, straight ahead driving position.

3) The front wheels are at zero inches toe.

These three factors are correlated by a process known as sighting the wheels. The process is the same regardless of the kind of rack used. It consists of the following steps:

1) Measure toe of the vehicle with either a toe bar or an alignment machine.

2) Center the steering wheel. Determine whether the steering wheel is in its correct position on the shaft. For full data refer again to Chapter 5.

3) Sight along the side of each front wheel, noting the amount of each rear wheel seen. From this observation determine which front wheel toes out or toes in more than the other.

4) Adjust the toe-in on the front wheel needing the most correction. Do this by turning sleeves on the tie rod. Be certain in this operation that you use the sleeve nearest the wheel you wish to adjust.

5) Resight the wheels. If the same amount of the rear wheel is not visible with the toe-in set, then adjust both sleeves equally until the wheels sight the same, keeping the steering wheel in the same straight ahead position.

s. Centering the Steering on the Visualiner. One rear wheel is set on zero degrees toe—or in a straight ahead position—as shown on the screen. To achieve this position, clamp a mirror to a rear

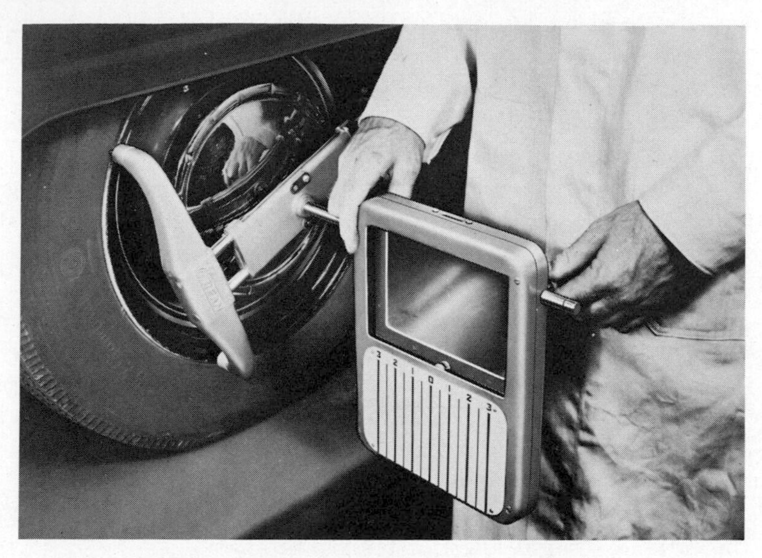

Fig. 25. Rear mirror installed on left rear wheel.
(John Bean Corp.)

wheel (usually the left rear wheel) in a manner similar to that used with regard to the front wheel. See Fig. 25.

A light beam is projected from the rear of the alignment head to the mirror mounted on the rear wheel. The mirror then projects an image in the shape of a cross on the screen. By turning the knob on the rear of the projection head, a rear wheel toe chart can be made to appear on the screen. See Fig. 26.

Before an accurate reading may be taken, the lateral run-out of the rear wheel must be taken into account. To compensate for

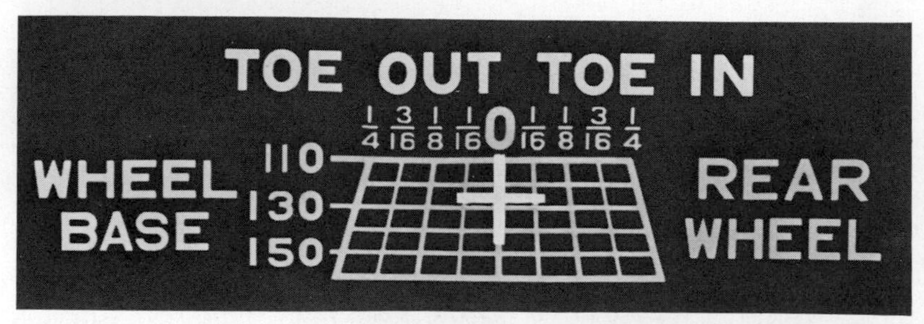

Fig. 26. The cross on the rear wheel toe chart shows the rear wheel is on zero or straight ahead.
(John Bean Corp.)

this factor, jack up the rear axle and rotate the left rear wheel. The cross on the screen will move on the left rear wheel chart if the wheel or axle shaft is bent. For example, if the cross moves from one-half inch toe-out to one-quarter inch toe-in, the total run-out is three-quarters of one inch. Rotate the wheel to split the total run-out. This maneuver will place the cross hair on one-eighth of one inch toe-out. Lower the wheel and remove the jack. Move the vehicle sideward on the alignment rack until the left rear wheel toe reads zero inches. See Fig. 26. The left rear wheel is now in the straight ahead position.

Adjust the left front wheel toe-in at zero inches by means of the tie rod adjusting sleeve. Then turn the tie rod adjusting sleeve on the right front wheel until it reads the toe-in specified by the vehicle manufacturer. Make certain the steering wheel is in the straight ahead position.

t. Recheck All the Nuts and Bolts You Have Loosened. Make certain they are tight. Remove the mirror assembly and push the vehicle off the turntable. Back the vehicle off the rack and road test it before delivering it to the customer.

In the foregoing procedure the corrections involved at each step were indicated. This same procedure will be used for both inspection and correction in your everyday work after you have an understanding of the material in this book.

Know how to interpret your diagnosis. Learn to remedy the faults you find to the satisfaction of your customer. Learn how to start with a known fault and, by a study of the conditions revealed in the course of an inspection, learn the specific remedies for specific faults. Learn also to make corrections without requiring costly and extensive rebuilding of the entire suspension system to create a "like new" situation. Be able to explain to an owner why his vehicle behaves in a certain way. These fine points of training, knowledge, and skill are but a few of the considerations of the accomplished wheel alignment specialist.

TRADE COMPETENCY TEST

1. What is the purpose of making a pre-alignment visual inspection before attempting correction? (pp. 186, 187)
2. What misalignment conditions may be indicated by tire wear? (pp. 188-191)

3. Why should a vehicle be road tested before checking for misalignment? (pp. 191, 192)
4. If worn suspension and steering parts are not repaired before an alignment job is done what may be the results? (p. 192)
5. How often should you check the wheel alignment equipment? (p. 192)
6. Why should springs be replaced in pairs? (p. 194)
7. How do you adjust front wheel bearings? (p. 194)
8. Why should the left front wheel have more positive camber, in most cases, than the right wheel? (p. 201)
9. What different types of adjustments may be used to control camber setting? (pp. 203-206)
10. Why is caster usually adjusted first during the alignment procedure? (p. 206)
11. What factors are found relative to the relationship between the vehicle and road when a properly aligned vehicle is traveling straight down the road? (p. 209)
12. What is meant by *sighting the wheel?* (p. 209)

CHAPTER 9

BRAKES

		PAGE
I.	Purpose of Brakes	213
II.	Factors Controlling the Stop	214
III.	How Brakes Stop the Vehicle	216
IV.	Construction of Brakes	216
V.	Self-Energization of Brake Shoes	221
VI.	Brake Shoe Actuating Mechanisms	224
VII.	Construction of Hydraulic Brake System	232
VIII.	Hand Brakes	238
IX.	Power Brakes	240

I. PURPOSE OF BRAKES

The purpose of the brakes on an automotive vehicle is to stop the vehicle, or to slow down its rate of travel, as required at any time during the operation of the vehicle. Whenever an automotive vehicle is in motion the safety of the operator, passengers, pedestrians, other vehicles, and public property depends upon the condition of the brakes with which that vehicle is equipped. The brakes on such a vehicle must be capable of stopping the vehicle quickly, reliably, at all times and under varying conditions, to avoid collisions and to permit the operator to retain control of the vehicle.

In many countries, and in many communities, regulations exist which require that vehicles be equipped with brakes which possess such definite performance characteristics. In many instances these standards are set by law. A number of communities require periodic brake examinations, carried out by qualified authorities, to insure the highest possible standards of safety.

Automotive vehicles are usually provided with two braking systems to conform to existing regulations. One is the service brakes, which operate on all four wheels and are applied through hydraulic pressure created by the operator applying foot pressure on the brake pedal. The second system is the hand or parking brakes which may operate the service brake shoes on the rear wheels only, through a hand lever and cable arrangement, or may, through the same linkage, operate a brake band contracting around a drum on the transmission shaft. In some vehicles this parking brake lever is arranged to be operated by foot pressure also.

II. FACTORS CONTROLLING THE STOP

The speed of the vehicle and the type and condition of the road are usually considered the chief factors which control the vehicle's stop. Actually, a number of factors are involved. They are:

a. Vehicle Speed and Load. Since stopping involves the absorption of energy, the greater the speed and the greater the vehicle load, the more the energy that must be absorbed to stop the vehicle.

b. Road Surface. The maximum work the brakes can do is to hold the wheels from turning. However, the quickest stop is made not with the wheels sliding, but with the wheels just ready to slide. The coefficient of friction between the road surface and the tire is highest just before the wheels start to slide. The coefficient of friction between the tire and the road varies for different types and conditions of road surfaces.

(1) *COEFFICIENT OF FRICTION. Friction is the resistance to motion which takes place when one body is moved upon another and can be defined generally as the force acting between two bodies at their surface contact so as to resist their sliding upon each other. The ratio of the force required to slide a body at constant velocity along a horizontal plane surface, to the weight of the body is called the coefficient of friction.*

c. Tire Tread. The condition of the tire tread is an important factor in controlling the stop. A new tread with adequate grooves between the rolling ribs provides a greater coefficient of friction than a smooth tire.

d. Hills. If the vehicle is traveling up a hill at the time of the stop, the force of gravity will assist the vehicle in making the stop. If a vehicle which is under load is traveling down a hill at the time of the stop, the force of gravity will tend to keep the vehicle moving, therefore increasing the braking effort required.

e. Number of Tires Braking. All wheels, which carry any part of the load, should be equipped with brakes in order to provide the maximum braking effort. Any part of the load being carried by a wheel not equipped with brakes will increase the time required for the stop. For this reason, most automotive vehicles are equipped with brakes at each wheel (four-wheel brakes).

f. Friction Between Brake Lining and Brake Drum. The ability of the brakes to prevent the wheels from turning is controlled by the coefficient of friction between the brake lining and the brake drum. Several types of materials having different coefficients of friction are in common use as brake linings. Grease-soaked or otherwise glazed linings may have either a tendency to slip over the brake drum surface rather than hold to it, or to cause the brake to grab.

g. Pressure Applied By Leverage. Another factor controlling the stop is the multiplication of the applied (driver pushing brake pedal) force by means of leverage. The increase over the applied physical force depends upon the ratio of levers between brake pedal and the brake shoes. This application of the laws of leverage applies equally to either mechanical or hydraulic brake systems.

h. Pressure Applied Through Energization. When the brake shoes are forced into contact with the rotating brake drum, there is a tendency for the shoe to follow the drum in the direction of rotation and thus to wedge the shoe more tightly against the drum. This factor is referred to as self-energization. Brake design makes use of this tendency to increase the applied pressure and thus reduce the physical effort required to apply the brakes. Location of the anchor pin is an important factor in self-energization.

i. Transfer of Load. The weights on both the front suspension and the rear axle are approximately equal in most vehicles when carrying average loads properly distributed. However, when the brakes are applied, there is a transfer of weight from the rear wheels to the front wheels, caused by the tendency of the vehicle to continue in its forward motion. The greater the deceleration (braking action), the greater the transference of weight from rear to front wheels. During the stop, the weight on the rear wheels is lessened, while the weight on the front wheels is increased by exactly the same amount. For this reason, brakes are designed so that the applied effort is greater on the front wheels than on the rear wheels, usually through the use of larger wheel cylinders.

j. Braking Force of Engine. The engine is used as a braking force, particularly when descending long grades. The braking effect of the engine is less in direct drive than it is in the lower gears.

III. HOW BRAKES STOP THE VEHICLE

The stopping distances shown in Table I are based on favorable road conditions and on average driver reaction time. Stopping distances will vary from those shown, depending on the type and condition of the road surface, the mechanical condition of the vehicle, and the variation of individual driver's reaction time.

TABLE 1. STOPPING DISTANCES

Vehicle Speed m.p.h.	Distance Traveled During Driver's Reaction Time	Distance Traveled After Application of Brakes	Total Stopping Distance
20	22 ft.	18 ft.	40 ft.
30	33 ft.	40 ft.	73 ft.
40	44 ft.	71 ft.	115 ft.
50	55 ft.	111 ft.	166 ft.
60	66 ft.	160 ft.	226 ft.
70	77 ft.	218 ft.	295 ft.
80	88 ft.	285 ft.	373 ft.

Brakes are designed to stop a vehicle within the indicated distances while it is carrying its rated load on average road surfaces.

Poor road conditions or an overloaded vehicle will also increase the stopping distance. Worn linings or drums, glazed linings, or grease-soaked linings lower the coefficient of friction, also contributing to increased stopping distances.

NOTE: The ideal lining is not necessarily the one with the highest coefficient of friction. Linings are selected according to the design of the brake and the particular vehicle on which they are to be used.

Poorly adjusted brake shoes prevent the full application of braking effort due to lack of full contact between shoe and drum. Lack of leverage, due to improper adjustment or wear, also prevents the full application of braking force.

IV. CONSTRUCTION OF BRAKES

Both front and rear wheel brakes used on passenger automobiles are of the internal expanding, hydraulically operated type. Hydraulic pressure operates pistons inside wheel cylinders to force the brake shoes into contact with the inside diameter of the brake drum, when the brakes are applied.

Certain parts are common to all passenger vehicle wheel brake

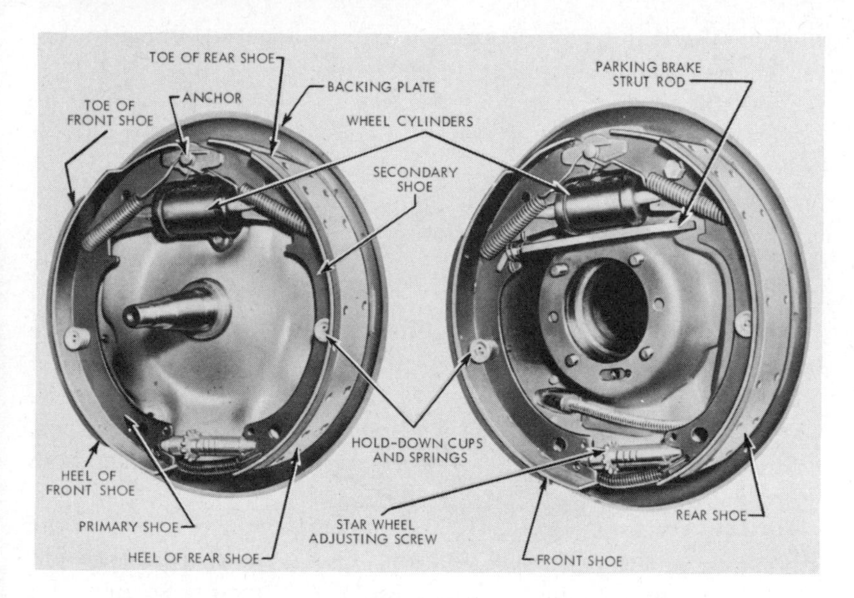

Fig. 1. Typical brake assembly.
(*Cadillac Div.—General Motors Corp.*)

assemblies. Included among these are a backing plate, brake shoe anchors, brake shoes, retracting springs, brake linings, brake drum, wheel cylinder or cylinders and adjusting mechanisms. Figure 1 illustrates a typical brake assembly with the drum removed.

a. Backing Plate. The backing plate, usually of ribbed pressed-steel construction, is rigidly bolted to the rear wheel axle housing for the rear brakes and to the steering knuckle assembly for the front brakes. This plate acts as a support for the anchor pins, wheel cylinder, retracting springs, adjusting mechanism and brake shoes. The brake backing plate carries the entire braking load for each wheel. It also forms a dust shield for the operating parts of each wheel brake.

b. Anchors. Anchor bolts (pins) provide a means of mounting the brake shoes to the backing plate and provide a pivot for the brake shoe. On some vehicles a single anchor bolt may be used for both shoes, while on others one anchor bolt may be used for each shoe. Some anchors are adjustable to permit adjustment of the anchored end of the shoe toward or away from the drum, to secure proper clearance between brake shoe and drum.

c. Brake Shoes. Brake shoes are of a T-section steel construction which is curved to fit the drum. A frictional material (brake lining) is either riveted or cemented (bonded) to the brake shoe.

One end of the brake shoes are attached to or held against the anchor bolts or pin. At the opposite end of the shoes, pressure is applied (by the wheel cylinder on passenger vehicles) to force the shoes outward toward the drum. The shoes and lining are free to move outward to the drum, pivoting on the anchor bolt or bolts. Springs or spring clips of various designs hold the shoes in proper position on the backing plate.

Brake shoes are classified as either *primary* or *secondary* brake shoes. The primary brake shoe is the first shoe in the direction of forward wheel rotation from the point of brake shoe actuation (wheel cylinder). The opposite shoe is, of course, the secondary shoe. In a brake assembly using two wheel cylinders both brake shoes are primary shoes.

d. Retracting Springs. Retracting springs are used to return the brake shoes to their released position. This is necessary to prevent any possible drag. In hydraulic brakes, the retracting springs also return the hydraulic fluid to the master cylinder. The location and number of retracting springs vary with the design of the brake. See Fig. 1.

e. Brake Lining. A molded type of brake lining (friction material) is used on automotive vehicles. The basic material of all brake lining is asbestos, used because of its high heat-resistant quality. Since the amount of work done by the secondary brake shoe is usually greater than the amount of work done by the primary shoe, the use of lining with a different coefficient of friction on each shoe is not uncommon.

f. Wheel Cylinders. Hydraulically operated wheel cylinders are used to force the brake shoe assembly into contact with the drum. Common practice is to use one wheel cylinder with two opposed pistons at each wheel. Each piston moves one brake shoe. If two separate wheel cylinders are used at one wheel, each wheel cylinder contains only one piston and operates one shoe.

g. Brake Drums. Brake drums are usually made of cast iron fused to a pressed steel disk. This type of construction usually has cooling ribs cast around the drum providing the assembly with a better dissipation of heat. The drum, when mounted, is accurately centered on the hub and wheel. The friction surface of the drum is machined to present a smooth surface to the brake lining. The inner edge of the drum generally has an annular groove located between two flanges to assist in keeping dirt and moisture from entering the brake mechanism. A coil spring (dampener spring) is sometimes used around the outside of the drum to reduce brake noises.

Fig. 2. Cast aluminum alloy brake with cast iron liner.
(Pontiac Div.—General Motors Corp.)

Another type of brake drum construction is that made of cast aluminum alloy with a cast iron liner, as shown in Fig. 2. This type of installation has ribs and fins to help dissipate heat to the air.

h. Disk Brakes. A disk brake was used for some time on one American made automobile. The construction and operation of the disk brake is somewhat different than that of the shoe brake. The disk brake utilizes two pressure plates, mounted back to back, within a rotating brake housing. A cross-sectional view of a typical disk brake is shown in Fig. 3. The pressure plates are flat disks which have brake lining segments fastened to their outer faces. The brake housing is constructed in two halves which are bolted together. This type of brake uses two wheel cylinders, each of which actuates the outer disk when the brakes are applied.

During application, the brake cylinder push rods move the outer pressure plate forward. This movement forces a series of steel balls which are located between the two plates, to move up ramps on

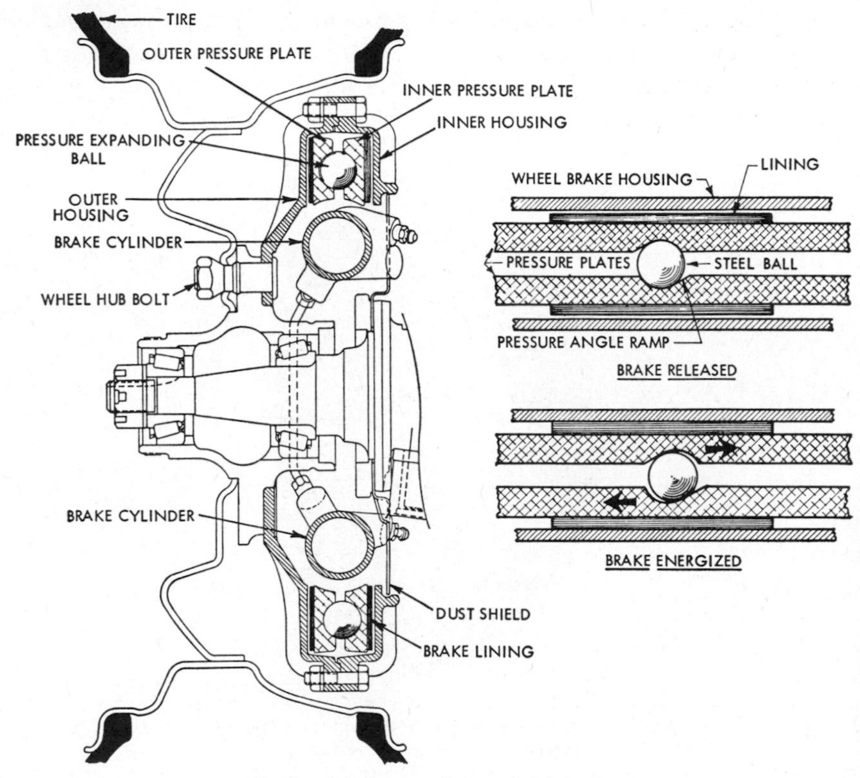

Fig. 3. Cross sectional view of disk brake.
(Chrysler Corp.)

the inner faces of both plates. The balls force the pressure plates apart so that the brake linings contact the inner faces of the brake housing. In the released position, the steel balls are in the bottom of the ramps between the pressure plates.

The disk brake is self-energizing in that when the outer pressure plate contacts the brake housing, it tends to rotate with the housing. This forward movement forces the steel balls further up the ramps to provide a greater pressure on both plates against the inner faces of the brake housing.

Disk brakes are self-adjusting so that the proper clearance between the brake linings and the brake housing is always maintained regardless of lining wear. When the brakes are released, the brake return springs move the outer pressure plate back toward its released position, that is, away from the brake housing. Automatic adjusters, mounted on the inside face of the inner pressure plate, stop the return movement of the outer pressure plate at a point which compensates for lining wear.

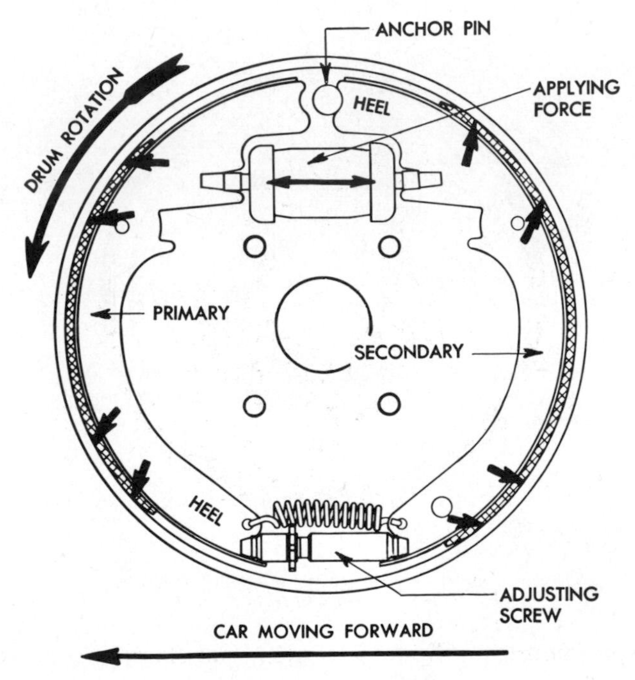

Fig. 4. Energizing action.
(*Buick Div.—General Motors Corp.*)

V. SELF-ENERGIZATION OF BRAKE SHOES

When brakes are applied and the lining contacts the drum, the shoes have a tendency to follow the drum and rotate with it. After the initial movement, the anchor prevents further movement at the anchored end of the shoe. The unanchored end, however, still tries to rotate with the drum, wedging the shoes more tightly against the drum, Fig. 4. The utilization of this frictional force (wedging the shoes more tightly against the drum) to increase the pressure of the shoes against the drum is called a *self-energizing* action. This action is utilized to lessen the physical effort necessary to apply the brakes. Various degrees of self-energization are employed, the degree of energization depending on the design of the brake. When the utilization of the force in one shoe is used to apply the opposite shoe, the applying force is known as *servo* action. If self-energizing force is applied in both forward and reverse motions of the vehicle the brake may be called a duo-servo brake instead of a fully energized brake.

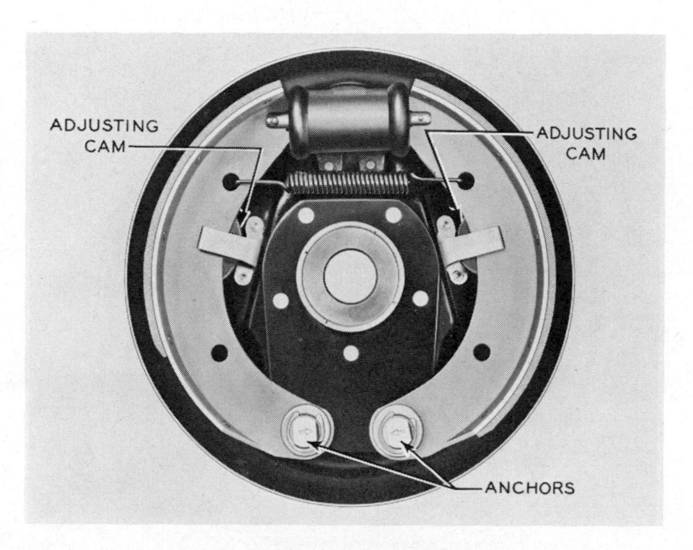

Fig. 5. Semi-energized brake assembly.
(*Plymouth Div.—Chrysler Corp.*)

a. Semi-Energizing Brake. In the semi-energized brake illustrated in Fig. 5, the brake shoes are anchored at one end to the backing plate. In some cases both shoes are anchored to one anchor bolt, while in other designs each shoe is anchored individually to its own anchor bolt. The shoes in brake assemblies of this type are not free to float within the drum. The front (primary) shoe tends to move outward with the drum, but is restrained by the anchor. The revolving drum tends to force the rear (secondary) shoe inward away from the drum. Because of these actions the brake lining of the primary shoe generally wears faster than the brake lining of the secondary shoe.

Most anchor bolts used with this type of brake are in the form of an eccentric, relocating the brake shoe closer to the drum when necessary. In addition, adjustable cams are located on the backing plate to permit the shoes to be moved closer to the drum to compensate for normal lining wear.

In the semi-energizing brake illustrated in Fig. 6, often referred

Fig. 6. Total contact brake assembly.
(*Dodge Div.—Chrysler Corp.*)

to as a total contact brake, the shoes are free to float within the drum but are not interconnected. Therefore, one shoe does not assist in applying the other. The end of the shoe opposite the wheel cylinder is inserted between two support plates and sits against an anchor. By permitting the shoe to float it is possible to obtain a more uniform contact between the lining and drum.

An adjusting cam at each shoe is used to compensate for brake lining wear.

b. Fully Energizing Brake (Duo-Servo Brake). In the fully energized brake, the ends of both shoes are coupled together by an adjusting mechanism, as shown in Fig. 7. As the lining contacts the drum, the friction between the lining and the rotating drum moves the forward (primary) shoe downward against the adjusting screw mechanism, which acts as a link transmitting the movement of the primary shoe to the lower end of the rear (secondary) shoe. With the upper end of the rear shoe held stationary by the anchor bolt (pin), the rear shoe lining is wedged against the drum. This wedging action, due to frictional force, imparts the self-energizing action to the braking effort, and thereby decreases the effort required by the driver to stop the vehicle.

The adjusting mechanism connecting the heel ends of the shoes

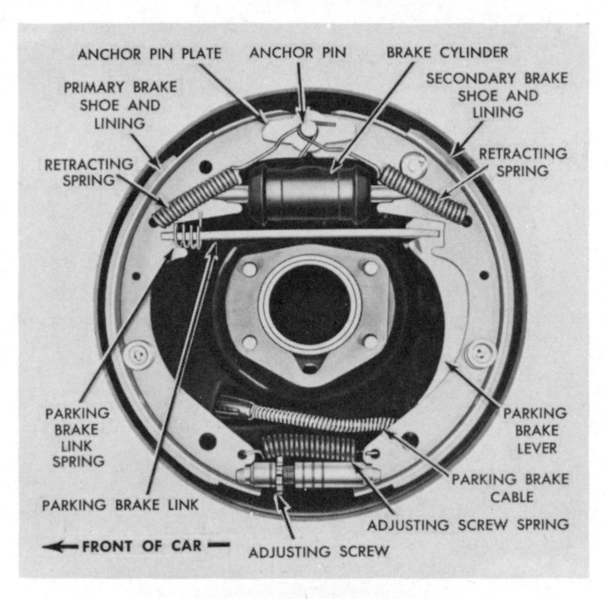

Fig. 7. Fully energized brake assembly.
(Ford Div.—Ford Motor Company)

is in the form of a screw, nut, and sleeve. The nut is used to adjust the clearance between the lining and the drum. The anchor bolt or pin may be movable to permit the adjusting and the toe end of the shoes.

VI. BRAKE SHOE ACTUATING MECHANISMS

Several methods of applying the brake shoe assembly to the drum have been used in the past. The brake shoes on all present day passenger vehicles are actuated by hydraulic pressure. The hand brake usually is applied by mechanical means through the use of cables and levers.

a. Mechanical Brakes. Older passenger vehicles used a system of levers, rods and/or cables to create a mechanical advantage for expanding the brake shoes when the driver depressed the brake pedal. This was known as the mechanical brake system, the components of which are shown in Fig. 8. The rods and cables were usually adjustable to permit removal of slack or free play, keeping the levers at the correct angle. When the brakes were fully applied, the lever angle was not to be at greater than a right angle to the rod in direc-

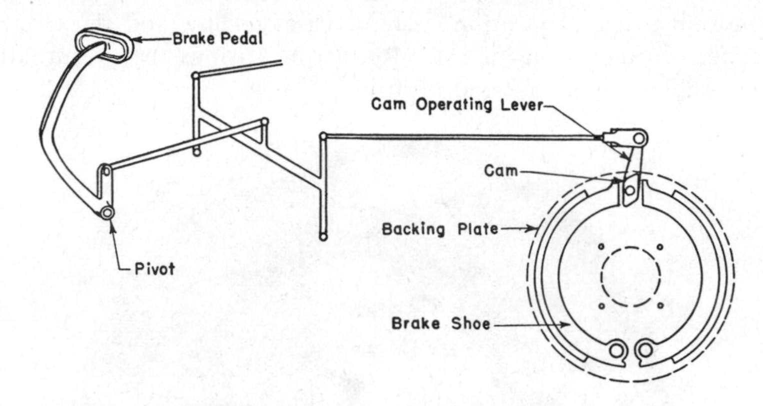

Fig. 8. Components of a mechanical brake system.

tion of travel. A cam, toggle, or wedge, located between the ends of the brake shoes, was used to expand the shoe assembly. Various types of adjustments located within the brake assembly were used to adjust the lining to brake drum clearance.

b. Electric Brakes. The present usage of electric brakes is confined primarily to house trailers. The use of electricity to operate the brakes of a detachable unit permits a simplified hook-up between the two units. An electric cable from the brake controller (rheostat) in the vehicle to a detachable plug connector at the trailer hitch provides a convenient coupling for separating the control circuit from the trailer brake circuit.

The brake shoes are actuated by an electromagnet which is attached to the brake backing plate. As the control lever of the controller (rheostat) is moved toward the apply position, current flows through the electromagnet energizing the magnet. The magnetic field developed causes the magnet to be shifted which in turn moves the brake shoe actuating mechanism. The actuating mechanism may be in the form of a lever operated cam or a cam which is shifted by the revolving of the armature. As more current is supplied to the magnet, more force is developed on the actuating mechanism.

One type of electric brake is illustrated in Fig. 9. An armature (in this case a metal ring which revolves to complete a circuit) (1) revolves with the drum. As current is supplied to the electromagnet (2), the magnet attempts to cling to the armature which causes the magnet to shift, forcing the cam (3) against the end of the brake shoes. This action applies the brake. When the control is moved to the off position current ceases to flow and the electromagnet becomes demagnetized. Retracting springs then return the brake shoes to their released position.

Fig. 9. Electric brake assembly.

c. Air Brakes. Air brakes are used on most heavy duty trucks and buses. In an air brake system, compressed air is employed to actuate the brake mechanism. Air pressure in a closed system is transmitted equally in all directions, the same as fluid pressure in a hydraulic brake system.

The brake mechanism is the same as that used in a hydraulic brake system except that a cam for actuating the shoes is located between the ends of the shoes in place of a hydraulic wheel cylinder.

The air brake system consists of a compressor, a governor, a reservoir, a brake control valve, a brake chamber containing a dia-

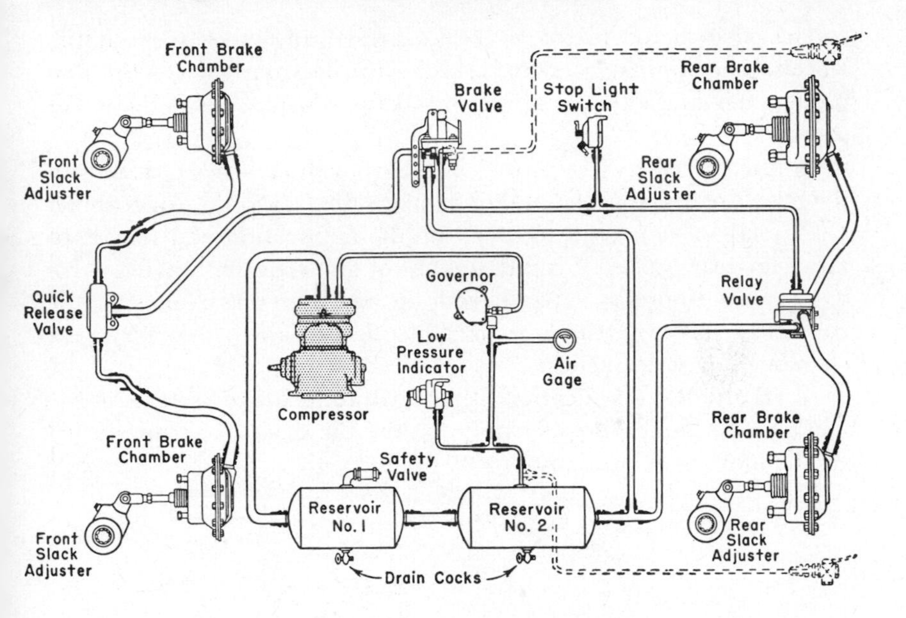

Fig. 10. Air brake system.

phragm, a quick-release valve, and a relay valve. Figure 10 illustrates a typical air brake system.

The engine driven, piston type air compressor supplies air under pressure to the reservoir for storage.

A governor regulates the pressure in the reservoir and prevents the building up of excessive pressure in the system. The reservoir is usually in the form of a welded steel tank designed to withstand pressure greatly in excess of the pressure required to operate the system. A safety valve is incorporated within the system (usually located at the tank) to relieve air pressure when it reaches a predetermined high.

The brake control valve is placed in the air line between the reservoir and the lines leading to the individual wheel brakes. When the brake control valve is in the applied position, air under high pressure from the reservoir is admitted to the diaphragm in the brake chamber at each wheel. In the off position, the air pressure from the reservoir is cut off and the lines are opened to the atmosphere. The valve is so designed as to permit controlled application of the brakes.

The brake chambers are equipped with a movable diaphragm

connected by a rod to the brake shoe operating mechanism at the wheels. The admission of air pressure to the front side of the diaphragm moves the diaphragm and linkage which actuates the brake shoes.

A quick release valve is used in the front brake lines to speed up the release of air from the brake chambers directly to the atmosphere.

A relay valve is used to speed up the application and release of air at the rear brakes. A small amount of air from the brake control valve opens the relay valve directly to the reservoir, by-passing the control valve, permitting a more direct flow of air to the rear brake chambers for faster action.

d. Hydraulic Application. In a hydraulic brake system, movement of the brake shoe assembly against the drum is accomplished by the movement of a column of liquid.

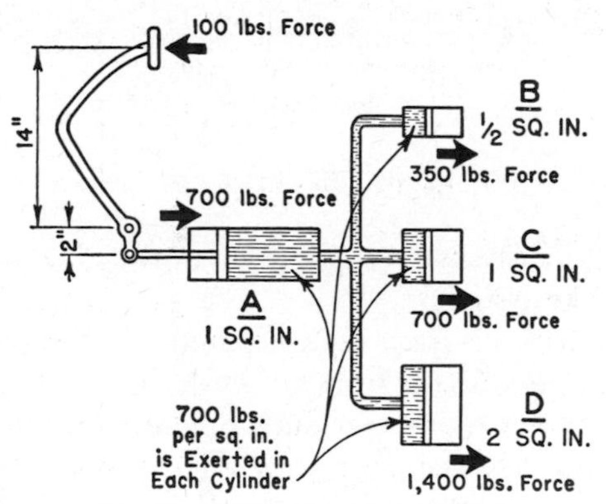

Fig. 11. Hydraulic brake principle.

Before attempting to describe the hydraulic braking system in detail, it is necessary to take into account two important elementary principles of hydraulics:

(1) No liquid can be appreciably compressed. To all intent and purposes a column of liquid confined in a tube represents a solid linkage, when pressure is applied to the liquid. The pressure is transmitted just as though the liquid was a solid rod.

(2) The pressure in every part of a hydraulic system is the same. When pressure is applied to a column of liquid, confined within the system, that same pressure exerted by the piston on the liquid is transmitted equally in all directions.

Four cylinders of various diameters are shown in Fig. 11. The cylinders are connected by means of suitable tubing and the entire system is filled with liquid (hydraulic brake fluid). The piston in cylinder A, called the *master* cylinder, is linked directly to the brake pedal. The other cylinders in this system are called the *wheel cylinders*.

If a force of 100 lbs. is exerted on the brake pedal, the resultant force on the master cylinder piston will be 700 lbs. This increase in pressure is due to a mechanical advantage ratio of 7 to 1, since the length of the lever between the pedal and the pivot point of the brake pedal is 7 times as long as the length of the lever below the pivot point.

Therefore, the piston moves along the cylinder A with a force of 700 lbs. If the area of the piston is 1 sq. in., the pressure throughout the system will be 700 × 1 or 700 lbs. per sq. in. (psi).

Since the pressure is equal in all directions, wherever the lines lead, the pressure will be 700 lbs. per sq. in. In case of cylinder B having ½ sq. in. area, the force will be 700 × ½ or 350 lbs. Cylinder C, having the same area as cylinder A, will exert the same force of 700 lbs. The force in cylinder D, however, which has an area of 2 sq. in., will be 700 × 2 or 1,400 lbs.

By varying the size of the cylinder it is possible to distribute the available pressure throughout the system as desired.

In Fig. 12 the hydraulic brake principle is shown. In this system the brake shoe assembly is moved in contact with the drum by pistons, in the wheel cylinders, connected directly to the shoes by links.

When the brake pedal is depressed, the master cylinder piston is moved within the master cylinder, putting the hydraulic brake fluid under pressure. This hydraulic pressure is transmitted through the connecting tubing to the wheel cylinders, forcing the wheel cylinder pistons outward.

The pressure on the wheel cylinder pistons forces the brake shoes outward, overcoming the tension of the retracting springs and bringing the lining into contact with the drum.

When the driver removes his foot from the brake pedal, the strong action of the retracting (return) springs pull the brake shoe assemblies back to their normal released position so that they are clear of the drums. The return action of the foot pedal also permits the master cylinder piston to return to its original position, thus leaving space in the master cylinder for the return of the fluid which has been pushed into the lines. The strong action of the brake shoe retracting springs enables the wheel cylinder pistons to force the fluid back along the lines and into the master cylinder.

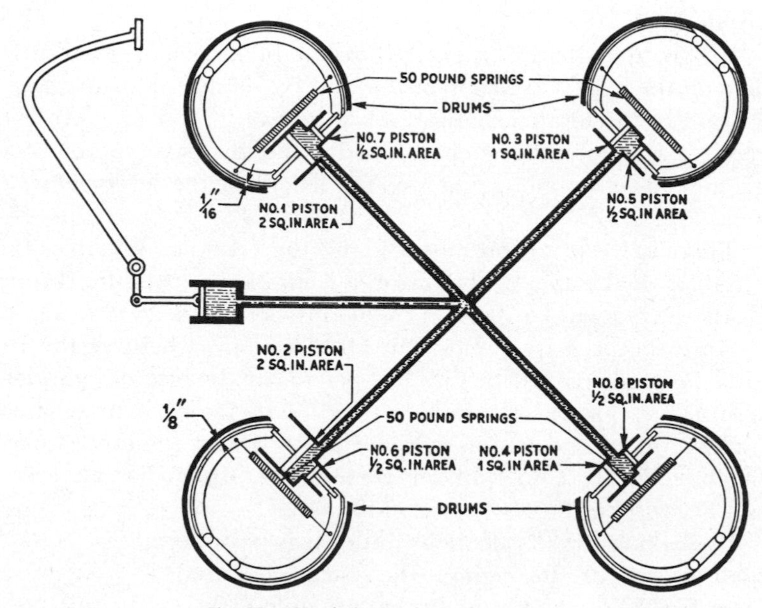

Fig. 12. Simple hydraulic brake system.

By using stepped cylinders (having one piston larger than the other) at the wheel cylinders, the applied force can be distributed differently to the two shoes. The stepped cylinder design is shown in Fig. 12. Also by using larger cylinders at the front wheels than at the rear wheels, a greater portion of the braking force can be distributed to the front wheel brakes. This compensates for the transfer of weight to the front wheels when stopping. Larger wheel cylinders are often used for the primary shoe so as to gain full advantage of the energizing action in the forward direction.

A typical hydraulic braking system is shown in Fig. 13. This system is a full-energizing system, the shoes being linked together at the bottom with an adjusting mechanism.

While liquids cannot be appreciably compressed this is not true of air or gases. A hydraulic system must be tightly sealed to withstand the pressures developed in the system and to keep out air and moisture. Sealing of the various cylinders is accomplished by the

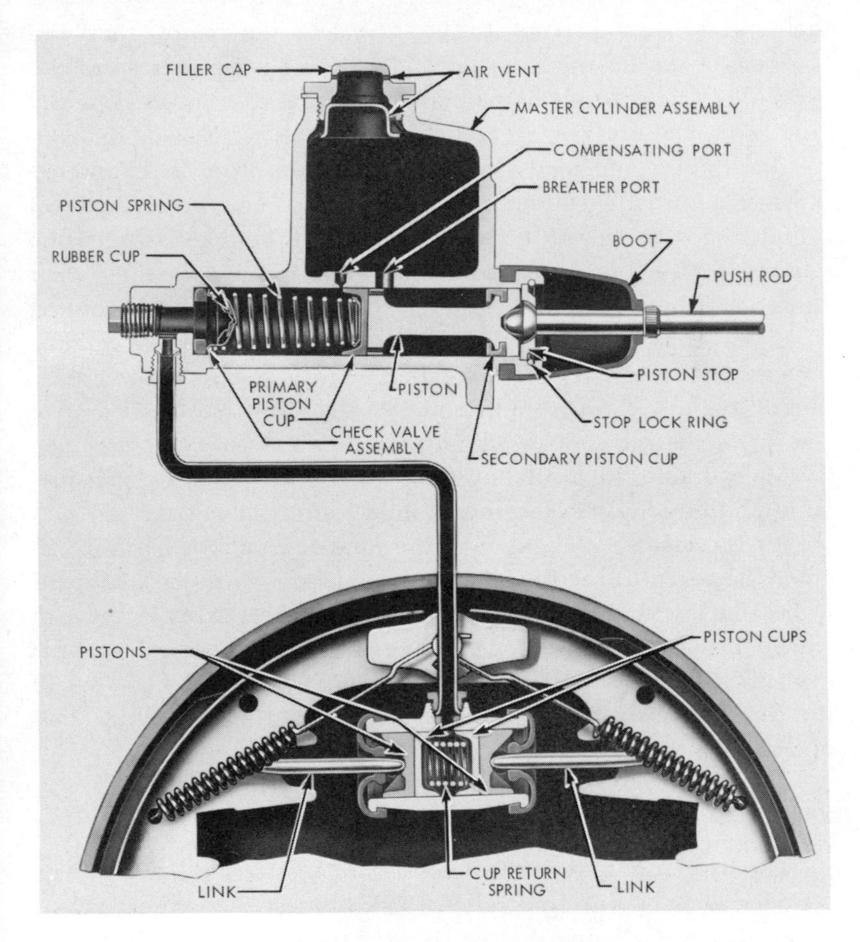

Fig. 13. Typical hydraulic brake system.
(Pontiac Div.—General Motors Corp.)

use of rubber cups on the compression side of the piston. These cups expand snugly against the cylinder bore when pressure is applied within the cylinder.

Since liquids cannot be compressed, any hydraulic pressure within the system must be applied pressure. When the brake shoes have been retracted back to their release position against the stops on the backing plate, the spring pressure is against the stop and not against the fluid. Likewise, when the movement of the fluid within the system stops, the valves in the master cylinder seat and their springs apply pressure to the valve seat—not against the fluid.

Some of the heat generated by the brakes is transferred to the hydraulic fluid, causing it to expand. When the brakes cool the fluid cools, and also contracts. If no provisions were made the contracting fluid would tend to create a pressure drop. This lowered pressure in the system allows air to enter the system around the wheel cylinder cups. However, the master cylinder is designed to keep the released pressure in the system about seven pounds greater than atmospheric pressure. This pressure is referred to as residual pressure.

Likewise, as the brake fluid contracts due to cooling, its volume become less. When the pressure in the lines drops below atmospheric pressure by an amount equal to the effort required to open the valves, the valves open, permitting more fluid to enter the lines.

All hydraulic tubes or hoses are fastened together by pressure-withstanding couplings to prevent fluid loss or the entry of air.

Air is present in the system at the time of assembly. Air also can enter the system if the fluid level of the master cylinder is allowed to become low. Valves are provided at each wheel cylinder through which this air may be expelled when the valve is opened and the brake pedal is operated, which will force the fluid and air out of the lines. Removing air from the system is called bleeding. This operation is described in Chapter 10.

VII. CONSTRUCTION OF HYDRAULIC BRAKE SYSTEM

The hydraulic brake system consists of a master cylinder, wheel cylinder, and the lines and hoses which connect the various parts.

a. Master Cylinder. Figure 14 illustrates a typical hydraulic brake master cylinder. It consists of two main chambers: the cylinder in which the piston operates, and an upper fluid reservoir. The reservoir permits additional fluid to enter into or return from the lines to maintain a constant volume when the fluid is affected by expansion (heat) or contraction (cold). In addition, any seepage of fluid, due to wear at sealed points, is compensated for by the reservoir.

The master cylinder piston is shaped like a spool and when in the released position as shown in Fig. 14, the space around its center is kept full of fluid which enters through the inlet or bypass

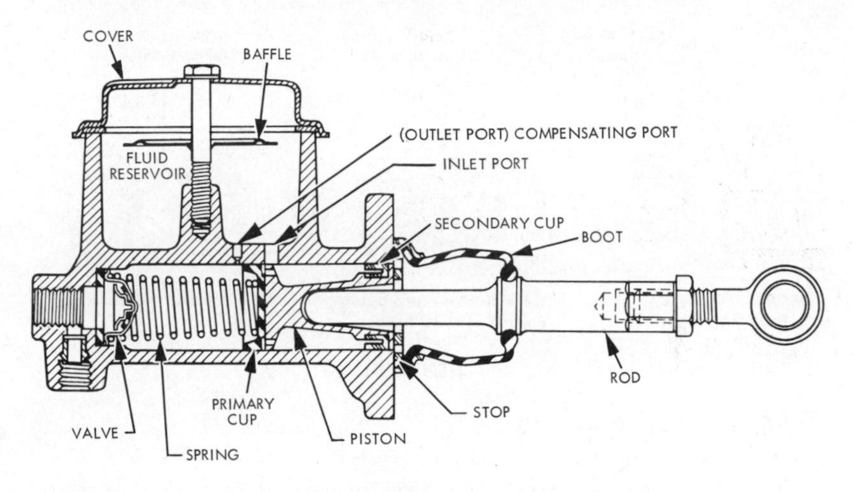

Fig. 14. Master cylinder piston in released position.
(*Plymouth Div.—Chrysler Corp.*)

port. A rubber cup which acts as a seal is provided at each end of the piston.

The rubber cup at the return spring end of the piston is called the primary cup and is designed to form a seal as the piston is moved forward toward the fluid outlet. A two-way fluid check valve is located at the cylinder outlet. The rubber cup mounted on the piston at the brake pedal rod end serves to prevent leakage of fluid at this point. This cup is called the secondary cup.

The pedal rod is connected to the foot pedal. A rubber boot over the back end of the master cylinder and around the pedal rod prevents dirt from coming in contact with the cylinder wall. When pressure is applied to the brake pedal, the pedal rod forces the master cylinder piston forward against the return spring. As the piston moves, it pushes the fluid through the small compensating (outlet) port into the reservoir. When the piston cup has moved sufficiently to cover the compensating port, the only remaining outlet through which the fluid can flow is the fluid check valve which leads into the hydraulic lines. The pressure exerted by the fluid forces the fluid check valve open against the tension of a small spring or diaphragm and fluid is forced into the lines. The pressure thus transmitted is exerted on the wheel cylinder pistons which forces the brake shoe assembly into contact with the drum.

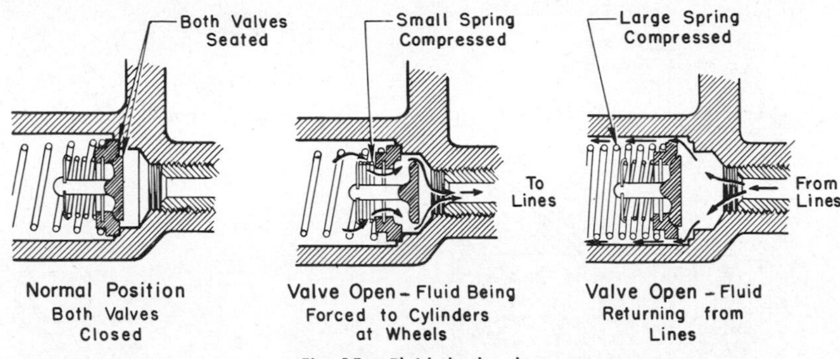

Fig. 15. Fluid check valve.

Figure 15 illustrates the action of the fluid check valve. Actually two valves incorporated within one unit are involved.

The fluid pressure exerted during brake application moves the small valve off its seat and fluid passes around the valve and into the lines.

When the brakes are released, the brake pedal is returned to its normal position by the brake pedal retracting spring. The master cylinder piston is returned to the released position by its return spring. This same spring holds the control valve momentarily closed, preventing the return of fluid from the lines to the master cylinder. As the piston moves away from the fluid check valve, the primary cup collapses, allowing the fluid from around the center of the piston to flow through holes in the head of the piston and into cylinder. The action of the powerful retracting springs on the brake shoes forces the fluid back through the lines and into the master cylinder. The master cylinder return spring, however, presses against a large valve and in order to enter the cylinder bore, the fluid from the lines must overcome the tension of the piston return spring and lift the large valve from its seat.

When the brake shoe retracting springs have returned the brake shoe assemblies to their stops, movement of the fluid in the lines also stops. However, the large valve has closed before the pressure in the system reaches zero, thereby maintaining residual pressure.

The master cylinder piston is returned very quickly to its released position, and since the fluid is slow in returning, a vacuum is created in the section of the cylinder vacated by the piston. When this vacuum is created within the cylinder, the rubber cup on the front end of the piston collapses. Therefore, atmospheric pressure on the fluid in the reservoir forces fluid to flow from the space around the piston through bleeder holes in the piston head, around the rubber cup, and into the front of the cylinder. See Fig. 16. The space around the spool portion of the piston is maintained full of fluid through the inlet port from the reservoir.

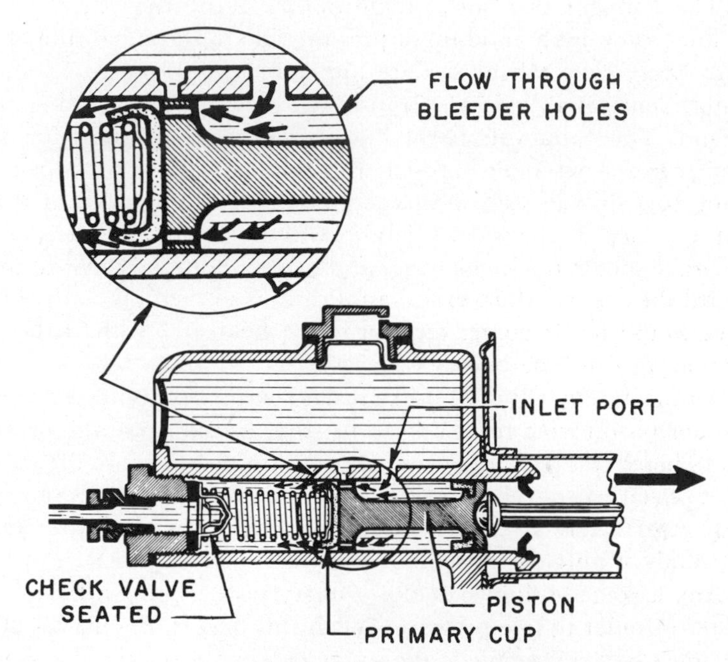

Fig. 16. Action of the master cylinder piston cup.
(*Buick Div.—General Motors Corp.*)

When the piston has been returned to its stop, the fluid in the lines is still being forced back into the master cylinder. The master cylinder, however, is already filled as explained and the excess fluid being returned by the tension of the brake shoe retracting springs is forced into the reservoir through the compensating port.

The tension exerted by the piston return spring closes the fluid check valve and maintains a residual pressure of about seven psi in the system. This pressure exerted on the lip of the wheel cylinder cups seals the system and prevents air from entering when the brakes are released.

If the clearance between the brake lining and drum is excessive so that a full stroke of the pedal will not bring about an effective pressure at the shoes, a quick release of the pedal will permit additional fluid to enter the cylinder. A second quick stroke of the pedal will force additional fluid into the lines. Sufficient fluid can usually be pumped into the system by this means until effective braking force is obtained. Adjusting the lining to drum clearance will usually correct a condition of this kind.

The compensating port, in addition to permitting the return of the fluid, prevents a build-up of pressure due to the expansion of the fluid. Every time the brakes are applied, heat is generated at the drums. Some of this heat is transferred to the fluid, causing it to expand. The extra volume of fluid represented by the expansion flows into the reservoir through the compensating port when the piston is against its stop. Without this compensating port, or if this port is blocked, the extra volume will overcome the tension of the brake shoe retracting springs and cause the brake shoes to move toward the drums. After several applications of the brakes, the brake shoes would be dragging, creating more heat and still further expansion, causing the brakes to seize.

An incorrectly adjusted brake pedal rod that prevents the master cylinder piston from returning to its stop, would cause the primary cup to block this port. Likewise, harmful fluids can cause the rubber cup to swell, effectively blocking the compensating port. Even with satisfactory fluids, it is possible for the cup to expand after many thousands of miles so as to block the port.

Any leakage of fluid past the primary piston cups will cause the master cylinder to lose pressure. When this occurs, the master cylinder must be disassembled, the cylinder surface cleaned and new rubber parts installed.

b. Wheel Cylinders. Each brake backing plate is equipped with one or two wheel cylinders connected to the master cylinder by means of hydraulic lines. A wheel cylinder having two opposed pistons is shown in Fig. 17. Each brake shoe either fits into a slot at the outer end of the piston, or is connected to the piston by a short connecting link. As the brake pedal is depressed, the master cylinder forces fluid along the brake lines and into the wheel cylinders, the fluid entering between the two pistons. Pressure is exerted between the two pistons, forcing the shoes and lining outward against the drum. Leakage of fluid is prevented by the rubber cups between the pistons and the fluid. A spring between the two piston cups keeps them firmly seated against the piston at all times. Each wheel cylinder is provided with a bleeder valve to permit the removal of any air in the hydraulic system. A rubber boot fits over each end of the cylinder to prevent dirt and foreign matter from entering the cylinder.

When it is desirable to have a greater pressure applied to one shoe, than to the other shoe, one end of the cylinder may be made larger and fitted with a larger piston. This is known as a step type of wheel cylinder.

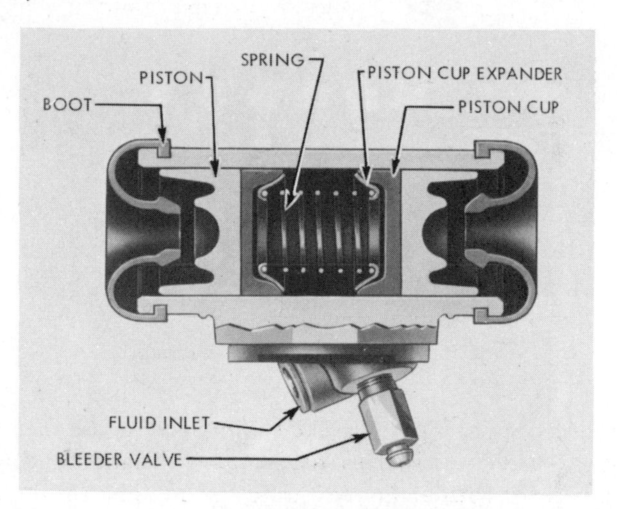

Fig. 17. Wheel cylinder with two pistons.
(Chevrolet Div.—General Motors Corp.)

Another type of hydraulic brake installation uses two single piston type of wheel cylinders on each backing plate, as shown in Fig. 18. The general operation is the same as on the installation having one wheel cylinder with two pistons. One end of the wheel cylinder is closed, and a hydraulic tube connects the two cylinders together. By using two wheel cylinders and locating the cylinders and shoe anchors directly opposite one another, both shoes become primary shoes and apply equal force to the drum.

Should fluid leak past the rubber piston cups and into the boots, the wheel cylinder must be disassembled, the cylinder wall cleaned and new rubber parts, after being lubricated with brake fluid, installed.

c. Brake Lines. Steel tubing which resists corrosion while withstanding high pressure is used between the master cylinder and frame connections, and between the rear flexible hose and rear wheel cylinders. Flexible hoses connect the tubing to the front wheel cylinders.

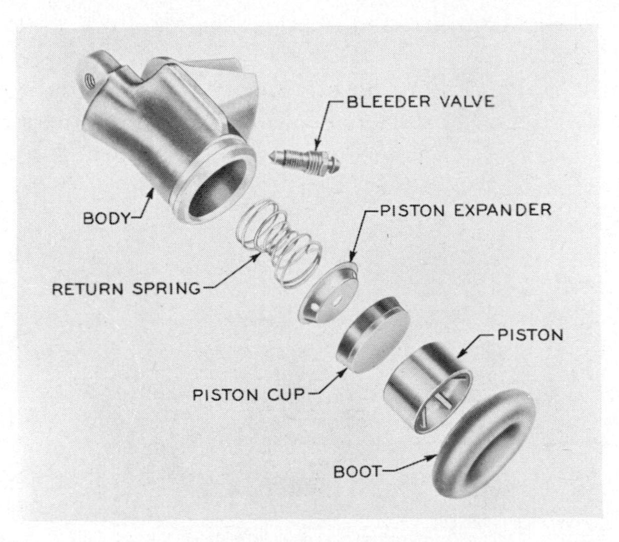

Fig. 18. Single piston type wheel cylinder.
(Dodge Div.—Chrysler Corp.)

If it is necessary to replace brake tubing, always use metal tubing which is designed to resist corrosion and withstand the high pressures encountered within the hydraulic system. The tubing must be double flared at the connections so as to produce a strong leak-proof joint. Low pressure copper tubing must not be used.

VIII. HAND BRAKES

Hand or parking brakes may be located either on the propeller shaft, or in the rear wheel brake assembly. The hand brake is actuated by means of cables and levers. The brakes are applied by either a hand or a foot lever in the driver's compartment.

a. Rear Wheel Brake. Figure 19 illustrates the cable and linkage arrangement used on the rear wheel type of hand brake. The control system consists of either a hand or a foot operated brake lever, brake cables which are enclosed within a conduit, and the brake shoe levers and struts which apply the rear brakes. The brake lever cable is connected to a sheave (equalizer) which is located at the center of the brake actuating cable. The actuating cable is provided with an adjusting nut to take up cable slack. One end of each brake cable is attached to the free lower end of a brake shoe lever which pivots on each secondary brake shoe. In each rear wheel and

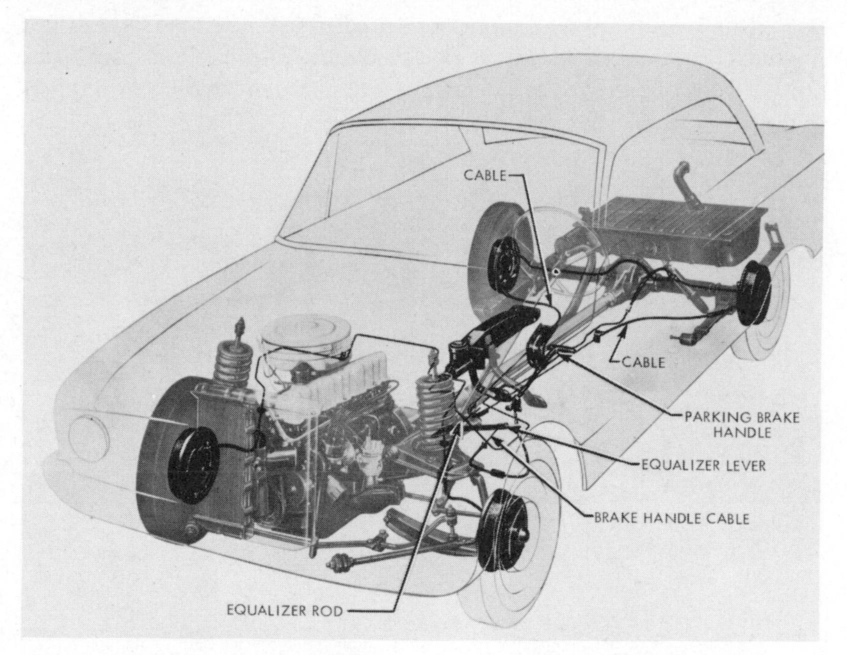

Fig. 19. Hand brake at rear wheels and the manual control system.
(Ford Div.—Ford Motor Company)

brake assembly, a strut is mounted between the secondary brake shoe lever and the front brake shoe. When the brake lever is actuated, the brake cables apply an equal pull to each brake shoe lever and strut forcing the brake shoe assembly into contact with the drum. Strut action against primary shoe causes servo-action, providing a good parking brake in the forward direction. However, the secondary shoe is not forced into the drum with sufficient pressure to give servo-action in the rear if the service brake is applied first and then the parking brake. The brake will hold in reverse. The brakes are adjusted by taking up cable slack.

b. Transmission Brake. An external contracting or an internal expanding brake is used as a parking brake on some automotive vehicles. In either type of installation, the brake is attached to the rear of the transmission and operates on a drum which is located at the front universal joint. In such a location, the brake has the advantage of operating through the rear axle gears; that is, it prevents rotation of the rear wheels by holding the transmission shaft.

The external contracting brake, as shown in Fig. 20, consists of a flexible steel band which encircles a drum. A flexible brake lining material is attached by rivets to the band. The band is contracted about the drum by means of a lever arrangement, which is actuated by a cable when the parking brake is applied.

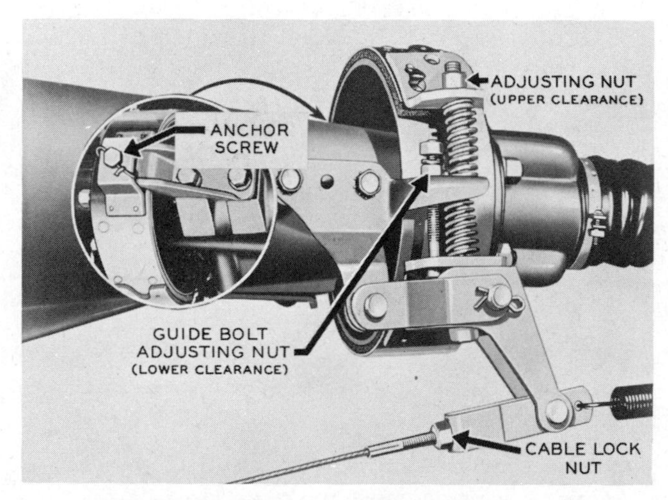

Fig. 20. External contracting brake.
(Plymouth Div.—Chrysler Corp.)

The cable arrangement for applying the brake is the same as the one used for the rear wheel type of hand brake. A clevis on one end of the cable is adjustable to permit the removal of cable slack.

The internal shoe type of transmission hand brake is illustrated in Fig. 21. It is controlled in the same manner as the external band parking brake. The actuating lever and strut arrangement is the same as that used on the rear wheel parking brake assembly.

When making an adjustment on either type of transmission brake, reduce the clearance between the brake lining and the brake drum to the point where there is a minimum of clearance; that is, almost but not quite to the point of contact.

IX. POWER BRAKES

For quick stops and severe braking, considerable pressure must be exerted on the brake pedal. The higher the speed of the vehicle and the greater its load, the more the effort that is required to stop the vehicle.

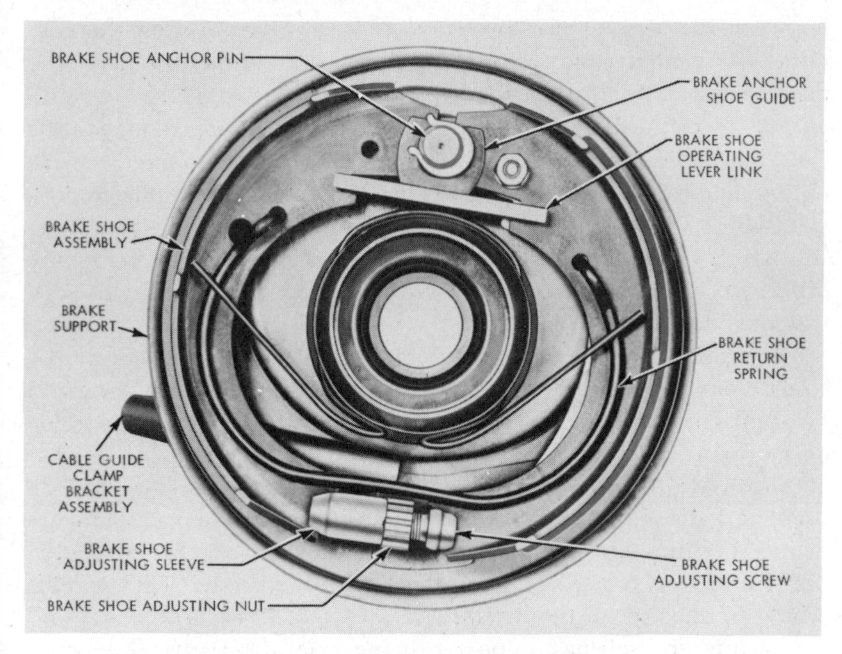

Fig. 21. Internal shoe type of internal transmission hand brake.
(Plymouth Div.—Chrysler Corp.)

In a hydraulic brake system there are limitations as to the size of the master and wheel cylinders which can be practically employed. Furthermore, the physical strength of the driver limits the amount of force which can be applied. These factors restrict the brake shoe to brake drum pressures obtainable.

To increase or boost the braking force, automobile manufacturers have made available vacuum assisted brake systems which are called *power brakes*. Different makes and designs of power brakes are on the market, but basically they all operate in the same manner. When the brake pedal is depressed, a valve arrangement is actuated, and engine vacuum from the intake manifold is then applied to one side of a diaphragm, bellows, or piston while atmospheric pressure is applied to the other side. Since the pressure is greater on the one side of the diaphragm, bellows or piston, it is then forced to the vacuum side. This movement assists (in varying degrees depending on the particular system) in supplying hydraulic pressure through the brake fluid to the different wheel cylinders.

a. Vacuum. When the pressure existing within a container is less than the atmospheric pressure (14.7 psi) surrounding the container—a vacuum condition then exists within the container. The measurement of vacuum is the difference between the pressure *within* the container and the pressure of the atmosphere *outside* the container. Vacuum is commonly measured in inches of mercury, with the reading representing the number of inches the atmospheric pressure will lift a column of mercury in its endeavor to flow into the container. Inches of mercury is merely a means of expressing the difference between the pressure within the container and the pressure outside the container.

If a container was completely emptied of air, the resultant pressure differential would be 14.7 pounds per square inch, which would be approximately 30 inches of mercury. As an example, an engine develops 15 inches of vacuum (comparable here to 15 inches of mercury), this 15 inches of vacuum would represent a pressure of 7.35 psi—one half of the value of atmospheric pressure since 30 inches of mercury equals 14.7 psi. If this vacuum was applied to a diaphragm having an area of 50 square inches a force of 367.5 pounds would be exerted on the diaphragm ($50 \times 7.35 = 367.5$).

Vacuum in itself has no power, being a negative valve. Any work done as a result of a vacuum or a partial vacuum is actually done by the pressure or weight of the atmosphere as it fills up the space where the lower pressure existed.

In the case of a power brake cylinder, the amount of work the unit will do is dependent upon how much engine vacuum, obtained from the intake manifold, is present on one side of the diaphragm, bellows, or piston and the area of the diaphragm, bellows, or piston.

The power brake cylinder may be either air or vacuum suspended. If the cylinder is air suspended, atmospheric pressure is present on both sides of the diaphragm, bellows, or piston until the brake pedal is depressed. In the applied position atmospheric pressure is cut off on one side of the diaphragm, bellows, or piston (brake pedal depressed) and vacuum is applied to the same side. Atmospheric pressure then forces the diaphragm, bellows, or piston toward the vacuum side.

If the cylinder is vacuum suspended, vacuum is present on both sides of the diaphragm or piston until the brake pedal is depressed. In the applied position (brake pedal depressed), vacuum is cut off on one side of the diaphragm or piston and atmospheric pressure is applied to the same side. One side of the diaphragm or piston now

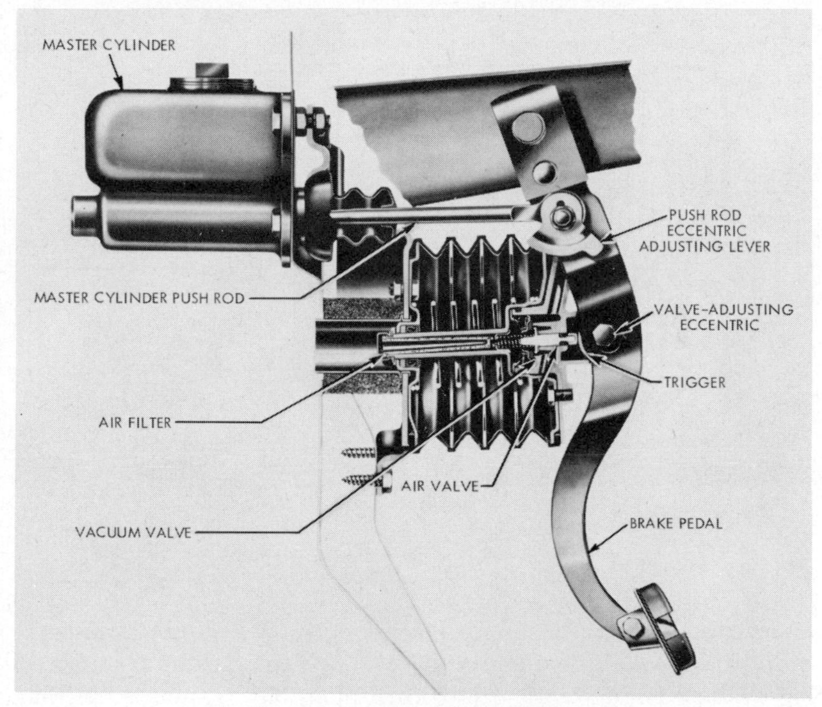

Fig. 22. Bellows type pedal-assist power brake.
(*Ford Div.—Ford Motor Company*)

has more pressure applied to it than the other side of the diaphragm or piston; therefore, atmospheric pressure forces the diaphragm or piston toward the side which has the least pressure, the vacuum side.

b. Power Brake Operation. The power brake unit involves the master cylinder and linkage only. Other parts of the brake system are usually like those in conventional brakes. Two external lines are generally connected to the power brake assembly, one of which is a vacuum connection to the intake manifold (vacuum reservoir on some installations); the other being a hydraulic connection leading into the hydraulic brake system.

On some installations a vacuum reservoir is inserted between the power unit and the intake manifold. The purpose of the reservoir is to make vacuum available for a short time to the booster unit, if the vehicle must make a stop without the engine running such as when it is being pushed or towed. Also, the reservoir maintains a uniform vacuum within the system should engine vacuum drop off

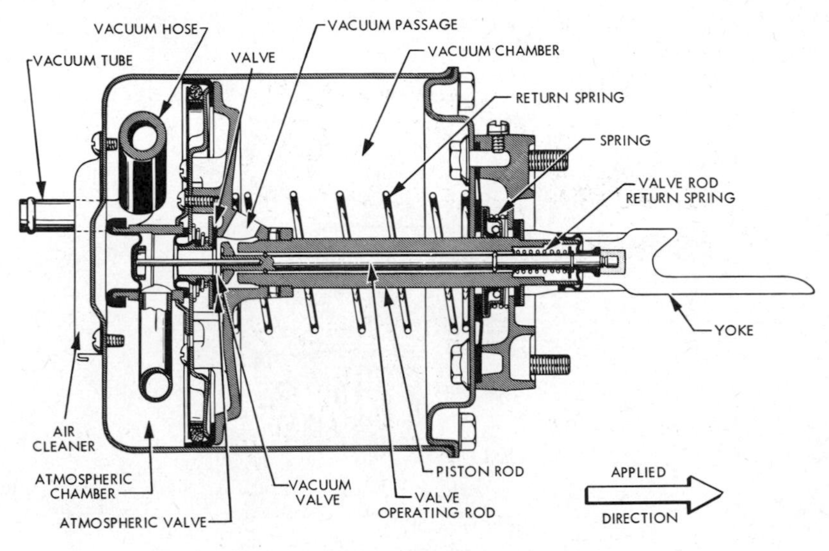

Fig. 23. Piston type pedal-assist power brake.
(Dodge Div.—Chrysler Corp.)

under certain operating conditions. A check valve must be used in conjunction with a vacuum reservoir to prevent vacuum from bleeding back to the intake manifold when manifold vacuum is less than the vacuum in the tank.

Three methods of transmitting the force created by vacuum to the hydraulic fluid actuating mechanism are used in the various designs of power units: a bellows, shown in Fig. 22, a piston, shown in Fig. 23, and a diaphragm, shown in Fig. 24. Regardless of whether a bellows, diaphragm, or piston is used, the operating principles and general construction features remain the same.

All power brakes retain some pedal resistance permitting the driver to maintain a certain amount of pedal feel. A light pressure upon the pedal will give a light braking force while a heavy pressure upon the pedal will give a more severe braking application.

If the vacuum section of the power unit should fail, brake application can still be obtained without the use of the vacuum assist.

There are two basic types of vacuum booster power brakes used on automobiles, the pedal-assist power unit, and the self contained hydraulic and vacuum unit.

c. **Pedal-Assist Power Brake.** The pedal-assist power brake is a separate booster unit which applies additional force to the master

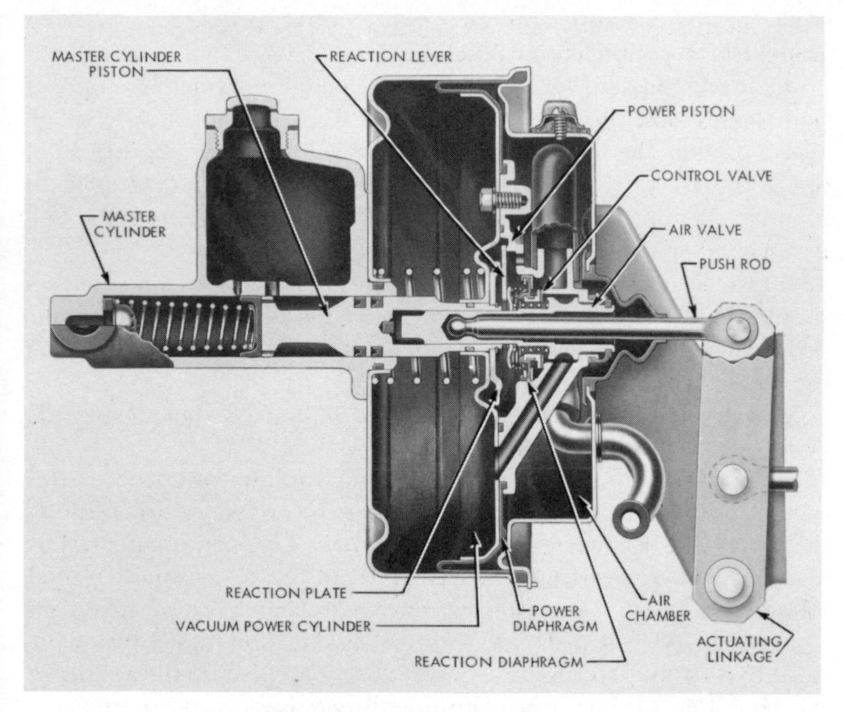

Fig. 24. Self contained diaphragm operated power brake.
(Pontiac Div.—General Motors Corp.)

cylinder through a linkage attached to the brake pedal. The power unit is located on the firewall (underneath the hood) either above or below the master cylinder. The pedal-assist power brake shown in Fig. 22 uses a bellows to transmit vacuum action.

The power unit is made up of an air-vacuum bellows, an air valve, and a vacuum valve. A reservoir is used on most installations of this type to supply vacuum. A check valve is located between the vacuum reservoir and the intake manifold.

When the brake pedal is in a released position, the air valve is open, admitting atmospheric pressure to the bellows chamber, and the vacuum valve is closed. These two valves are actuated by brake pedal movement. When the brake pedal is depressed, while the engine is running, the air valve is closed and the vacuum valve is opened. Intake manifold vacuum now removes the air from the bellows chamber causing the bellows to contract and assist the downward movement of the brake pedal. The vacuum assist provided is equal to the pressure applied on the brake pedal, thus making gradual brake applications possible.

If, at any time during application the pedal movement is stopped, both valves close, holding the unit in a fixed position.

As soon as the brake pedal is released, the trigger on the pedal opens the air valve, which in turn closes the vacuum valve. With the air valve open and the vacuum valve closed, air enters the bellows chamber stopping the power assist.

In the event there is a loss of engine vacuum, or if any situation should arise whereby the booster unit fails to operate, the brake pedal is free to function independent of the power unit, applying the brakes in the conventional manner.

An air filter located at the air valve filters the air entering the bellows chamber.

There are two adjustments which can usually be made to this type of power unit. An eccentric bolt on the trigger which actuates the valves can be adjusted to maintain correct valve movement. The master cylinder push rod can also be adjusted to maintain proper clearance between the master cylinder piston and the push rod.

Another type of pedal-assist power brake unit uses a piston instead of a bellows to transmit movement. The piston type of unit is shown in Fig. 23. This type of unit is usually air suspended and consists of a power cylinder, a vacuum piston and rod assembly, an internal poppet type of control valve, and an air cleaner.

The basic operation of this unit is the same as the bellows type of unit. As this assembly is located above the master cylinder the applied force is in a direction opposite to that of the assembly located below the master cylinder. By using a yoke on the valve rod, the mechanical contact between the power unit and the brake pedal linkage exists only when the power unit is assisting in brake application. In the event there is a loss of vacuum, the brake pedal is free to function independent of the power unit in applying the brakes in the conventional manner.

Pedal free play can be adjusted as can the power unit trigger device.

d. Self Contained Power Brake. Numerous designs of the self contained power brake have been used, but basically the operation is the same for all, whether they use a bellows, a diaphragm, or a piston, or are of the air or vacuum suspended type.

As the power brake unit reduces the amount of pedal pressure needed to stop the vehicle due to vacuum assistance, it is possible to reduce pedal travel and have the brake pedal height more nearly the same as the accelerator pedal height.

The master cylinder is attached to the front of the power unit and opposite the pedal push rod. Most of the power units being installed at the present time use a master cylinder constructed in the same manner as the conventional master cylinder. The major difference will simply be an extension of the master cylinder piston to receive the actuating rod.

Figure 24 illustrates a commonly used self contained power brake unit. The unit is air suspended and the vacuum reaction is imposed against a diaphragm.

The power unit is composed of two main sections: the vacuum power cylinder, and the hydraulic master cylinder, plus the actuating mechanism and linkage.

A front and rear housing interlock to form a chamber in which the power diaphragm and related parts operate. The section to the rear of the diaphragm is called the *air chamber* since it is open to atmospheric pressure at all times. The section to the front is called the *vacuum chamber* and is subjected to manifold vacuum during power application of the brakes. All air entering the cylinder passes through an air filter.

The air chamber is sealed off from the vacuum chamber by means of the diaphragm. Located on the center portion of the diaphragm is a plate which carries the actuating and valve mechanism. This plate is called the piston. A flexible hose connects the piston to a fixed tube at the top of the rear housing, thus permitting the piston to move back and forth while being connected to the intake manifold which supplies the engine vacuum. Air is exhausted out of the vacuum chamber through passages in the piston, and through a hose when the control valve is positioned for power application.

The power piston assembly contains the control valve and reaction mechanism. The control valve is made up of the air valve and a floating choke valve assembly. The reaction mechanism consists of a master cylinder reaction plate, a reaction disk, three reaction levers, and an air valve reaction plate. A push rod, which operates the air valve, projects out of the power cylinder housing through a flexible rubber boot.

The master cylinder is constructed in the same manner as the conventional brake master cylinder.

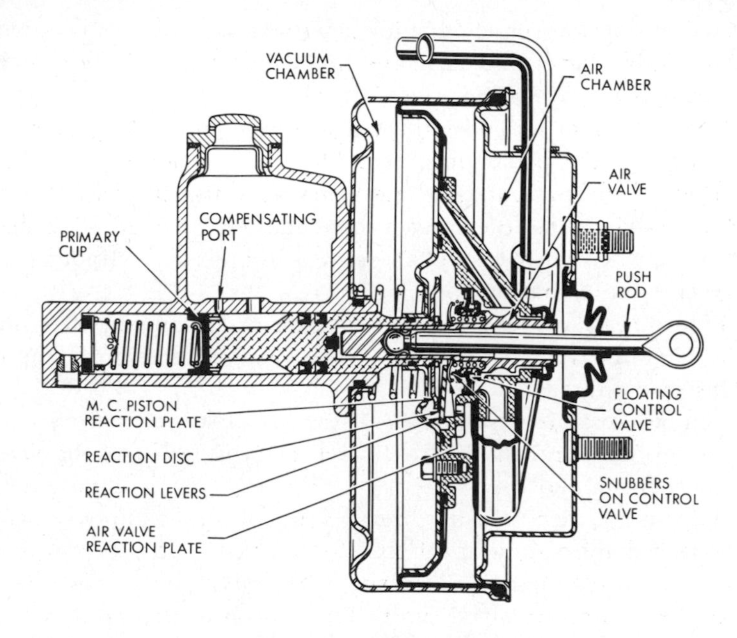

Fig. 25. Self contained diaphragm operated power brake in apply position. (*Buick Div.—General Motors Corp.*)

As the brake pedal is depressed, the push rod moves the air valve forward until its annular (ring like) seat contacts the floating control valve, at which point atmospheric pressure is sealed off from the vacuum chamber. Further movement of the air valve pushes the floating control valve away from its annular seat in the piston, connecting the vacuum chamber to the intake manifold which supplies the engine vacuum. As air is exhausted out of the vacuum chamber, atmospheric pressure in the air chamber moves the power piston forward.

When the power piston is moved forward, it carries the master cylinder piston forward, hence applying the brakes. As the pressure starts to build up in the hydraulic system, pressure on the end of the master cylinder piston causes the master cylinder piston reaction plate to move away from its stop, pressing against the reaction disks and reaction levers. The levers, in turn, swing around their pivots in the power piston and push the air valve reaction plate back against the floating control valve snubbers. The self contained diaphragm operated unit is shown in the applied position in Fig. 25. In this

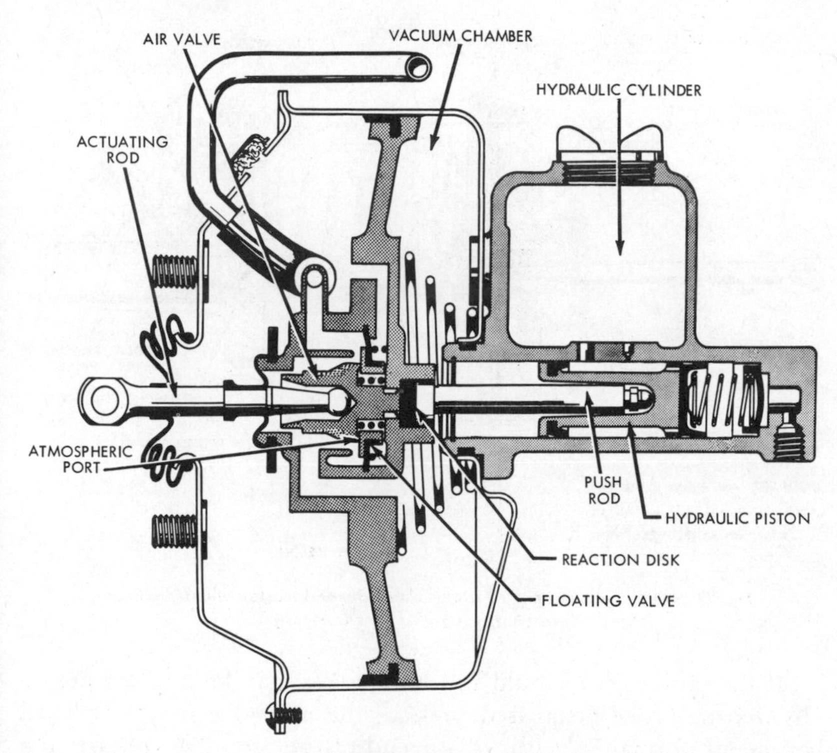

Fig. 26. Self contained piston operated power brake.
(Oldsmobile Div.—General Motors Corp.)

manner approximately 40% of the load on the master cylinder is transferred through the air valve and push rod assembly to the brake pedal, opposing the foot pressure applied by the driver. This reaction pressure gives the driver a brake feel which is proportional to the degree of brake application.

When the brake pedal is held stationary, the air valve and the floating control valve are also held stationary. The power piston, however, continues forward until its annular seat contacts the floating control valve. At this point, both the air valve and the power piston are seated on the floating control valve. Therefore, the passage to the vacuum chamber is closed to atmospheric pressure as well as to vacuum, and the power piston is held stationary.

When the brake pedal is released, the valves return to their normal positions cutting off vacuum; therefore, atmospheric pressure is present on both sides of the diaphragm.

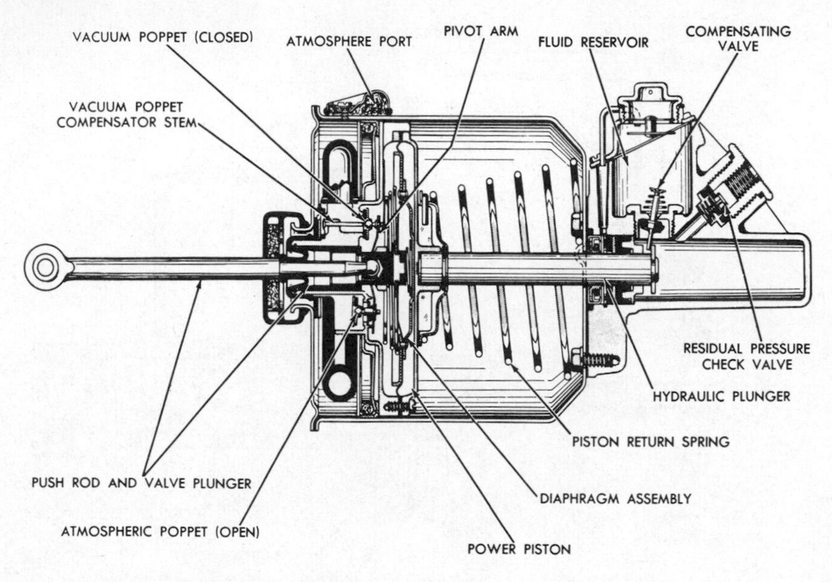

Fig. 27. Self contained power brake with extended master cylinder plunger.
(*Lincoln Div.–Ford Motor Company*)

If the power unit should fail, the brakes may be applied manually. As the brake pedal is depressed, the air valve moves forward beyond its normal travel until the end of the air valve contacts the rubber bumper in the master cylinder piston. Further movement of the brake pedal pushes the master cylinder piston into the master cylinder, causing the brakes to be applied in the conventional manner.

Another design of a self contained power brake unit is illustrated in Fig. 26. A sliding piston is used in this type of unit instead of a diaphragm. This type of installation is also air suspended and operates in the same manner as the unit which uses a diaphragm. Two push rods are used in conjunction with a conventional master cylinder piston, rather than a single push rod and an extended master cylinder piston.

Figure 27 illustrates a self contained power brake unit with an extended master cylinder plunger. The construction of the master cylinder differs somewhat from the master cylinder as used in the conventional brake system. A compensating port valve is used in the extended master cylinder type of unit rather than the customary compensating port. As the hydraulic plunger (master cylinder piston) moves forward, the compensating port valve closes. Fluid is displaced by the large diameter hydraulic plunger, forced past the residual pressure check valve and into the hydraulic lines. The basic vacuum and air valve construction and operation is the same as on other designs of power brake booster units.

e. Power Brake Troubles. The fact that the brakes will operate even if the booster unit fails, means that the regular brake system is left intact and the power system is simply added to the existing brake system. Trouble shooting is the same for the power brake system as for the conventional brake system until you get to the power unit itself. Air in the hydraulic lines will cause a spongy pedal feel and grease or oil soaked brake lining will cause the brakes to grab. Always check the regular brake system first; if the system is all right, then check the power unit.

Power brakes do not require adjustment other than the linkage, they either operate correctly or not at all.

For a quick check as to whether or not the power unit is working, the pedal should fall away slightly and less pressure will be required to maintain the pedal in any given position. Another more positive check of the same nature is to remove the brake light switch and replace it with a pressure gage. Depress the brake pedal and take a pressure reading. Start the engine and take another pressure reading with the brake pedal in the same position; there should be a substantial increase in pressure with the engine running.

If the power unit is not giving enough assistance, check the engine vacuum. If the engine vacuum is abnormally low (below 14 inches at idle) tune up the engine to raise the vacuum reading and try the brake assist. A steady hiss when the brake pedal is depressed indicates a vacuum leak which results in a hard pedal, that is, a lack of power assist.

If the brakes fail to release properly, the trouble is usually a tight or misaligned connection between the power unit and the brake linkage. If this connection is free and the brakes still fail to release properly, the power unit must be disassembled, providing the trouble is not a restricted line or trouble in the conventional brake system.

f. Power Brake Service. Consult the manufacturers' shop manual for specific procedures and specifications for the particular unit being serviced.

Make sure only clean, top quality brake fluid is used as more

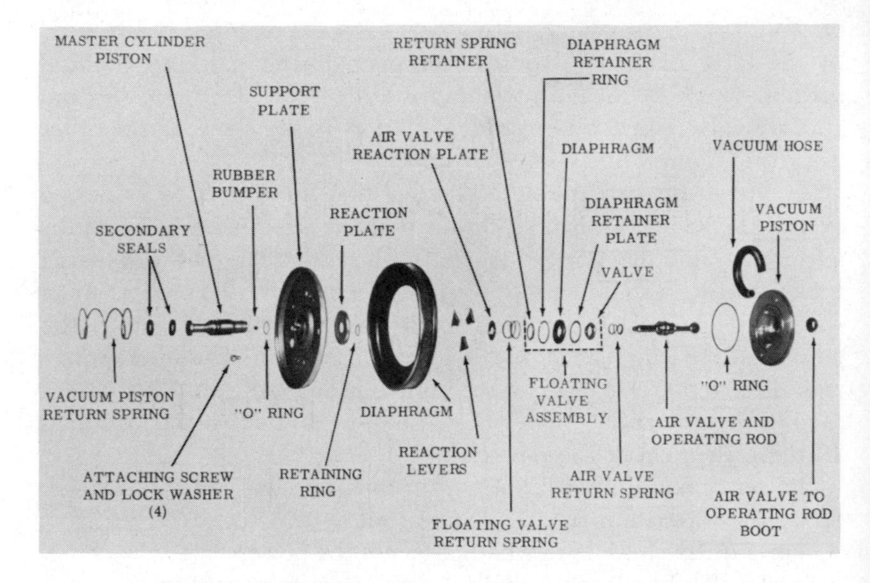

Fig. 28. Disassembled power booster valve assembly of self contained unit.
(*Oldsmobile Div.—General Motors Corp.*)

seals and valves are used in power brake systems than with conventional brake systems. Inferior or dirty brake fluid will usually do more damage to a power brake system than to the conventional brake system.

If an air filter is used it must be kept clean and free of foreign matter.

Pedal free play should be maintained the same as on a conventional brake system.

If the brake pedal must be depressed over one-half of its full travel distance before the brakes apply, the lining to brake drum clearance should be adjusted.

When a power unit fails the entire unit should be disassembled and overhauled. Figure 28 shows a disassembled power unit valve assembly.

Cleanliness is essential when working with a power unit. Use alcohol for parts cleaning rather than a cleaner with a petroleum base.

Complete overhaul kits are available and all parts should be used when overhauling the unit. Make sure all connections and matching surfaces are clean and vacuum tight when reassembling.

TRADE COMPETENCY TEST

1. What are the factors which control the stopping of a vehicle? (pp. 214, 215)
2. How does a wheel cylinder operate? (p. 218)
3. What is the purpose of the dampener spring around the outside of the brake drum? (p. 219)
4. Describe what happens in a hydraulic brake system when the driver removes his foot from the brake pedal. (p. 229)
5. Why is a step type wheel cylinder used in some brake assemblies? (p. 230)
6. What is the advantage of using two single piston wheel cylinders? (p. 237)
7. How are the rear wheel hand brakes equalized? (p. 238)
8. What multiplies the braking force in a transmission parking brake? (p. 239)
9. What is the basic operating principle of a power brake? (p. 241)
10. What factors determine the amount of effort a power brake will apply? (p. 242)
11. What is the advantage of using a vacuum reservoir? (p. 243)
12. How does a pedal-assist power brake operate? (pp. 244, 245)
13. What adjustments can usually be made to a pedal-assist power brake? (p. 246)
14. What adjustment should be made to power brakes if the brake pedal must be depressed over one half of its full travel distance? (p. 252)

CHAPTER 10

BRAKE SERVICE

		PAGE
I.	Common Brake Troubles	254
II.	Adjustment of Brakes	259
III.	Flushing Hydraulic Brakes	264
IV.	Bleeding Hydraulic Brakes	266
V.	Brake Relining	268
VI.	Brake Drum Service	273
VII.	Master Cylinder and Wheel Cylinder Repair	274

Brake service work should be of the highest standard of reliability and accuracy. Anyone doing such work should recognize and accept the responsibility which arises from the fact that the operator of the vehicle will be entrusting his safety and that of many others to the care and skill with which such brake work has been performed.

Automotive brakes require attention more often than most other major units on the vehicle. This chapter discusses some of the troubles experienced with automotive brakes, and explains as well the adjustments or repairs which may be required.

I. COMMON BRAKE TROUBLES

Brakes are designed to give satisfactory service over long periods of time with occasional adjustments to compensate for normal wear. Occasionally, some trouble occurs in the brake system which lessens the ability of the brakes to stop the vehicle within safe distances. Ordinarily, adjustment of the brakes may correct such troubles; however, further repairs or relining of the brakes may be necessary. Some of the common brake troubles are indicated as follows:

a. Brakes Lock During Vehicle Operation. It is possible for the hydraulic service brakes at all wheels to lock in the applied position and to fail to release, if the compensating port in the master cylinder is either partially or totally blocked, which would prevent the brake fluid from returning to the reservoir after a brake application had been made. Blocking of the compensating port can result if the brake pedal linkage is not correctly adjusted, which would permit the edge of the lip of the primary cup on the master cylinder piston to completely or partially cover the port. Correct adjustment of the pedal linkage requires a clearance of about 0.015 to 0.020 clearance between the brake pedal rod and the master cylinder piston. As a result of this clearance, the brake pedal can be moved between 1/4 inch and 1/2 inch (on most cars) before the master cylinder piston is moved (termed pedal free play). If this clearance is not maintained the lip of the primary cup will either totally or partially block the compensating port, preventing brake fluid from returning to the master cylinder reservoir. This would cause the brakes to drag.The heat resulting from the friction between shoes and drums would cause the fluid to expand in the wheel cylinders, forcing the brake shoes outward against the drums and locking them in the applied position.

A swollen primary cup, due to the use of inferior brake fluid, or the presence of mineral oil in the fluid, would also block the compensating port with the same results. Dirt or other foreign matter in the fluid can also block the port, which is of very small diameter.

NOTE: If the brakes are locked, preventing movement of the vehicle, momentarily open the bleeder valve at any wheel. The pressure holding the brakes applied will force out a small amount of fluid, freeing the brakes. Close the bleeder valve. This does not correct the trouble, but will permit the vehicle to be moved to a location where repairs may be made.

To correct this trouble, first check brake pedal free play, if it is not within the limits required for that vehicle, adjust pedal linkage to provide correct free play. Some late model vehicles do not have provision for adjustment of free play as they use a linkage of fixed dimensions, and thus require no pedal free play. If pedal adjustment does not correct the trouble, clean the master cylinder filler plug and the area around it and remove the filler plug. With a clean piece of tag wire, check through the filler port for clogging of the compensating ports either by dirt, or by a swollen primary cup. If inspection indicates dirt or possible swollen primary cup, master cylinder should be overhauled and hydraulic system flushed and bled.

b. Brakes Do Not Work. When foot pressure is applied, the hydraulic brake pedal should travel just far enough to develop the hydraulic pressure necessary to apply the brakes. If the pedal goes to the floor suddenly, it may be due to a leak in the hydraulic system (generally a faulty primary cup in the master cylinder), or the pedal linkage may be broken or disconnected. Check for broken or leaking lines or connections, especially in the flexible lines. Tighten any loose connections or replace any damaged parts. Check for leakage of the master cylinder piston cups and wheel cylinder cups. Fluid in the dust boots on the master cylinder or any wheel cylinder indicates leakage past the rubber cup at that point. Correction of such leaks requires overhaul of the leaking cylinder.

If air has entered the hydraulic system, the brake pedal will have a spongy feel when depressed (since air in the system may be compressed), and may travel all the way to the toeboard or firewall without developing sufficient hydraulic pressure to stop the vehicle.

Air will enter the hydraulic system if the fluid in the master cylinder is too low, if there is excessive clearance between the brake linings and the drums, if there is a faulty check valve in the master cylinder, or if the pistons of the wheel cylinders are not held firmly in place when the tension of the brake shoe retracting springs is removed while servicing the brakes.

Bleed the hydraulic system to eliminate any air that may have entered the system. Bleeding is explained further on in this chapter. Adjust the brake shoes if required.

c. Low Pedal Reserve. During the normal operation of any brake, a little of the brake lining wears away each time the brakes are applied. On hydraulic brakes the pedal reserve decreases as the wear increases. This wear is compensated for by means of a minor brake adjustment which restores the pedal reserve.

Pedal Reserve: This term refers to the distance between the brake pedal and the toeboard or firewall when the brakes are fully applied. Less than two inches of reserve is considered dangerous. During severe application, the drums get hot and expand, thus further reducing the pedal reserve.

d. Hard Brake Action. Hard brake action, or excessive brake pedal pressure required to stop a vehicle, may be caused by the normal wear of the brake linings, a heavy glaze on the lining, or grease soaked lining. Make a minor brake adjustment to compensate for lining wear. If this does not correct the trouble a major adjustment may be necessary or repairs required. Lack of lubrication of the pedal linkage can cause hard brake action. Check the brake lining for wrong type of lining, or brake shoes installed in the reversed position. Replace the linings if required. Check the hydraulic lines for obstructions, kinks, dents, or dirt. Clean out lines or replace parts as required.

Check the brake fluid. The wrong type of fluid will thicken and not flow freely through the lines and openings. If in doubt about the fluid, drain and flush the system. Refill with fluid recommended by the manufacturer of the vehicle. Bleed brake system. See procedure on pages 264 to 268.

On vehicles equipped with a brake booster, the booster may be inoperative and not giving any brake assistance. Tighten all connections in the vacuum system, clean the booster air cleaner, and service the vacuum check valve at the engine intake manifold.

e. Uneven Brake Action. If the brake action is uneven, that is, if one wheel brake operates faster than the others, adjust the brake shoes. If after a minor adjustment the brakes still operate unevenly, perform a major brake adjustment.

Check the flexible brake hoses for worn spots due to chafing against any part of the front suspension, and for cuts or tears of outer surface caused by flying stones or other objects passed over by the vehicle. Look for separation of the hose from the fittings at the ends, or for damage to the fittings, such as cracks, damaged threads, bends, etc. Check for soft spots in the hose, which can indicate softening of the rubber inside the hose.

If the hose is wetted externally at any spot, have an assistant apply pressure to the brake system by operating the brake pedal and thoroughly examine each hose, after cleaning, for any fluid leaking through a weakened part of the hose or around the fittings. If hose appears soft in any spot when compressed between the fingers, or if fluid appears to ooze from any spot, the hose should be replaced. After it is carefully cleaned to prevent entry of dirt, the hose can then be removed and the interior inspected visually with a strong light, if necessary. If it is suspected that the hose is in any way clogged by loose or swollen rubber lining, it can be checked by applying pressure to brake system with the brake pedal and observing whether fluid flows normally from bleeder valve when it is opened. Be sure to clean thoroughly around bleeder valve before opening in order to prevent dirt from entering the system.

If one wheel drags, or if the vehicle is pulling to one side when a stop is made, the adjustment of the front wheel bearings should be checked and corrected to give proper wheel movement with no endwise play of the wheel on the spindle. Loose wheel bearings permit the wheel to move in an endwise manner on the spindle, resulting in a misaligned contact of brake shoe and brake drum.

While the drums are off, check for a corroded or bent shoe mechanism, a sticking wheel cylinder piston, weak or broken brake shoe retracting springs, or grease or glaze on the linings.

If grease is found on the brake lining, examine the grease seals for wear, damage, or aging (hardness of the sealing lip) which will permit grease to escape from the seal and work down onto the drum and brake lining. Lubricant at too high a level in the differential (rear axle) can work its way past a rear wheel grease seal. On front wheels, check for an excessive amount of grease used in packing the front wheel bearings or in the cavity in the front hub. In addition, check the drums for an out-of-round condition and for deteriorated cups in the wheel cylinder. Repair or replace parts as required.

f. Spongy Pedal. A spongy pedal may be due to excessive clearance between the lining and the drum, or air in the hydraulic system. Adjust the brake lining to drum clearance and bleed the brake system.

If this has not corrected the trouble, perform a major brake adjustment. While the drums are off, look for bent or otherwise distorted brake shoes. Brake linings that do not fit the drum make it necessary to apply sufficient pedal pressure to develop sufficient hydraulic pressure to bend the shoe in order to obtain full contact with the drum. This also, at times, will result in a brake action as though you were pushing the brake pedal against a spring instead of something solid.

g. Brakes Grab. When brakes grab under light pedal pressure, it may be that the lining has absorbed grease, oil or brake fluid. Grease-soaked brakes will usually grab. Linings soaked with oil or brake fluid fail to hold, and will slip, giving the effect of a grabbing brake on the opposite wheel. Loose brake backing plates also are a cause of brake grab. Brake drums which are rough, scored, cracked, or out of round are also causes.

Damaged brake lining must be replaced. Brake drums which cannot be remachined within the limits described in relining or which are cracked must be replaced. Oil or grease seals should be replaced, if they are faulty. A check should be made for excessive amounts of oil or grease reaching the seals.

h. Loss of Fluid. Hydraulic brake fluid can be lost if a wheel cylinder leaks, if the master cylinder leaks, or if a line or connection (cracked line, cracked or defective fittings, cross threaded, or loose, cracked flare) leaks. Loss of fluid at the master cylinder necessitates its removal for repairs. Loss of fluid at the wheel cylinder necessitates overhaul of the wheel cylinder.

II. ADJUSTMENT OF BRAKES

Brake adjustments are divided into two classifications: minor adjustments, which compensate for normal lining wear; and major adjustments, which involves moving both the toe and the heel of the brake shoe. Consult the vehicle manufacturer's shop manual for the specific method of making either type of adjustments.

a. Minor Brake Adjustment. If the condition of the lining is unknown, it is advisable to remove one front wheel and look for the following conditions: brake drum scored, out-of-round, or bell-mouthed; brake lining soaked with oil, grease, or brake fluid, glazed or worn to less than $\frac{1}{32}$ in. from the rivet heads or $\frac{1}{32}$ in. from the shoe when bonded lining is used; brake lining does not make full contact with the drum. If any of these conditions exist, a minor brake adjustment will not suffice. It may be assumed that the condition of the linings and the drums at the other three wheels is approximately the same as found at the wheel removed.

Adjust all brake shoes at all four wheels to compensate for lining wear. An adjustment is provided at each brake that moves

Fig. 1. Left, front brake assembly. Right, rear brake backing plate.
(Plymouth Div.—Chrysler Corp.)

the brake shoes outward towards the drums, thus permitting the proper clearance to be established.

The procedure for making a minor brake adjustment is to reduce the lining to drum clearance to a point where the wheel just turns freely, without a lining drag.

Two methods of adjusting the lining to drum clearance are in common use on today's automobiles. One method involves the use of two adjusting cams, one cam being in contact with each shoe, as shown in Fig. 1. With vehicle hoisted or jacked up safely, so wheels can be spun, turn the adjusting cam for the front brake shoe, Fig. 1, until the shoe is tight against the drum. Then carefully back off the cam until the wheel can be spun freely. Next, turn the cam for the rear brake shoe until the shoe is tight against the brake drum. Then back off carefully on cam until wheel spins free. Repeat this procedure for all wheels. Check parking brake adjustment.

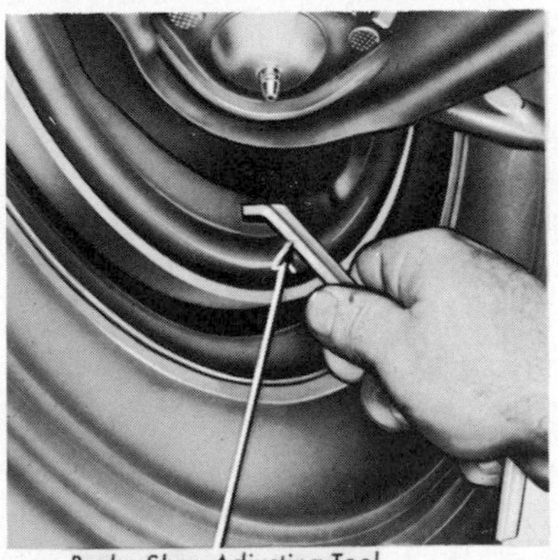

Fig. 2. Star wheel minor brake adjuster.
(Ford Div.—Ford Motor Company)

The other method of adjustment consists of a star wheel adjusting screw located between the lower ends of the brake shoes. This method of adjustment is shown in Fig. 2. Disconnect parking brake cables at equalizer so that the parking brake is not partially applied due to shortened cables. Remove the rubber plugs from the adjusting holes in the backing plate. Using a tool as shown in Fig. 2 and with vehicle wheels off the ground, turn the star wheel until the brake shoes are hard against the drum and there is a heavy drag on the wheel. Then back off the star wheel approximately 10 to 15 notches. Spin wheel to check drag. Brake shoes should be correctly adjusted if correct procedure has been followed. If there is still a heavy drag on wheel, the brake shoe anchor pin will need adjustment as described under major adjustment. If anchor pin adjustment is not required, replace the rubber plugs in adjusting slots. Then adjust the parking brake cables to give correct parking brake action.

After completing the adjustment of the shoes, check the pedal reserve. If the pedal reserve is less than half the total distance to the toe-board or firewall, readjust the shoes more carefully. If this does not establish normal pedal reserve, a major adjustment, including an inspection of each of the brake assemblies, is required.

Adjust pedal free play (except on '61 Chrysler products). The brake pedal is correctly adjusted when the pedal has more than 1/4 in. and less than 1/2 in. free travel (measured at the pedal pad) before the master cylinder piston starts to move. The brake pedal lash is usually adjusted by shortening or lengthening the rod linking the brake pedal to the master cylinder piston. Check the master cylinder reservoir and fill if necessary.

(1) *ADJUST PARKING BRAKE CABLES.* Adjusting the lining to drum clearance automatically adjusts the parking brake; however, if excess movement is necessary to apply the brakes, the cable should be shortened. The cables are adjusted by loosening the locknut on the equalizer several turns. If a clevis is used remove the clevis pin and turn the clevis until the cables are just tight enough to remove the slack. If a nut is used on the equalizer rod instead of a clevis, turn the nut forward until the cable slack is removed. Tighten the lock nut. Excessive tightening may pull the brake shoes off of their anchors causing the brakes to drag.

b. Major Brake Adjustment. A major brake adjustment is recommended after installation of new or relined shoes, after the drums have been turned down, and in all cases where satisfactory braking is not obtained by the minor adjustment.

A major adjustment involves, as a first step, the removal of all brake drums to permit an inspection of the braking parts.

Inspect the linings, drums, retracting springs and hold-down springs. Look for signs of hydraulic fluid leakage. Replace the linings if they are oil soaked or excessively worn, if they are loose on the shoes, or if the drums are to be turned oversize. Correct the cause of the oil leak if oil is getting on the lining. Turn down the drums or replace them if they are badly scored or grooved.

Make sure the brake shoes are correctly installed and that all points of friction are lubricated (sparingly) with zinc oxide lubricant. Make sure the retracting springs have the correct tension.

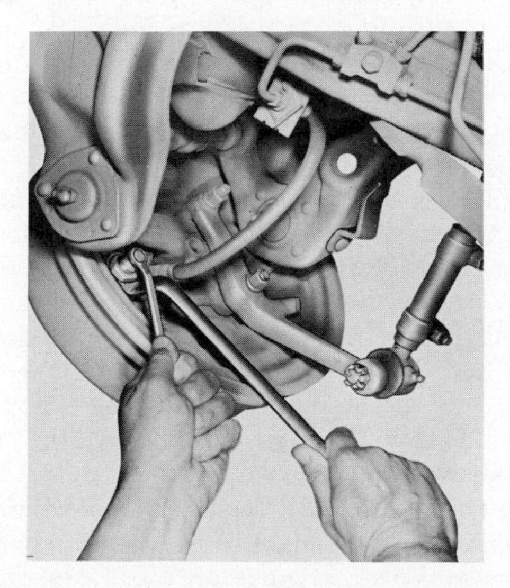

Fig. 3. Setting anchor pin for major adjustment.
(Pontiac Div.—General Motors Corp.)

A major adjustment also includes inspection of the hydraulic system, and bleeding of the system if necessary. A number of brakes are provided with adjustable anchors. A major adjustment involves the resetting of these anchors along with brake shoe adjustment by means of the regular star wheel adjusting screw or cams to obtain the desired clearance.

Consult the manufacturer's shop manual if there is a question as to whether or not the anchor or anchors are adjustable as well as the correct specifications of the anchor settings.

When each brake shoe has a separate anchor bolt, the head of the anchor carrying the shoe is generally in the form of an eccentric. Turning the eccentric will move the shoe away from or in toward the drum. This type of adjustment is shown in Fig. 1.

When both brake shoe ends are in contact with one anchor pin, the anchor may be in the form of an eccentric, and shoe to drum clearance is adjusted by turning the anchor pin, as shown in Fig. 3. On some installations the anchor pin is mounted in a slot. Loosening the anchor pin lock nut, expanding the star wheel adjuster, and tapping the pin upward will raise the brake shoes and reduce the lining to drum clearance.

Special adjusting gages or drums should be used to obtain the exact anchor setting. If a special gage is not available move the anchor until the drum locks. Then, move the anchor in the opposite direction until the drum just turns without a drag.

Adjustment of the hand brake is also generally considered as a part of a major brake adjustment.

c. Self-Adjusting Brake. Some automobiles are equipped with a self-adjusting type of brake. This brake is of the fully energized type with a self-adjusting mechanism added, and is shown in Fig. 4.

The self-adjusting mechanism consists of a link, actuating lever, pawl, and pawl return spring. The looped end of the link is attached to the anchor pin and the hooked end of the link is attached to the actuating lever. This connection is shown in Fig. 4. The actuating lever is held against the secondary shoe by means of the hold-down cup and spring assembly. The pawl is connected to the actuating lever and held in position by the pawl return spring.

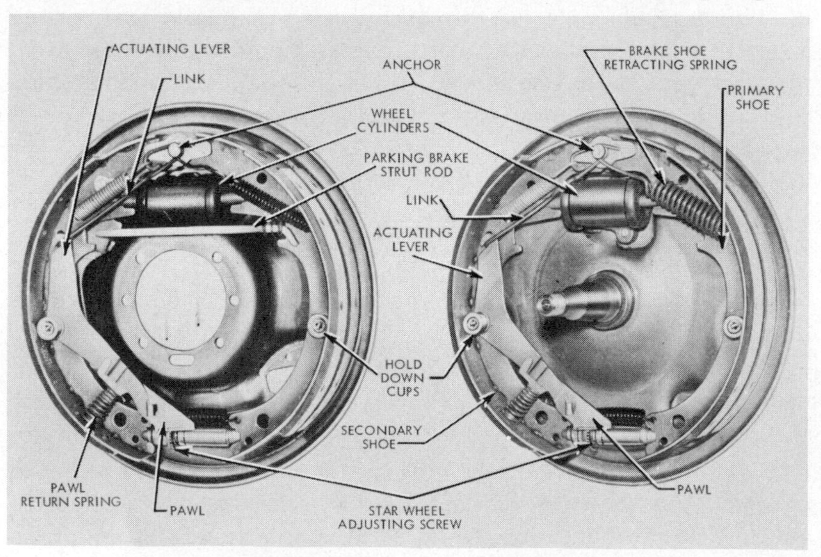

Fig. 4. Cadillac self-adjusting brake.
(Cadillac Div.—General Motors Corp.)

The automatic adjuster operates only during reverse brake application. The energizing action of the shoes following the drum while moving rearward, forces the upper end of the primary shoe *against* the anchor pin, and the secondary shoe *away* from the anchor pin.

The link holds the top of the actuating lever stationary, forcing the actuating lever to pivot on the secondary shoe. The pivoting action forces the pawl downward against the end of a tooth on the star wheel adjusting screw.

If the lining to drum clearances are correct, the downward movement will stop before the star wheel is turned. If the clearance is too great, however, the secondary shoe will move outward and the pawl will move downward far enough to turn the star wheel one notch and thereby take up the adjustment. When the brake lining is worn to its maximum serviceable limit, the self-adjuster will not operate. Increased brake pedal travel will warn operator that lining must be replaced.

When the brakes are applied as the vehicle is moving forward, the self-adjuster does not operate because the energizing action of the shoes forces the *secondary* shoe and not the *primary* shoe against the anchor pin.

This type of brake can also be adjusted manually by inserting a small screw driver in the access hole and holding the pawl from the star wheel adjusting screw. Adjust in the same manner as a conventional brake using a star wheel adjuster.

III. FLUSHING HYDRAULIC BRAKE SYSTEMS

The hydraulic brake system must be drained, flushed out, and refilled with new brake fluid of the correct type if the fluid in it becomes thick, dirty or contaminated with rubber or metal particles from the parts of the system. Mixing of two different brake fluids in the system may produce a chemical reaction between the fluids which can harm the rubber or metal parts, or reduce the braking efficiency. If any mineral oil, such as engine oil, has been put into the system either in error, or in an emergency when brake fluid was not available, the rubber parts would be damaged by swelling. In any such instance flushing would be necessary as part of the procedure to restore the braking system to normal efficiency. When flushing a brake system, use only the special flushing fluid recommended by the car manufacturer. If no such flushing fluid is available, clean, denatured alcohol may be used.

Remove all grease and dirt from the bleeder valve and the area around it at each wheel by wire brushing. No dirt should be permitted to enter the system. Attach a bleeder hose to each bleeder valve, placing the end of the hose in a clean container to catch the fluid pumped from the system. Open all bleeder valves one turn. Pump the brake pedal with full strokes until all of the fluid has been forced out of the system. Now, clean thoroughly around the master cylinder filler plug by wire brushing. Remove filler plug. Install a *gravity type* filler (Fig. 5) filled with the approved flushing fluid in the filler plug opening. This will keep a supply of clean flushing fluid in the master cylinder. Now pump the brake pedal through full strokes to force the flushing fluid through the system. Continue until all flushing fluid in filler has been forced into and through the system. Where absolutely *dry,* clean, compressed air is available, air pressure can be used, if care is exercised, to force the balance of the flushing fluid out of the line. Otherwise, the system should be refilled with new, clean brake fluid, and bled until all air and the remaining flushing fluid have been removed.

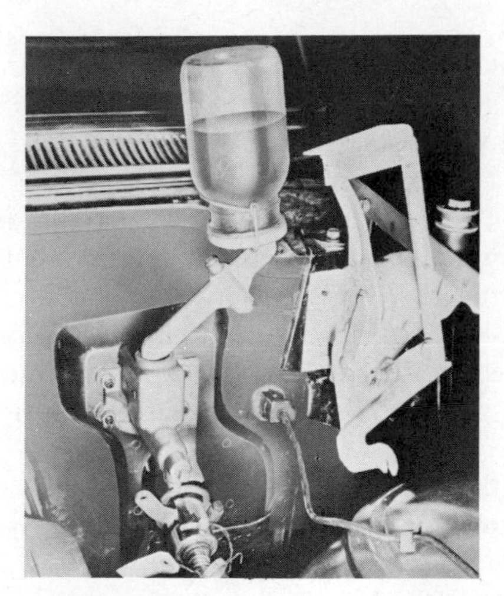

Fig. 5. Gravity type brake fluid filler.
(Chevrolet Div.—General Motors Corp.)

IV. BLEEDING HYDRAULIC BRAKES

Removing air from the hydraulic brake system is referred to as *bleeding*. The procedure is essentially the same on all vehicles having hydraulic brakes. The only variations in the procedure are the differences in the method of keeping the master cylinder full during the operation.

Remove all surface dirt from the area around the reservoir filler plug. Even one grain of sand in the brake fluid can cause serious damage to the hydraulic system. *Never* reuse brake fluid that has been bled from a brake system.

If you do not have a filler, or if you have a gravity filler, the job is best performed by two people, one at the brake pedal and the other observing the discharge at each wheel.

a. Manual Bleeding Procedure (without Gravity Filler). Following is the step-by-step description of the manual bleeding procedure (without gravity filler). Note that two persons are required to do the job properly:

STEP 1. Install a bleeder hose into the bleeder valve at the wheel having the longest brake line (right rear wheel). Insert the free end of the hose into a clean glass partially full of clean brake fluid. The end of the hose must be kept below the level of the fluid in the jar while bleeding the system. The glass jar permits you to see bubbles in the fluid leaving the bleeder hose. Keep bleeder valve closed until pressure on the system is built up as explained in Step 3.

STEP 2. The person in the car should remove the master cylinder reservoir filler plug (previously cleaned) and fill the reservoir with clean brake fluid of the type approved by the car maker. He should keep the reservoir filled during the bleeding operation to avoid the possibility of air entering the system.

STEP 3. The person in the car should now pump the brake pedal slowly while the bleeder is closed, until pressure is built up in the brake system and the pedal no longer moves downward but has a hard, springy feel. Hold the pedal down hard and firmly at this point to maintain the pressure in the system.

STEP 4. The person doing the bleeding should now open the bleeder valve quickly, being alert for bubbles in the fluid leaving the bleeder hose in the jar. IMPORTANT: *Before the brake pedal goes more than halfway to the floorboard, the bleeder valve must be*

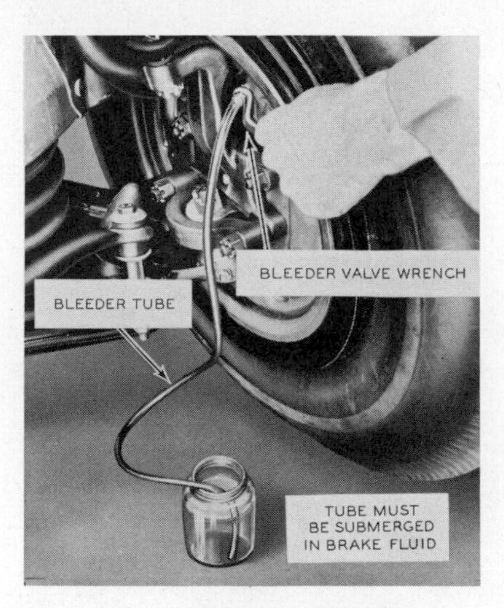

Fig. 6. Bleeding brakes.
(Oldsmobile Div.—General Motors Corp.)

closed again to prevent loss of pressure in the system and to avoid drawing air or dirty fluid back to the system.

STEP 5. Repeat Steps 3 and 4, making sure the master cylinder reservoir is kept filled with clean brake fluid, until no air bubbles are observed in the fluid leaving the bleeder hose. Keep pressure on the system at all times. Close bleeder valve tightly while pressure is still on the system after you are sure there is no more air in the line being bled. Remove bleeder hose and wipe bleeder valve dry.

STEP 6. Repeat bleeding procedure at left rear wheel, then the right front wheel, and finally left front wheel (Fig. 6). NOTE: *On vehicles having two wheel cylinders on front wheels, be sure to bleed the lower wheel cylinder first, then the upper wheel cylinder last, to insure that all air is removed from that brake line.*

STEP 7. After bleeding has been completed at all wheels, refill reservoir to correct level and install filler plug. Wipe clean.

STEP 8. Check brake pedal action, test for proper free play of pedal. Make brake adjustment as required, or test brakes to determine if there is any need for adjustment. Double check to make certain all bleeder valves are tightly closed.

b. Manual Bleeding (with Gravity Filler). If a gravity filler is used, as shown in Fig. 5, the procedure (also with two people) will

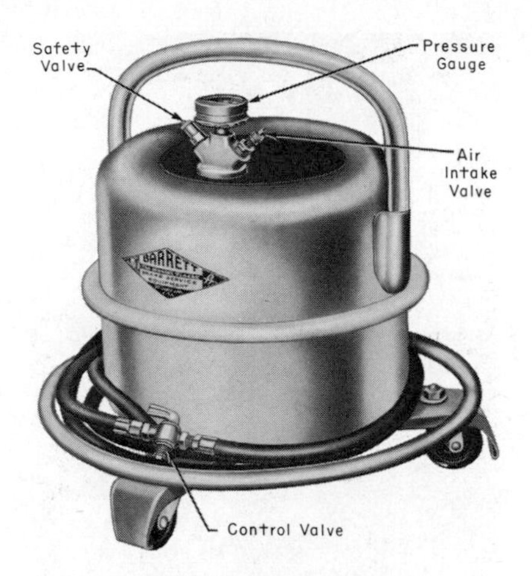

Fig. 7. Pressure bleeder.
(Barrett Equipment Company)

be exactly the same, except that the master cylinder will not have to be filled by hand. The gravity filler will automatically keep the correct level of fluid in the reservoir as long as there is sufficient fluid in the gravity filler jar.

c. Pressure Bleeding. A pressure bleeder, such as the one shown in Fig. 7, makes bleeding a one-man operation. The pressure bleeder not only maintains the correct level in the master cylinder reservoir, but eliminates the necessity for brake pedal manipulation. The pressure bleeder consists of a pressure tank partially filled with clean brake fluid. The tank is then sealed and compressed air at 20 psi is introduced into the tank through a valve, such as used for filling a tire.

The pressure tank is connected to the master cylinder reservoir with a pressure tight connection. After the pressure bleeder line is tightly connected, the valve in the bleeder line is then opened. This places 20 psi of pressure on the entire hydraulic system. Open the bleeder valve at each of the wheel cylinders, in turn, until the air bubbles stop and the fluid runs clear. When the bleeding operation is finished, close the valve in the bleeder line before disconnecting it from the master cylinder.

V. BRAKE RELINING

To maintain effective brakes, do not install new linings on the

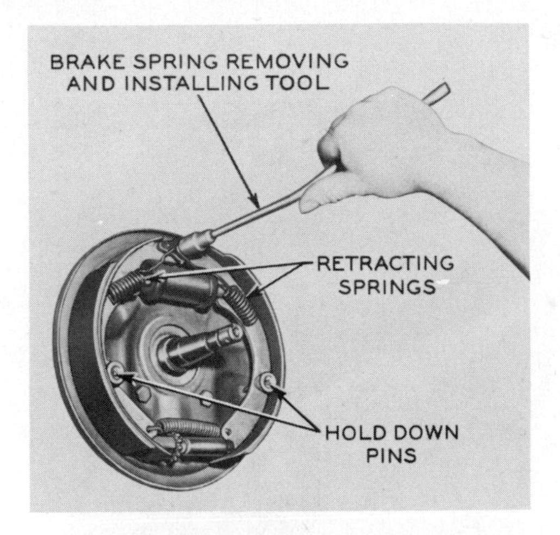

Fig. 8. Removing brake shoe retracting springs.
(Chevrolet Div.—General Motors Corp.)

shoes of only one wheel. Replace the lining on all shoes of all four wheels.

The first step in replacing brake lining is to remove the brake shoes. The brake shoes can generally be removed by removing the hold down spring pins and the brake retracting springs, as shown in Fig. 8. Install a brake cylinder clamp on the wheel cylinder to prevent the pistons from coming out of the wheel cylinder. If the hand brake is of the rear wheel type disconnect the cable from the lever at each rear shoe. If horse shoe locks are used on the anchor bolts to retain the lower ends of the shoes, remove the locks to permit the removal of the shoe from the anchor.

If the lining is riveted to the shoe, the rivets may be driven out from the end opposite the head with a punch which will pass through the rivet hole. Brake relining machines, shown in Fig. 9, are equipped with a punch to press out the rivets.

Most automobile parts stores, or automobile dealers, carry a complete line of brake shoes with the linings already attached (either bonded or riveted) and sell them on an exchange basis. Shoes with bonded lining should be exchanged, as bonding requires special equipment.

It is essential that the exact type of lining specified by the manufacturer for the particular vehicle be used when relining brakes. Any change in the coefficient of friction of the lining from what is

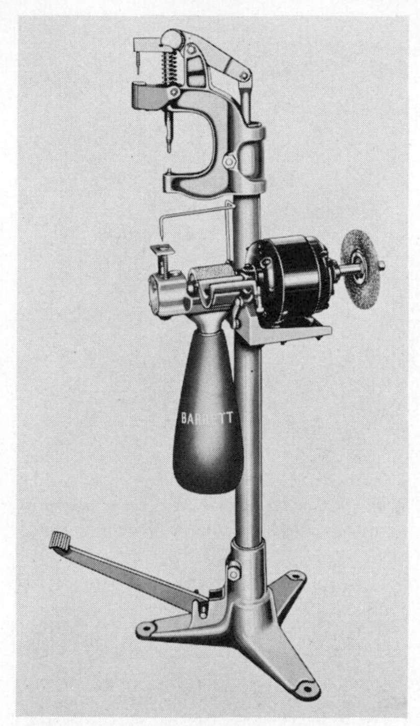

Fig. 9. Typical brake relining machine.
(Barrett Equipment Company)

intended for the specific brake may result in improper brake action.

Most manufacturers of brake lining package their lining in custom sets for specific vehicles. The linings in these sets are cut, chamfered, drilled, and counterbored for the particular brake it is to be used on. The lining will also be of the correct thickness for standard drums.

It is important that the lining be installed on the shoe in such a manner that the lining contacts smoothly and evenly throughout the entire curve of the shoe or band. If gaps occur between the brake lining and shoe at any point between the rivets, it will be impossible to get satisfactory brake action. To insure complete contact, and to prevent gaps, a brake lining clamp, such as the one shown in Fig. 10, or lining stretcher should be used to hold the lining tightly against the shoe while it is being riveted.

If a clamp or stretcher is not available, rivet the lining by applying the center rivets first, then working outward, drawing the lining

Fig. 10. Typical brake lining clamp.
(Dodge Div.—Chrysler Corp.)

tightly over the shoe before inserting each pair of rivets. If a brake riveting or brake relining machine is not available to attach the lining, a punch the same size as the rivet head clamped in a vise will serve as an anvil. A special rivet set is used to roll the end of the rivet over. The rivets must be set tight. Use a "roll" rivet set only, never a "star" rivet set.

When the brake drums are to be turned, postpone installing the new lining until after the drums are turned. Oversize (thicker) lining or shim stock between the lining and the shoes will usually give a better contour fit between the lining and the turned oversized drum. To check lining fit, secure it to the shoe. Hold the shoe and lining against the braking surface of the drum. If it is possible to rock the shoe against the drum, the lining is only contacting the drum at the center of the lining and oversized lining or shim stock should be used.

If only the ends of the lining contact the drum, the lining or shim stock is too thick. Either thinner shim stock or lining may be used; however, if the necessary equipment is available, the lining can be ground to properly fit the drum after the lining and shoes are installed on the backing plate. Molded, noncompressible, flexible, shim stock is available in two thicknesses: .020 in., or .03125 in. More than one thickness of shim stock may be used between the

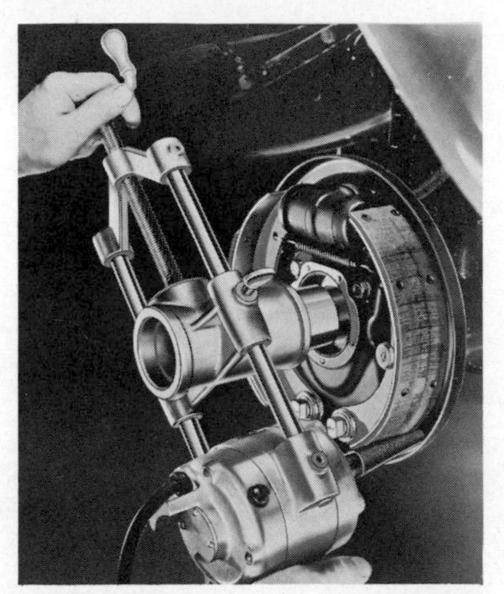

Fig. 11. Portable brake lining grinder.
(Dodge Div.—Chrysler Corp.)

lining and shoe if needed. Oversize riveted lining is more commonly used in brake work today.

Many brake riveting or relining machines have a grinding attachment which is used for grinding the lining after it has been installed on the shoes. High spots usually form around the counterbores during the riveting operation. These are removed and the ends of the lining are chamfered with the grinder.

New brake linings or unevenly worn old linings can be ground to the correct radius, and concentric with the wheel bearings with a portable brake lining grinder, such as the type shown in Fig. 11. Before using the grinder, the brake shoes are usually set to drum size at both the heel and toe. The brake grinder is then centered on the axle or spindle with such a setting so as to remove the minimum amount of lining to give the correct diameter with a true and concentric surface.

Most brake shoes are now cam ground by the brake shoe supplier or the brake specialist before he installs the shoes on the vehicle. Cam or radius grinding of brake shoes means grinding the shoes to fit a drum approximately .020 less than the drum size. A cam ground shoe will rock in the drum slightly, but will give a better initial braking action on vehicles that have fixed anchors on the brake backing platės. However, the cam ground technique is not

Fig. 12. Typical brake drum lathe.
(Barrett Equipment Company)

recommended for all brake designs. Most cars now use fixed anchors, for which oversized lining must be installed. A spindle mounted grinder or a bench type grinder employing an anchor pin similar to the one used on the car must be employed to establish the desired shoe contact surface.

VI. BRAKE DRUM SERVICE

Brake drums that are out-of-round, tapered, grooved, scored, or having rough spots, should be remachined on a brake drum lathe, like the one shown in Fig. 12. A telescoping gage or a brake drum gage is used to check for brake drum out-of-round or bell mouthing. If the scores in a drum are over 0.010 of an inch in depth, or the drums are out-of-round, the drums should be turned on a lathe to restore a concentric surface. If the brake drums are to be remachined, do not reline the brake shoes until after the new size of the drum has been established. It may be necessary to install oversize lining or shims under the lining to compensate for the decreased diameter of the drums. Using oversize lining or shims may eliminate the need for making a major adjustment.

Remove only the amount of material necessary to clean up the braking surface. If too much material is removed from the drum, distortion will result when the drum is subjected to heavy usage. Most manufacturers give 0.060 in. as the maximum which can be safely removed from the diameter of the drum.

Before installing clean the drums thoroughly with alcohol if the turned surface becomes greasy or dirty.

Drums usually have cast iron rubbing surfaces and therefore should be turned with a tool bit. However, some drums in use will develop work-hardening spots in the center of the lining contact surface of the drum. These spots usually cannot be removed with a tool bit. Most drum lathes employ a grinder attachment to remove these hard spots. Refer to drum manufacturer for recommendations.

VII. MASTER CYLINDER AND WHEEL CYLINDER REPAIR

Consult the manufacturer's shop manual for exact specifications, removal, overhaul, and reassembly procedures. The master cylinder may be located on the firewall in the engine compartment or attached to the frame under the vehicle near the flywheel housing. When removal of the master cylinder is necessary, clean all dirt from the hydraulic line fittings at the cylinder before loosening the connection.

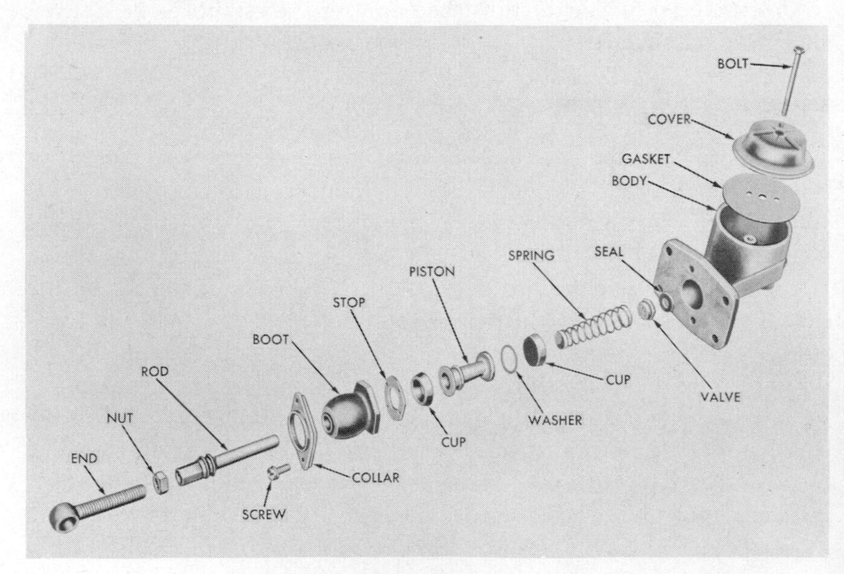

Fig. 13. Disassembled master cylinder.
(Dodge Div.—Chrysler Corp.)

Disassemble the master cylinder by removing the push rod boot, the snap ring, and the stop plate. An exploded view of a master cylinder is shown in Fig. 13. Use extreme care to keep all parts clean and free from oil and grease. If the cylinder is scored or rough, it should be polished with a hone. If the scores cannot be removed, the assembly should be replaced. Check the fit of the power piston in the master cylinder and if not within specifications, replace both the master cylinder and the piston. Maximum allowable clearance between the piston and the master cylinder is .006 in. Maximum allowable clearance of the piston within the wheel cylinder is .005 in. Replacement parts for the master cylinder are sold in kit form, as all the rubber parts should be replaced when overhauling a master cylinder. On reassembly, lubricate all parts with clean brake fluid, and after installation, bleed the hydraulic system.

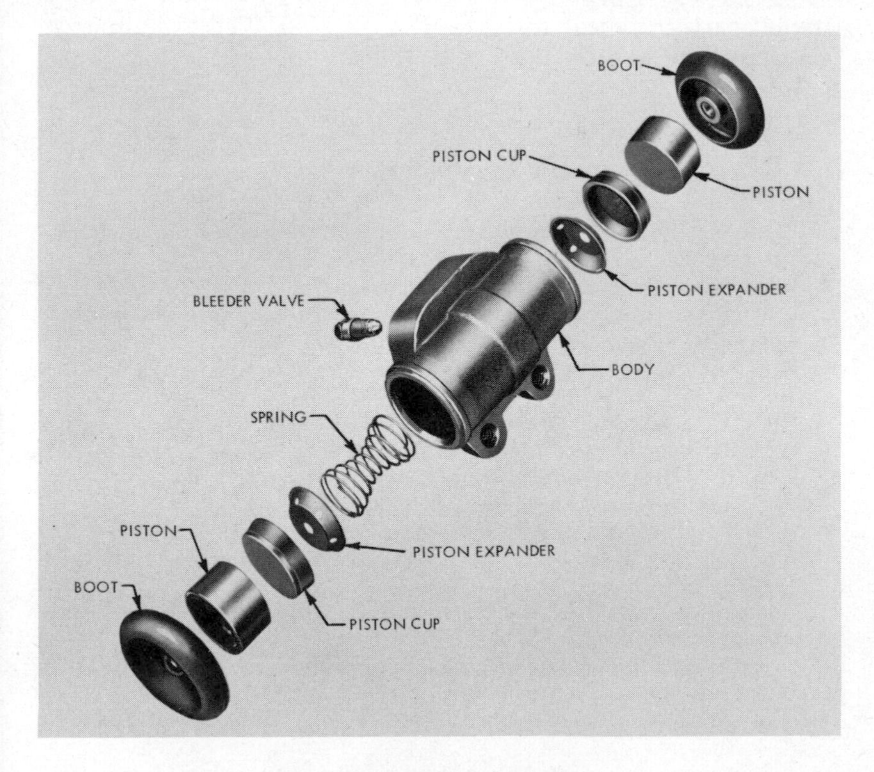

Fig. 14. Disassembled wheel cylinder.
(Dodge Div.—Chrysler Corp.)

The wheel cylinders are usually fastened to the brake backing plate by means of bolts or cap screws. If wheel cylinder replacement is necessary, loosen the flexible hose (front wheel cylinders) at the wheel cylinder. Remove the wheel cylinder, then hold the hose, and unscrew the cylinder from the hose. This saves time because the hose does not need to be disturbed where it fastens to the brake line.

Wheel cylinders usually do not have to be removed from the backing plate for disassembly or for honing. The wheel cylinder can be disassembled by removing the rubber boots or covers after the brake shoes have been removed. A disassembled wheel cylinder is shown in Fig. 14. If the cylinder is scored, polish with a hone. If the scores cannot be removed the cylinder must be replaced. As with the master cylinder, all rubber parts are generally replaced when overhauling a wheel cylinder. Clean all parts with alcohol before assembly (except rubber parts) and, on assembly, lubricate all parts (rubber parts included) with clean brake fluid. The hydraulic system must be bled after the overhauling of any of the four wheel cylinders.

TRADE COMPETENCY TEST

1. What will cause brakes to lock up while the vehicle is being operated? (pp. 254, 255)
2. What can be done to temporarily free-up locked brakes? (p. 255)
3. What are some of the things that can happen to the brake system which will result in complete brake failure? (pp. 255, 256)
4. How can you tell if the wheel cylinders or master cylinder is leaking? (p. 256)
5. What is considered to be ample brake pedal reserve? (p. 256)
6. What are some of the causes of hard brake pedal action? (pp. 256, 257)
7. What does a spongy brake pedal usually indicate? (p. 258)
8. What are the causes of brake grab? (p. 258)
9. How do you make a minor brake adjustment? (pp. 259-261)
10. What is the correct brake pedal free play and how is it adjusted? (p. 261)
11. What things should be checked before making a major brake adjustment? (pp. 261, 262)
12. Can you explain how to bleed brakes manually? (pp. 266-268)
13. When is it necessary to remachine brake drums? (p. 273)
14. How are wheel cylinders serviced? (p. 276)

INDEX

PAGE

A

Aligner, body and frame 15
Alignment, customized 186–212
  equipment check 192–193
  pre-alignment inspection 186–191
  pre-alignment road test 191–192
  vehicle alignment 193–211
  vehicle repair 192–212

B

Balancer, wheel 146–151
  Acra-speed, ...147
  mechanical type 150
  on-the-car 148–149
  stationary or off-the-car 150
  Stewart-Warner 149
  Visualiner 151
Ball and socket joint 112–113
Ball joints 37
Ball shank press 128
Banjo housing 55
Bead block 140
Bleeding 232
Body press 15
Brake adjustment 259–264
  major 261–263
  minor 259–261
  parking 261
  self-adjusting type 263–264
Brake cylinder repair 274–276
Brake drum service 273–274
Brake fluid filler, gravity type 265
Brake relining 268–273
Brake troubles 251–259
Brakes 213–253
  air 226–228
  construction of 216–221
  disk 219–220
  electric 225–226
  factors controlling the stop ..214–215
  fully-energizing 223, 230
  hand 238–240
  how it stops the vehicle 216
  hydraulic application of 228–232
  hydraulic system, construction of 232–238
  mechanical 224–225
  power 240–253
  purpose of 213–214
  semi-energizing 222–223
  shoe-actuating mechanisms ..224–232
  shoes, self-energization of ...221–224

PAGE

C

Calibration 192
Cam and lever gears 93
Camber 59, 165–168, 187, 197, 200–206
Camber reading gage 176
Caster 155–165, 181, 200, 206–209
Caster effect 156
Control arm 35, 53
Curb height 187, 193
Curb weight 70

D

Deflection rate, spring 73–75
Diamond sight gage 8
Disk, wheel 170
Drag links 115, 118
Dubonnet suspension 43

E

Elliot axle 45
Engine braking 215

F

Fatigue and breakage, spring 75
Frame 1–31
  clamp 27
  correction sequence of repair ..14–29
  estimating 29–31
  general description of 1
  kinds of damage 6–14
  principles of repair 5
  types of 2–4
    box type 3
    unitized 4
    with bracing 3
    X-type 2
Frame damage 6–14
  center section 6–12
    diamond 6–10
    sag and raise 10–12
    sway 12
    twist 8–10
  rear section 12–14
Frequency, spring 75
Friction, coefficient of 214–216

G

Gage
  camber reading 176
  diamond sight 8
  height 17

PAGE

Gage—*continued*
- magnetic, portable 180
- pressure 126
- run-out 57
- self-centering 9–10, 14
- steering axis 184
- toe-in 179
- torsion-air 193
- Tru-way 13
- two-point tram 8
- wheel alignment, portable ...175, 183

Gaging 6

H

Hand brakes 238–240
Height gage 17
Horn pull plate 27
Hotchkiss drive 50–51
Hydraulic brake systems
- bleeding 266–268
- construction of 232–238
- flushing 264–265

Hydraulic ram 15

I

Idler arm 128

K

Kingpins 39–42, 162, 170, 200

L

Leaf springs 42, 44–46

M

Magnetic gage, portable 180
Master cylinder 229, 232, 236
Mechanical advantage 88

O

Oxygen-acetylene welding unit ..17–19

P

Parallelogram linkage 42–44
Pedal free play 255
Pedal reserve 256
Pitman arm 90, 100, 111, 117–118
Pivot pins 41
Pivot shafts 35
Power brakes 240–253
- operation 243–244
- pedal-assist 244–246
- self-contained 246–251
- service 251–252
- troubles 251
- vacuum 241–243

Power steering 94–111

PAGE

Power steering—*continued*
- adjustments 124–129
- hydraulic type 96–99
- integral type 101–111
  - coaxial 103–107
  - constant control 101–103
  - Saginaw in-line 107–108
  - Saginaw offset 109–111
  - Saginaw rotary valve 108–109
- linkage type 99–101
- other types 111

Pressure gage 126
Protractor, use in alignment 174

R

Radius rods 52
Rear axle housing 55–56, 60–61
Recirculating ball 93
Relay rods 100, 115, 118
Reverse Elliot axle 44
Rim flange 140–141
Road test, pre-alignment 191–192
Rubber bushings 69
Run-out
- lateral 136, 176, 196
- radial 136

Run-out gage 57

S

Scriber, tire 178
Self-centering gage 9–10, 14
Self-energization of brakes .215, 221–223
Shimmy 171, 189
Shock absorbers 52, 80–87
- service 87
- types 81–87

Springs 62–80
- bumpers 72
- bushings 69
- characteristics 73–75
- mountings 68–73
- replacement 77–80
- service 76–77
- types 62–67
  - air cylinder 66–67
  - coil 65
  - multiple leaf 62–64
  - single leaf 64–65
  - torsion bar 66

Stabilizers 72–73
Steering, hard 192
Steering, power 94–111
Steering axis gage 184
Steering axis inclination 183–184
Steering gears, manual 89–94
- construction 90–91
- servicing 118–124

PAGE

Steering gears, manual—*continued*
 types 91–94
  cam and lever 92–93
  recirculating ball 93–94
  worm and roller 91–92
Steering knuckle 37, 40–41, 111–112, 158
 angle 163–164
 sidewise inclination 162
Steering linkages 111–128
 ball and socket joint 112–113
 centering 209
 drag links 115, 118
 relay rods 100, 115, 118
 tie rod 111–118
 types 115–118
Stopping distances 216
Straightener, frame 15
Straightening equipment 15
 body and frame aligner 15
 body press 15
 frame straightener 15
 hydraulic ram 15
Strobe light 150
Struts 52
Suspension, axle
 with leaf springs 44–46
Suspension systems, front ...32–48, 112
 component parts 35–39
 Dubonnet type 43
 independent 33–35, 112
 parallelogram linkage 42–44
 service 46–47
 transverse leaf 42
 with ball joints 39
 with kingpins 39–42
Suspension systems, rear 49–61
 air bellows 49
 alignment 56–61
 Hotchkiss drive 50–51
 independent 53–55
 torque tube drive 51–53

T

Tie rod 111–118
 adjusting sleeve 172
Tire pressure 137
Tires 130–152
 construction of 142–143
 inflating 145, 188
 servicing 144–145
 sizes of 144
 types of 143–144
 wear of 171, 187–190

PAGE

Toe-in 59, 128, 168, 179, 189–198
Toe-in gage 179
Toe-out ..59, 168, 172–176, 179, 189, 199
Toe-out on turns 172–176, 199
Torque 49
Torque tube drive 51–53
Torsion-air gage 193
Track bar 50, 56–57, 74
Tracking 50, 73, 190
Tram gage, two-point 8
Trammel 178–179
Tru-way gage 13

V

Visualiner 58–60, 177, 183, 193, 209

W

Wheel
 construction 130, 140
 servicing 145–152
  balancing 133–135, 146–152
  bearing adjustment 145, 194
  checking run-out 145–146
  checking wobble 145
Wheel and tire assembly 130–152
 construction 130, 140–145
 corrections and adjustments 137–139
  incorrect tire pressure 137–138
  switching tires 139
  uneven tire wear 138–139
 operation 131–133
 static and dynamic balance..133–135
Wheel alignment gage, portable 175–183
Wheel alignment factors 153–172
 caster 155–162
 camber angle 165–168
 point of intersection 168–170
 steering knuckle inclination .162–165
 toe-in 170–172
 toe-out on turns 172
Wheel alignment machine, mechanical 183
Wheel balancer 147–151
 Acra-speed type 147
 mechanical type 150
 on-the-car type 148–149
 Stewart-Warner type 149
 Visualiner 151
Wheel cylinder 229, 236
Wheel wobble 136
Worm and roller gears 91–92